Rey M. Wik Science and American Agriculture

Sept 20, 1966

Science and Society in the United States

THE DORSEY SERIES IN AMERICAN HISTORY

EDITOR   IRVIN G. WYLLIE   *UNIVERSITY OF WISCONSIN*

Science and Society

in the United States

Edited by

David D. Van Tassel *and* Michael G. Hall
both of the University of Texas

1966
The Dorsey Press, Homewood, Illinois

First Printing, May, 1966

Library of Congress Catalog Card No. 66–14552

PRINTED IN THE UNITED STATES OF AMERICA

Preface

The aim of *Science and Society in the United States* is to provide an introduction to the ways in which the modern scientific revolution has become interwoven in the political, economic, and social institutions of the United States. The book is not intended as history of science, but is based on the conviction that the history of science can no longer be ignored in the traditional approaches to this country's history. It reflects the editors' dismay at how difficult it has been for the teacher and student of United States history to find scholarly treatment of this subject anywhere short of highly specialized and uncoordinated monographs. The reader will quickly see that despite some popular traditions, the pursuit of scientific knowledge in the United States has been of long standing, and that the printed and manuscript materials for worthwhile studies in the area are plentiful. Nevertheless, it is a patent fact that the relationships between modern science and the fabric and dynamics of society have not reached the level of consciousness of the textbook and the university examination.

The editors, who are not historians of science, have asked the contributing authors, who are, to write essays appropriate to the interests of the social, economic, and political historian. An effort has been made to focus attention on pure science rather than technology, as far as that has been possible, because it becomes increasingly apparent that the traditional emphasis on "Yankee ingenuity" and a nation of "doers, not thinkers" neglects an important part of United States history. For like reason science has been narrowly construed as the natural and not the social sciences. Humbly aware of their own limitations in the history of science, the editors hope, in a kind of self-denying article of faith, that this introduction to an important subject will soon become obsolete.

The editors would like to take this opportunity to thank at least a few of the many people to whom we are indebted for aid, advice, and inspiration that helped give form to this book. Merle E. Curti of the University of Wisconsin, Richard Shryock of the American Philosophical Society, A. Hunter Dupree of the University of California—pioneers in the field—not only set the pace, supplied the inspiration, but gave valuable advice. Irvin Wyllie of the University of Wisconsin, who first saw merit in the idea, is responsible for the inception of the project. We wish to thank our colleagues in the Department of History of the University of Texas for lending tolerant ears to our problems and for suggestions; particularly George Basalla, who read over the entire manuscript, Robert M. Palter, William H. Goetzmann, and H. Wayne Morgan. Mrs. Bettie Butcher and Mrs. Phyllis O'Keefe typed the voluminous correspondence and portions of the manuscript, often under trying circumstances; Helen Van Tassel and Jean Hall as typists, proofreaders, sounding boards, and spender of money, helped speed the work to completion. We acknowledge our debt to many other unnamed individuals, but accept full responsibility for the shortcomings of this book.

DAVID D. VAN TASSEL

MICHAEL G. HALL

Austin, Texas

March, 1966

Table of Contents

Introduction

David D. Van Tassel and Michael G. Hall*

I. THE EUROPEAN BACKGROUND

It seems useful, before undertaking a survey of ways in which modern science has affected modern society, to review very quickly the major stages of progress in the sciences themselves. This is particularly desirable inasmuch as the discoveries and the formulation of novel scientific theories took place in Europe, whereas this book is concerned with the United States. The pages that follow attempt to give a topical and chronological sketch of nineteenth- and early twentieth-century science as a heuristic aid to using the later chapters.

No introduction to the nineteenth century was more prophetic than the experiments of Luigi Galvani and Alessandro Volta with electricity in the 1790's. Electricity has become the magic wand of the modern world. It drives the industrial machine and provides the scholar his understanding of the world's structure. Galvani, a deft Bolognese anatomist, demonstrated that impulses along animal nerves are electrical in character. Alessandro Volta, also from northern Italy, and eight years Galvani's junior, helped explain Galvani's experimental results, discovered electrolytic action, and created the voltaic battery, which gave the scientist his first source of continuous electrical current. The results of these discoveries will be seen to run with increasing significance through every area of modern science and technology.

In the world of the chemical sciences, the eighteenth century may be said to have reached a climax with the appearance in 1789 of *Traité Elémentaire de la Chimie*, by Antoine Lavoisier. Henceforth chemists were to start from the basic proposition that matter is con-

* Part I, "The European Background," was written by Professor Hall and Part II, "The American Setting," by Professor Van Tassel.

served in chemical reactions, and, equally important, they were to accept the proposition that laboratory technique must be based on the measurement of weights—fundamental principles of conceptualization and of method.

The nineteenth century had barely opened before John Dalton, a Quaker scientist in Manchester, England, proposed a new theory for the structure of matter. In his *New System of Chemical Philosophy* (1806), Dalton transformed the ancient hypothesis of corpuscular or atomic structure, in which all atomic particles were supposed to be alike, to the hypothesis that matter is composed of particles in which all atoms of a certain element are identical with each other, but differ from the atoms of any other element. Almost simultaneously a Swedish chemist in Stockholm, Jöns Jakob Berzelius, and another Englishman, Humphry Davy, at the Royal Institution in London, were carrying on experiments which stemmed from Volta's discovery of the electric potential produced by chemical reaction. The result was that the chemical affinity which bound together the atoms newly described by Davy was understood to be electrical in nature. Berzelius became the leading figure in chemistry in the first quarter of the nineteenth century. From his post in Stockholm he did more than any other to make the science an autonomous profession. It was Berzelius who established the abbreviations for the elements and the modern forms of chemical formulae and equations. Following Dalton, his principal goal was to determine precisely the atomic weights of known elements. But included in his understanding of affinities were misconceptions which led Berzelius to reject another hypothesis, advanced in 1811 by the Italian physicist Amadeo Avogadro. Not until the second half of the century would chemists agree with Avogadro and then discover methods for actually measuring the numbers of atoms which make up compounds.

Such advances as those of Berzelius and Davy were largely theoretical and had little effect on life outside the scholar's study. It is fair to say that the first quarter of the nineteenth century saw fundamental advances in theories of inorganic chemistry which were to wait a generation before their full exploitation and practical application. Meanwhile, in the second quarter of the century, particularly after 1830, the field of organic chemistry made startling progress, with immediate consequences for the industrial world.

Inorganic chemistry encompasses many minerals and thousands of compounds, each of which has a simple and distinctive molecular structure. These inorganic compounds were readily susceptible to analysis in terms of the relative amounts of combining elements. Organic compounds, on the other hand (Berzelius, by the way, introduced the modern distinction between organic and inorganic), are characterized by a confusing variety of spatial arrangements into which rather few elements are combined. Some isomers (again, we owe the term to Berzelius!) have identical proportions of combining elements but very different properties. In such cases the analytical techniques fruitful in inorganic chemistry, the analysis of relative weights, proved to be insufficient; spatial arrangement was the key.

As the second quarter of the century opened, the discoveries of Friedrich Wöhler and Justus von Liebig about these organic compounds foreshadowed the rise of German chemistry. Since then Germany maintained a position of preeminence in the chemical industry which was unchallenged until the sale of German chemical patents to U.S. industry after World War I. Wöhler studied under Berzelius at Stockholm and returned to Germany to take academic positions at Berlin and then Göttingen. But of the two it was Liebig's influence which did most to stimulate German chemical studies. After coming back from study at the Ecole de Pharmacie and Ecole Polytechnique where he had been inspired by Baron von Humboldt and the French chemist Gay-Lussac, Liebig established himself at Giessen. There he created a chemical laboratory which was to become world-famous and in particular was to be a mecca for young scientists from the United States.

Liebig was one of the great originators of agricultural chemistry, especially in the field of nitrates and chemical fertilizers. No wonder, then, that young scientists from the United States, where agriculture was the first area to give sustained institutional support to science, gravitated to his laboratory.

Liebig's and Wöhler's pioneering work was in the analysis of organic isomers. One branch of this study was begun in 1828 when Wöhler (in Berzelius' laboratory) synthesized, for the first time, an organic compound, urea. It had been widely believed that such compounds could only be created by a vital process peculiar to living organisms. By synthesizing urea from inorganic ammonium cyanate, Wöhler struck at the roots of the doctrines of vitalism and at the same time brought into one framework the study of living and nonliving chemical compounds. Here also began the trail of synthetic organic compounds which was to revolutionize the industrial potential of the world. One may think, then, of two interlocking lines of progress stretching from the work of Liebig and Wöhler. One was the understanding of molecular arrangement, which was to explain the existence of isomers; the other was the ability to synthesize organic compounds. The first of these trails leads through Liebig to his pupil Friedrich August Kekulé, who more than any other single person contributed to the picturing of molecules in their varieties of structural arrangements. The climax of his architectural descriptions came in 1865, when he struck on the closed hexagonal arrangement of carbon atoms in the benzene molecule, one of the most important and most stable of all compounds. From this threshold proceeded, in the twentieth century, the study of electrical affinities between atoms and those researches into the molecular structure of proteins, enzymes, and amino acids which are today revolutionizing biology.

Meanwhile, the ability to synthesize in a laboratory the products of living nature had startling results. Pierre Berthelot, in the 1850's, led the field in producing, in his Paris laboratory, complex organic compounds like ethyl alcohol and even compounds unknown in the natural world. Man would soon be able actually to improve on the resources which nature offered to satisfy his manufacturing appetite. The first industrially significant development came via Liebig, through his student, August Wilhelm von Hofmann, who settled in at London's Royal College of Science, and from Hofmann's student and protégé, William Henry Perkin. Perkin, on the track of something else, synthesized a compound which had a rich mauve color and which was to be the first aniline dye. Within months Perkin developed and patented industrial techniques for producing cheap, synthetic dyes—one of the most dramatic of the instances of the symbiosis between science and industry which mark the contemporary world. The fate of exotic and expensive sources for textile dyes—indigo, madder, brazil wood, the *Murex* mollusc (Tyrian purple), the *Dactylopius coccus* ("cochineal")—was sealed. Not all colors were synthesized at once, and the discoveries were spread over the second half of the century. Hofmann returned to Germany, where the aniline dye industry expanded to enormous importance.

If synthetic dyes were the first industrial consequences of organic chemistry, plastics are the most recent and most dramatic. The industrial story here begins with the work of the Belgian-born American chemist Leo Baekeland, who created Bakelite early in the twentieth century. Simply to list the important discoveries since then would take a volume. Whatever the branch of industrial synthetics, be it plastics or fibers or rubbers, the foundations are to be sought in the spatial structure of the organic molecule.

Chemistry in the second quarter of the nineteenth century was dominated by discoveries about organic compounds. After 1860, however, inorganic chemistry once again made great strides, and a wide-sweeping organization of all chemical knowledge brought the science of chemistry to a new position by the turn of the century. An international conference of chemists at Karlsruhe in 1860 was the occasion for the reannouncement and final acceptance of Avogadro's hypothesis through the fervent advocacy of his countryman Stanislao Cannizzaro. The rule that the same volumes of different gases (if kept at the same pressure and temperature) contain the same number of molecules gave chemists an important new technique to ascertain relative atomic weights for the elements. Before the decade of the 1860's had passed, a German, Lothar Meyer, and more importantly a Russian, Dimitri Mendeleev, were able to arrange all known elements in a systematic way—the periodic table. That was in 1869. Mendeleev left blank spaces in his table, predicting that unknown elements would be discovered to fill in the hypothesized order of nature. Already Robert Bunsen and Gustav Kirchhoff, both at Heidelberg, had developed the spectroscope (1859), a crucial laboratory instrument, which was used to discover elements unknown before. Soon Mendeleev's predictions began to be fulfilled.

By the century's end chemists had arrived at an understanding of matter based on elementary atoms and their combinations into molecular groups. They were able to apply Lavoisier's principle of measurement of weights and assign relative weights to the unseeable atoms; and they had also developed laboratory techniques which gave them (and industry) undreamed-of control over the elements. In 1896 the discovery of radioactivity by Antoine Henri Becquerel opened an entirely new era in chemistry.

But before carrying the study of chemistry into the twentieth century, it is necessary to go back to 1800 and retrace a hundred years of history, this time visiting another kind of laboratory—the physicists'.

The continuous electrical current produced by the voltaic pile opened the door to the nineteenth-century study of electrical energy. Like many another in the early years of the century, the Danish physicist Hans Christian Oersted was looking for the supposed relationship between electricity and magnetism. In 1820, during a routine lecture-room demonstration, Oersted saw that he could make a magnetized compass needle rotate by sending a current through a nearby stationary wire. When Oersted's discovery was published in a small

Latin treatise, European physicists were galvanized into action. André Marie Ampère at the Ecole Polytechnique quickly elucidated the magnetic attraction between electrical currents and established a mathematical description, including the familiar practical unit of electric current, the ampere. Dominique Françoise Arago very soon used the new information to develop the electromagnet. And Michael Faraday, assistant to Humphry Davy at the Royal Institution in London, noted a program of research in his journal: "convert magnetism into electricity." Oersted produced movement in a magnet by an electric current; Faraday went on to reverse the transformation by inducing an electric current from the motion of a magnet.

Within the decade 1820–1830 a new age was born, with Faraday officiating as the principal midwife. The long-suspected electromagnetic relationship was confirmed. For the workaday world the principles, if not yet the useful application, of the electric motor and the electric dynamo were established. Application was to develop in the evolution of technology, outside the province of this paper. But the magnitude of what was to come can be appreciated by recalling here that the dynamo and the motor have in the twentieth century virtually replaced the steam engine as the source of industrial power.

Electromagnetic phenomena had a fascination for the physicist, partly because of the ease with which they could be studied in the laboratory. Quickly physicists learned to measure and manipulate the strange forces which acted at a distance. Karl Friedrich Gauss established the unit of magnetism; Georg Simon Ohm the unit of resistance to a current. Lavoisier's arch principle was being put to practice: what man can measure he controls. But it was Faraday again who pushed matters into the realm of abstract speculation. How is it that things can operate on each other across a distance at all? Faraday hypothesized electromagnetic fields of force pushing out into space and retracting again. All space, he argued, was filled with an invisible substance which is the medium of the fields of force as they ebbed and flowed.

Another, and at first thought, a wholly different subject, the propagation of light, had also turned men to speculating about what happens in emptiness. What happens when a beam of light leaves its source and travels across space to illuminate an object? Isaac Newton, at the start of the previous century, had said that light was made up of corpuscles, particles. Christian Huygens, a Dutch contemporary of Newton's, argued to the contrary that light was propagated in wave fronts, like ripples in a pool of water. Newton won the argument in his day, and for the rest of the eighteenth century, men based their concepts of light on Newton's *Opticks*. Then in 1801 Thomas Young, an incredible prodigy in many fields, the man who later was to take up oriental languages and to translate the inscription on the Rosetta stone, proposed that Huygens had been right after all. Light traveled in a wave action, which could be demonstrated by interference patterns in simple laboratory experiments. Newton's prestige died hard; but in 1820 the Frenchman Augustin Fresnel devised experiments conclusively supporting the wave theory advanced by Young.

Two characteristic features of nineteenth-century science were now becoming prominent. One was the greater and greater role of abstruse mathematics, used in this instance to describe wave mechanics. The other was the positing of a physical model, in this case an elastic matter called ether which filled space but which was invisible, weightless, and unapproachable by laboratory techniques. The ether was in fact a purely abstract construct; but its reality was thought necessary to explain the propagation of light by transverse waves, and in Faraday's case, to explain the movement of electromagnetic fields of force.

James Clerk Maxwell, educated at Edinburgh and then at Cambridge, where he supervised the planning of the famous Cavendish Laboratory in the 1870's, was a master of mathematics. He was also the first of the great modern physicists to dispense with the imagined physical model and to rely solely on mathematical understanding of phenomena. Maxwell took Faraday's electromagnetic lines of force and, doing away with the clumsy expression of an elastic ether, Maxwell expressed the operation of electromagnetic waves in pure mathematical notation. He did not by any means dispel the generally held belief in the ether; but he apparently ignored it as unnecessary for an understanding of the equations, which by themselves described the phenomena. Maxwell's equations could satisfy the requirements of light wave propagation too. And more than that.

Near the beginning of the nineteenth century, William Herschel held a thermometer just beyond the spectrum cast by sunlight passing through a prism, and the temperature climbed. Apparently at this end of the spectrum there was a margin of light, whatever that was, that was not visible. Similar experiments soon proved that the same was true at the ultraviolet end, and it became apparent that visible light was only a part of a larger kind of radiation. Maxwell's equations showed all these radiations to obey the same rules as electromagnetic waves! Light, radiant energy, electromagnetism, wave propagation were one, and all were susceptible to mathematical description. Just as Mendeleev had predicted the discovery of new elements, Maxwell predicted the existence of waves of energy which were both longer and shorter than any that had yet been known. In 1877 H. R. Hertz discovered the long radio waves. At the other end of the scale short X rays and gamma rays, when *they* were discovered at the century's end, would fall into their proper place. Maxwell's mathematical concepts were one of the great unifying inventions of the human mind.

Another imagined matter besides the ether had been conjured up before the nineteenth century opened. It was caloric—a weightless material substance which was supposed to be heat. This material, heat, could be released from its association with physical bodies when, for example, they were rubbed together producing friction. The story of how such a belief was finally dispelled and replaced by theories of thermodynamics begins with an American refugee from the War for Independence, Benjamin Thompson, Count Rumford. In 1798, Count Rumford was engaged in boring canon in Munich. He noticed that increasing the cutting ability of the boring tools did not liberate more heat, as it should according to theory; on the contrary, blunt instruments, which could not cut into the iron and liberate its caloric at all, seemed to produce more heat. Heat then seemed to be, not a substance to be let out of materials, but a product of work. A few years after Count Rumford published these speculations, Thomas Young also posed criticisms of the caloric theory through a study of radiant heat associated with the radiation of light.

Then in 1824 a brilliant French theorist, Sadi Carnot, speculating on the relationship between heat and mechanical energy in the steam engine, laid the foundation of thermodynamic theory in a little book, *Reflections on the Motive Force of Fire.* From Sadi Carnot's analysis it followed that the energy of heat was not lost as it passed through the engine, but did become unavailable for work. Carnot's book was not immediately influential, perhaps because it was too theoretical and too difficult to apply to laboratory experiments. Carnot was not to receive the recognition he deserved until the 1850's.

Investigation of the relationships between heat and energy were the particular triumph of an English brewer, James Prescott Joule. Joule was a master of delicate laboratory techniques. In the 1840's he became convinced that no caloric matter existed. Rather, heat was produced (as Rumford had argued without precise experimental evidence) by mechanical work. At approximately the same time two German scientists, Robert Mayer and Friedrich Mohr, a student of Liebig's, came to the belief that both the heat of animal bodies and the mechanical work animals are capable of are derived from the chemical nature of their food. Particularly to Mayer did mechanical energy, heat, and chemical energy seem equivalent. Each could be transformed into the others. Hermann von Helmholtz, a sort of universal genius of the century, took up these researches in physiology and used them to attack the vitalist school. The energy manifest in life was due not to some vital force but to the conversion of chemical energy. Helmholtz went on to restate the eighteenth-century law that the energy of the universe (motion, heat, work, or whatever) was constant. Here was in effect the "First Law of Thermodynamics."

None of these works was popular. Papers by Joule, Mohr, Mayer, and Helmholtz were all at first rejected by learned journals. Common to all of them was the rejection of the idea of a caloric substance and the acceptance of the idea that heat and work are interconvertible. These positions were summed up at mid-century by Lord Kelvin in 1850 and Rudolf Clausius in 1851. These men started their arguments from where Sadi Carnot had left the subject in 1824, included the experimental research in the intervening quarter century, and concluded with the "Second Law of Thermodynamics"—namely that energy in the universe tends to become unavailable for conversion into work. Energy may be conserved in the universe; but when mechanical or chemical energy is converted into heat and the heat dissipated, that energy is never again available. Clausius' expression for the quantity of unavailable energy is "entropy." The study of thermodynamic theory had developed from this theoretical position into a rich specialty of its own.

As we have seen, the international conference of chemists at Karlsruhe in 1860 opened new opportunities for the understanding of the molecular nature of gases. From this point Maxwell was able in the 1880's to clarify concepts of energy and heat at the level of molecular motion. With Maxwell, and even more with Ludwig Boltzmann, an Austrian physicist, the now-familiar pattern of increased mathematical sophistication appeared in thermodynamic studies, this time in the guise of mathematical statistics. Boltzmann also showed how the theoretical structure of thermodynamics offered a new tool for the study of radiation. Highly abstract and mathematical in its origin and development, the study of thermodynamics has been at the center of pure sciences like astrophysics and geophysics; it played an important role in Josiah Willard Gibbs's elegant phase rule; it lies at the foundation of modern industrial techniques like gaseous diffusion processes. Just as Maxwell could dispense with the substance ether, so in the first fifty years of the nineteenth century could the concept of caloric substance be abandoned.

Looking backward from the exhilarating shores of twentieth-century biological studies, it seems possible to trace two more streams of investigation working their way through the ocean of nineteenth-century science. One had to do with the classification of living forms and the explanation of their origins and continuation. The other had to do with the structure and functioning of living material in whatever form it might take. The former was the study of evolution, the latter, of cell biology. The one considered, chiefly, the gross forms of life; the other concentrated on, chiefly, microscopic organization of life. By the twentieth century, both lines of thought came together, the successful theories of evolution giving meaning and purpose to the study of molecular biology.

In about 1800 a physician in southern France, Xavier Bichat, established the study of histology by carefully distinguishing the various kinds of tissues which compose the animal body. It was a great step forward in conceptualizing the object of biological investigation, and it also represented the farthest a biologist might go until he had new tools to work with. The critical tool was the microscope. Not, to be sure, new, for it had been invented in the seventeenth century. But a succession of revolutionary improvements were at hand. In Italy, in Czechoslovakia, in England, the microscope was improved in the first three decades of the nineteenth century. The achromatic microscope was invented by 1830, and significant improvements (immersion lenses, substage condenser) added to its versatility through the rest of the century.

Bichat's tissues were, of course, known to be made up of cells. The cellular structure of plants had been observed by the first generation of observers in the seventeenth century: Hooke, Leeuwenhoek, Malpighi, Swammerdam. But why almost a century was to elapse before this line of investigation was resumed remains an enigma. In 1809 Jean Baptiste Lamarck could go so far as to say that "cellular tissue is the general matrix of all organization." A more refined and more confident statement of cell theory waited upon improved instruments. In 1831, a year after the invention of the achromatic microscope, Robert Brown, an English doctor, identified the nucleus within the cell. But it was Matthias Schleiden at Jena who put forth in 1838 the general theory that the cell is the basic unit of all plant life. The next year Theodor Schwann, anatomy professor at Louvain, extended the proposition to include all animal life as well. No biological concept has led to more far-reaching consequences than the cell theory that was now taking shape. The cell was seen to be the critical unit in which living matter is organized. In 1858 the German pathologist Rudolf Virchow showed that the cell is also the unit at which disease impairs life. Ordinary symptoms of disease are but reflections of the disruption of the normal functions of cells. Not long afterwards, cells were seen to reproduce asexually in the process called mitosis. Another German, Walter Flemming, invented techniques for staining fixed cells and was able to describe in 1879 the longitudinal splitting and reduplication of chromosomes.

Meanwhile, in the 1850's and 1860's, the Frenchman Louis Pasteur, a chemist, set to work on a succession of utilitarian projects: control of fermentation in brewing, how to keep wine from going sour, how to save France's silkworms from an epizootic. The consequences of Pasteur's work—besides gratifying French businessmen—were to put an end to the belief in spontaneous creation and to identify microorganisms as the carriers of disease. The modern study of microbiology sprang from Pasteur's empirical demonstrations and from his techniques. The English surgeon Lord Lister (whose father had developed the achromatic microscope) saw the importance of Pasteur's work for the operating room. Lister started the practice of sterilization, rather roughly, to be sure, with carbolic acid. In 1876 Robert Koch in Germany identified the microorganism responsible for cattle anthrax. Knowledge of the nature of infection has since then led to an indescribable number of preventions and cures in plant and animal life.

The fullest exploitation of the cell theory, however, makes us turn back to the beginnings of theories of biological evolution. Many elements of European thought converged at the start of the nineteenth century to create a climate of opinion favorable to Darwinian evolution. In Germany, *Natur-philosophie* and the rising school of history set people to explaining things and events as processes in time. In France, Lamarck at the Musée d'Histoire Naturelle argued a descent of animal species from one another, the process closely tied to environment. In England, as well as on the continent, geological knowledge, particularly the stratigraphy of fossil-bearing rocks, emphasized the secular character of species. And in England, with its belief in progress under laissez-faire capitalism, the young Darwin had read Malthus' essay on population, where the human population is described as engaged in a perpetual battle for a never sufficient food supply. All these ideas prepared Charles Darwin (and Alfred Russel Wallace) for his work at mid-century in stating evolutionary theory. Papers by both men appeared in 1858, and Darwin's book *On the Origin of Species by Means of Natural Selection, or the Preservation of Favoured Races in the Struggle for Life* appeared in 1859. In 1871 he published *Descent of Man.*

Even before the publication of *Origin of Species*, Gregor Mendel, a modest, cherubic-faced monk in Sudeten Germany, had started an epoch-making series of experiments in his kitchen garden. Mendel's explanation of the patterns of inheritance provided an operational explanation for Darwin's theories of evolution. By crossbreeding a species of pea through successive generations, and by keeping meticulous qualitative and quantitative records, Mendel came to the conclusion that single inheritable features, like tallness and yellowness, were due to discrete, independent factors ("genes"), and that these factors were distributed in successive generations of a given population according to predictable statistical patterns. Ignored in 1866 by the elite of the scientific world, Mendel's papers lay forgotten until 1900. Today they mark the foundation of modern genetic theory.

Even before the discovery of Mendel's papers, however, study of the cell nucleus had led scientists to identify it as the unit through which inherited characteristics are exchanged. Mendel's statistical patterns contradicted in some cases the observed chromosomal patterns. This anomaly was resolved in 1911 by Thomas Hunt Morgan, working at Columbia University in New York on *Drosophila*, the fruit fly. By demonstrating from empirical evidence the possibilities of linkage and crossover in chromosome structure, Morgan united the study of genetics and evolution with the study of the cell.

By 1890 science had developed extraordinary power for the understanding of natural phenomena and for changing the environmental conditions of human life. But the most startling discoveries were yet to come, and by the time the dust began to settle, man's understanding of the physical and chemical world had been thoroughly upset.

A chronology of the revolution begins in the early 1890's and begins appropriately with electricity. One branch of the study of electrical phenomena which drew much attention at the end of the century was electrical discharges in gases at low pressures, i.e., in vacuum tubes. As early as 1876, experimenters discovered a fluorescence or glow on the glass wall of such tubes, a glow produced by rays emanating from the negative electrode or cathode. (This glow is familiar to every owner of a television set.) As the last decade of the century opened, William Crookes in England developed laboratory techniques for producing these cathode rays, and astonishingly was also able to deflect the rays with a magnetic field. Crookes proposed that the rays were more than electromagnetic radiation; that they were indeed a new kind of matter. The problem intrigued European physicists, and experiments with cathode rays became the rage. In 1895 Wilhelm Conrad Roentgen in Germany, while engaged in such experiments, noticed that the rays from his "Crookes tube" exposed photographic paper even when it was carefully shielded from the tube. These so-called X rays had an uncanny power to penetrate most opaque objects. In France, Henri Becquerel, who had long been interested in fluorescence, turned to see what he could learn from Roentgen's discovery. Quite by accident Becquerel found that uranium compounds emitted rays without any vacuum tube at all. That was 1896. Within two years Marie Curie, overcoming crushing burdens of poverty, isolated the new element, radium, with the power to emit X rays nine hundred times greater than uranium.

Back in England J. J. Thomson, director of the Cavendish Laboratory, was still interested in the vacuum tube discharge phenomena. He experimented to see "what effect the passage of these rays through a gas would produce on its electrical properties." The result was (in later terms) to ionize the gas and permit an easy flow of current. Thomson was able within the year (1897) to corroborate Crookes's earlier suggestion: the rays in the tube were indeed previously unknown particles of matter. They had mass and velocity, and these properties could be measured by deflecting the new particles within a controlled electromagnetic field. Thomson had identified the electron.

The range of experimental and theoretical work which these discoveries of the 1890's launched has become so great that only the briefest account can be attempted here. Traditional views of physics and chemistry were alike challenged, and it was a collaboration between a physicist and a chemist which produced the next revelations. Ernest Rutherford came to England from New Zealand, became Thomson's assistant, then went on to McGill University in Canada; Frederick Soddy, who had been born in southern England and educated as a chemist at Oxford, also took a position at McGill. By the first year of the new century, Rutherford detected the existence of a strange and extremely massive particle (the alpha particle). He and Soddy worked out the existence of isotopes and the transmutation of elements resulting from their radioactive decay. A satisfactory statement of these innovations in what had previously been the domain of the chemists alone came in 1913.

But before then Ernest Rutherford had returned to England (to Manchester this time), and there undertaken experiments with his alpha particle. From the now-famous experiments in which Rutherford bombarded thin sections of gold leaf with alpha particles, and his collaborator Hans Geiger plotted the scatter pattern of those particles which got through, Rutherford hypothesized in 1911 an atom made up of a massive core or nucleus with a positive electrical charge, surrounded at relatively huge distances by a number of electrons with negative charge.

Before discussing what the Danish visitor to Manchester, Niels Bohr, made of this Rutherford model, it is necessary to turn back to the beginnings of quantum theory. That story begins at Berlin University with Professor Max Planck. In the exciting decade 1890–1900, Planck devoted himself to traditional problems posed by electromagnetic field theory. He wanted to devise equations which would describe the radiation of energy from an ideal ("black body") radiator at any temperature to which it is heated. It was supposed that such a body could radiate energy over a continuous range of temperatures, the wavelengths becoming increasingly shorter as the temperature increased. (That could be illustrated visually, for example, by the changing color of a bar of iron as it is heated from cherry red to white hot.) Planck found, however, that to write adequate equations he had to introduce a disturbing new idea, taken partly from Boltzmann's mathematical statistics. The range of possible radiation is not continuous but composed of a series of discrete units, which Planck called quanta.

Energy, according to this new concept, could be produced in any number of whole packets but not in fractions of packets. The amount of energy in a packet could be determined by multiplying the frequency of the radiating waves by a factor which seemed to be a universal constant and for which Planck calculated a numerical value. Planck was unhappy with his own conclusions, for they violated too many established ideas in classical physics. Albert Einstein, however, in 1905, used Planck's constant and the conceptualization behind it, to explain the hitherto mysterious photoeloectric effect. Einstein suggested that light energy can be thought of as being localized in packets rather than being spread over a wave front, as it is in electromagnetic field theory. The packets, so similar to Planck's quanta of energy, were later called photons, and by supposing their existence, the photoelectric effect can be adequately described. All one has to do is be willing to abandon the essence of nineteenth-century optics, which from Thomas Young to Maxwell was based on treating light as a wave and not a particle phenomenon.

Let us return to Niels Bohr. Fresh from receiving his Ph.D. from the university of Copenhagen, Bohr went abroad for a year of study. He spent the last four months at Manchester under Rutherford in 1912, the very time that Rutherford and Geiger were putting the finishing touches on their model of the atom. Bohr reworked Rutherford's primitive atomic model by applying to it the principle that energy (in this case the energy of the orbiting electrons) comes in discrete packets. In Bohr's new model, electrons orbit about a nucleus only in specific possible orbits, determined by their energy level expressed in conjunction with Planck's universal constant. Bohr's theoretical picture and rigorous mathematical analysis received early experimental confirmation in the emission spectra of hydrogen.

The initial success of Bohr's model assured the acceptance of both the newly discovered structure of the atom and the revolutionary quantum theory. World War I, 1914–1918, caused a slowing down of the pace of discovery, but in the 1920's a large number of physicists turned to explore the implications of these innovations. Louis de Broglie postulated in 1924 the dual (i.e., wave and particle) character of electrons. At Göttingen Max Born, Wolfgang Pauli, Werner Heisenberg, and P. Jordan developed a mathematical treatment of the electron which became known as "quantum mechanics." In 1926 Erwin Schroedinger at Copenhagen and Paul Dirac in England developed independent mathematical descriptions, Schroedinger still clinging to classical emphasis on waves in preference to quanta. The two approaches to the problem of the electron—the more conservative of Schroedinger, and the more radical of Heisenberg—were hoped to be mathematically equivalent. Nevertheless, fundamental philosophical questions were involved, particularly Heisenberg's formulation of the proposition that the natural world is at its roots indeterminate. The resulting argument divided physicists into opposing camps. Einstein, De Broglie, Schroedinger never accepted the full implication of the quantum theory of Born, Pauli, Heisenberg, and the disagreement between the two groups lasted well into the 1950's.

But already what Maxwell had done for Faraday's fields of force, Heisenberg had done for Bohr's atom: the visual model was completely abandoned for a description in mathematical terms alone. There is no doubt of the immense utility such a development gives the scientist. Nor is there any doubt that it has been this same process which makes some areas of science almost impossible for the public to understand as long as it remains unfamiliar with advanced mathematics.

Albert Einstein, a German graduating from a Swiss university, could not get a university appointment. In 1905—at the age of 26— he held a minor position in a Swiss patent office in Berne. That year he published three articles in the now-famous seventeenth volume of the *Annalen der Physik*. One was his paper on the photoelectric effect, which we have already mentioned. Even more upsetting to the premises of nineteenth-century science was a paper "On the Electrodynamics of Moving Bodies." The background of this paper was not the Roentgen-Becquerel discoveries of the 1890's, but a quite different series of experiments. In 1887 Albert Michelson and Edward Morley reported from Cleveland, Ohio, on a very simple but very precise experiment that failed. According to classical or Newtonian laws of motion, a beam of light directed in the direction of the earth's movement should have an absolute speed which is the sum of the earth's speed through space and the light beam's speed across the earth. But, unfortunately, the Michelson-Morley experiment could detect no difference between light moving with the earth's motion and light moving across it.

An Irish physicist, G. F. Fitzgerald, suggested a reason for the experimental result. The instruments contract, said Fitzgerald, when they are in motion. It was this "Fitzgerald contraction," short yardsticks, slow clocks, etc., which the public was later to seize on as the most exotic consequence of the theory of relativity. Fitzgerald and the Dutchman Hendrik Lorentz worked out mathematically the degree of contraction required to explain the observed phenomena, and Lorentz, who was interested in electromagnetic phenomena, expanded the mathematics to describe the contraction in the size of an electron at increasingly high speeds, when measured along the direction of motion, assuming that the speed of light was constant in all reference systems. The new mathematical tool was knows as the Lorentz Transformation.

The next year Einstein published his paper on the electrodynamics of moving bodies and by so doing established the framework for the theory of relativity. Ether, assumed tacitly by Michelson and Morley, was abandoned. More importantly, Einstein also abandoned the assumptions of Newtonian laws of motion and the implicit belief in absolute time and absolute space. The Lorentz Transformations were expanded. The most famous equation of all physics, $e = mc^2$, is itself a product of this development. With Einstein's later work on general relativity, non-Euclidean geometrics were used for the first time to describe real space-time and as was the case with quantum mechanics, the general public was left outdistanced by a science which utilized unfamiliar mathematical and geometrical tools. Einstein himself is supposed to have said, "Since the mathematicians have invaded the theory of relativity, I do not understand it myself any more."

The biological sciences have not been rocked as the physical sciences were by an overturning of classical or nineteenth-century concepts. Evolution, genetics, and cell biology remain fruitful concepts. Perhaps for this reason achievements in biology have been less widely publicized. Just as physics and chemistry were brought together in the early years of the twentieth century, biology and chemistry have fused into an immensly productive union—biochemistry. New experimental techniques like the electron microscope, the ultracentrifuge (1920's), and paper chromatography (1940's) have played in this century the role of the achromatic microscope in the last.

After the cell had become identified as the unit of biological life, one outstanding problem was the chemistry of protein molecules, which make up the bulk of the cellular material. Protein chemistry advanced steadily through the first half of the century and reached one milepost in 1951, when Linus Pauling and Robert Corey in California proposed the helical shape for polypeptide chains. By that time the English biochemist Frederick Sanger was already at work on determining the structural order of amino acids in a peptide chain, and by 1953 the structure of an important protein molecule (insulin) was for the first time described.

Although proteins make up the greater part of the cell, the nucleus is composed in large measure of a nonprotein substance, roughly identified in the nineteenth century by the German, Friedrich Miescher, and nowadays called nucleic acid. The search for an understanding of the nucleic acid molecules also occupied much of the first half of the twentieth century. Building on work done primarily in England, J. D. Watson and F. H. C. Crick at Cambridge University constructed in the early 1950's a helix model of the nucleic-acid molecule comparable to Pauling's model of the protein molecule. What is of particular importance here, of course, is the suggestion that the nucleic-acid molecule is the structure which carries genetic information from one generation to the next.

Evolutionary biology, tracing a line of development through Darwin and Mendel into modern genetics, has come into immediate interplay with cellular biology and hence with chemistry. The circle of disciplines thus linked together is completed with the application of evolutionary thinking to the molecular chemistry outside cellular organization. Molecules themselves are seen to have had an evolutionary history prior to their organization as the building matter of cellular life. In 1952 Stanley L. Miller in California subjected a hypothetical primitive atmosphere to electrical discharge simulating lightning. The results were a number of more complex molecules, including several of the amino acid variety. Such experiments give empirical evidence to support the hypothesis that life itself began from a natural situation, and also allow this chronological sketch of one and a half centuries of science to end as it began with an electrical discharge.

II. THE AMERICAN SETTING

The sudden eminence of science in American life since 1945 is largely a matter of degree. For instance, in 1898 William J. McGee told the readers of the *Atlantic Monthly* that "scientific progress . . . is so closely interwoven with industrial and social progress that the advance of one cannot be traced without constant reference to the other. . . . In truth, America has become a nation of science." Actually, America was not then, nor had it ever been, a nation of science, although there has always been an important reciprocal relationship between science and the development of America. No history of the United States can be complete without taking into account the role of science in its intellectual, economic, and cultural growth.

The history of this relationship between science and society in the United States is *terra incognita*, an area unknown to the political historians, and yet since 1776 it has strongly affected local and national politics. In 1876 Professor John W. Draper, New York physician and philosopher, deplored the ignorance displayed by his countrymen when they indulged in the intellectual fashion of depreciating American culture, and particularly scientific achievement. He warned, "They mistake what is merely a blank in their own information for a blank in reality."

In this part of the Introduction, as background for the more specialized treatments given in the succeeding chapters. I shall attempt to sketch briefly two major areas important to understanding the relationship between science and society. The first area is the development of the political structure and economic conditions which furnished the background and explanation for the peculiar development of science in America. In dealing with the second area, I hope to outline the development of the various sciences in the United States through a sketch of the organization of institutions for the promotion of science and the diffusion of knowledge.

Political and Economic Conditions

During the long period of exploration and settlement, the plantations of North America were economically dependent on England. "Yankee ingenuity" contributed a few important innovations, such as the American ax, superior in design and balance to the European, Benjamin Franklin's "Pennsylvania fireplace" (1742) or Franklin stove, his lightning rod of 1750, and finally, in 1776, David Bushnell's one-man submarine. It is doubtful, however, that much more could have been achieved. The constant scarcity of labor in the thinly settled coastal colonies inhibited significant growth of industry. All of the Thirteen Colonies were, therefore, to one degree or another economically dependent on the mother country for long-range credit, favorable trade legislation, or outright subsidies. Since each of the Colonies was also independent of the other, having legal identity as a business corporation or proprietorship, each Colony had its own unique history, recruiting its own settlers and fighting its own battles over parliamentary regulation and cooperating only under the stress of self-preservation.

This ambiguous condition of being at once economically dependent and politically autonomous carried over to the culture of British-Americans; that is, there was a small group in each Colony who wrote books and poetry, painted pictures and engaged in scientific or philosophic investigations, and to this extent there was an independent literature, art, and science. Colonial authors, however, sought publication in London; artists welcomed recognition by noble patrons in England; and scientists wanted recognition by the Royal Society of London. In other words, the colonists considered themselves to be Englishmen in every respect, sharing equally in the British heritage with any native of the British Isles. All young colonists, equipped with the ability and financial wherewithal, went to Oxford or Cambridge for classical degrees and to Edinburgh and London for training in medicine, admission to the bar, or for clerical orders. Colleges established in the Colonies were not conceived as universities but as convenient local institutions for religious and classical education. Most of these colleges, indeed, were supported to some extent from England. Even colonial philosophic and literary societies seemed to be unnecessary except as convenient local forums for discussion of papers, perhaps prior to submission to the Royal Society.

Among the colonials there were many outstanding naturalists, collectors, amateur astronomers and horticulturalists, who carried on a lively and voluminous correspondence with the scientists of Europe. There were even a few individual colonists who had sufficient wealth to patronize the arts and sciences, a function performed by the crown and nobility in Europe. Given the relative poverty and sparsity of population of the North American Colonies, however, it is surprising that there was any scientific achievement at all, that any colonist could engage in basic or theoretical research unrelated to practical problems or to the unique natural features of the new world, let alone make a major contribution to scientific theory. On the other hand, it is not at all surprising to find more Americans elected to the Royal Society prior to the Revolution than since.

Americans in 1776 renounced their English citizenship, threw off colonial status, and by force of arms won international recognition of their political independence. The victorious patriots, however, not only found themselves excluded from the economic benefits and foreign privileges they once enjoyed as Englishmen, but were in an ambiguous cultural situation which they only vaguely understood. The American Revolution stands at the beginning, as we can see now, of two great modern trends. It initiated the violent phase of modern nationalism— the so-called age of democratic revolutions—and the long series of explosive battles for colonial independence. Today we might look upon the United States of the 1780's and 1790's as an emerging or "developing" nation. But Americans and Europeans alike saw the new Republic as full-grown, complete in every detail. The leaders of the new nation sought to undertake the impossible task of building all the institutions of a national state, *in toto*, and at once. Many agreed, for instance, on the need for a site for the national capital, independent of any of the original Colonies, symbolizing the unity of the nation and untainted by a colonial past. That the federal capital should be the center for art, architecture, and education went without saying. But such national institutions did not materialize, as they did later and with greater success during the French Revolution.

Since the leaders of both Revolutions shared similar ideas and ideals, the differing results must be explained by the history of the two events. The French Revolution, led by the middle class against monarchy and hereditary aristocracy, was from the beginning highly centralized in direction and solidified by the threat of invasion and war with the most powerful nations in Europe. The French Revolution sought to destroy the *ancien régime*; but the new Republic erected national institutions and raised science to a professional status, establishing the Ecole Centrale and in 1749 the great Ecole Polytechnique in a frantic effort to reconstruct a society to face the challenge of war. Almost all of the new institutions of the Republic, and even those founded by Napoleon, rested on firm foundations. The French educational system had long been centralized. The Ecole Centrale and Ecole Polytechnique did nothing new in this respect. What they did was to emphasize science and mathematics as utilitarian requirements for building the new society. Jean Baptiste Pierre Antoine de Monet de Lamarck (1744–1829) served as botanist for the Jardin du Roi before the Revolution, and continued in that position in the same institution, renamed the Jardin des Plantes. The old academies, including the Académie des Sciences, were closed, but the buildings, equipment, and libraries formed the basis for the new national schools and academies; and since most of France's outstanding scientists favored the Revolution, they were installed immediately in the new schools. Only a few outstanding men of science and learning were executed, like Antoine Laurent Lavoisier (1743–1794), founder of modern quantitative chemistry.

After the American Revolution, on the other hand, the states sought to maintain their longstanding political autonomy, which rested on their right to tax and to pass their own legislation. Articulate and enlightened foreigners were quick to point out to the New World rebels just what the world expected of the new nation. The Marquis de Condorcet did so in his *Influence of the American Revolution on Europe* (1786), as did Richard Price, an English liberal. Both rejoiced in the new prospect for the future of human progress, liberty, and humanity. The revolutionary leaders, caught up in this enthusiasm, were quick to abolish the vestiges of English rule, and steps were taken in some of the new states for the separation of church and state, establishment of republican forms of government, and subordination of the military to civilian rule. But the program for an enlightened society was cultural as well as political. George Washington and others were already planning for a great new national capital and a national university. John Adams enthusiastically drafted a clause in the Massachusetts Constitution of 1780, making the state responsible for the support of science education and the arts. Dr. Benjamin Rush of Philadelphia called for the immediate building of such institutions, hailed "patriots . . . come forward! Your country demands your services. Philosophers . . . your country demands your studies and speculations. . . ." He asserted that the American War was over, but ended with the ringing declaration, "THE REVOLUTION IS NOT

OVER!" Many members of the Constitutional Convention of 1787 shared these sentiments and proposed various clauses for national institutions supporting the arts, sciences, and education.

Although there was no disagreement on the need for such institutions among the leaders in the Convention and later in Congress, their vision ran aground on the submerged reef of localism. Each and every step toward centralization was jealously watched and hedged around with safeguards against "tyranny." Such centralization as did occur with the ratification of the Constitution of 1787 was inspired by financial problems and won by producing an ingeniously vague patchwork of compromise and political manipulation. The new nation started off in debt at home and abroad, sunk in depression, and with a highly unfavorable balance of trade, little foreign recognition, and less credit. Conditions scarcely favored the founding of scientific or cultural institutions. With a large proportion of U.S. capital sunk in western lands and the whole economy racked by periodic depressions, even institutions as well-established as the American Philosophical Society seem to have had only marginal economic vitality.

The Society thrived briefly after its founding in 1743, but by 1745 Franklin complained that things were not going well, for the members were "very idle gentlemen" who would take no responsibility. Between 1744 and 1768, the Society limped along, but in January of 1768, it took on new life, stimulated by the activity of a local rival, The American Society for Promoting and Propagating Useful Knowledge. The American Philosophical Society resumed regular meetings, elected new members, and allied itself with the Proprietary party. The American Society for Promoting and Propagating Useful Knowledge, on the other hand, represented the democratic party. However, the importance of the coming transit of Venus in 1769 encouraged a union of the two groups on equal terms, combining the membership as of 1768. In 1795 the enlarged American Philosophical Society had funds enough to offer a prize of $100 for essays on a system of "liberal education" for the new nation, as well as for the best method for computing the longitude from lunar observations, improvements on ships' pumps, construction of stoves or fireplaces, preservation of peach trees from premature decay, American vegetable dyes, and the best construction or improvement of lamps, especially for lighting streets.

The American Philosophical Society also obtained a piece of property in Statehouse Square near Independence Hall and erected a building of its own. During construction, however, the money ran out. Donations were solicited from members, and Franklin was the chief contributor. Even then the building had to be completed on credit, and the Society was forced to rent all of the rooms, with the exception of two, in order to pay its debts. The Society again ran into financial difficulties when, in 1835, the city of Philadelphia offered to buy its lot and building, and in anticipation of this windfall, it bought property for a new building, mortgaging all of its assets, including its library and its scientific and artistic collections. The city, however, reneged on its purchase proposal because of the financial depression of 1837, and as a result the Society came very close to bankruptcy and ruin. As before, subscriptions and members' donations saved the day. Many another less fortunate organization, however, failed within a few years of its founding. Scientific journals were generally short-lived for the same reason. Colleges foundered for lack of funds; and museums or cabinets, often begun in the interests of scientific education, were either dispersed by sheriffs' sales or forced to charge admission fees, becoming commercial ventures. The American Museum of John Scudder was bought by P. T. Barnum and became the cornerstone of his career. Individual monographs often remained in manuscript for lack of funds, or were privately published. Nathaniel Bowditch, a wealthy merchant of Salem, spent a good part of his fortune (over $12,000) to publish his annotated translation of four volumes of LaPlace's monumental five-volume *Celestial Mechanics*.

The situation did not improve until well after the Civil War. During the whole span from the close of the Revolution through 1865, neither the economy nor the political structure of the country was conducive to any continuous or large-scale public support of scientific or other cultural institutions. The country would continue to be a debtor nation technically until 1915, and would suffer scarcity of investment capital because of an unfavorable balance of trade through 1877.

The immense acquisition of western lands after the Louisiana Purchase enhanced the power and potential wealth of the federal government, sustaining continued economic expansion. The race to tap the untold riches of the West spurred on vigorous state and national projects to build canals, highways, and railroad systems. Every major coastal port city and eastern state vied in the competition to gain access to the natural wealth of the Mississippi Valley. Their optimism inspired a resurgence of foreign investment and encouraged immigration. Scientific activity shared in this stimulus through exploration, both state and national, to survey and map the region and, as it were, take inventory on the natural wealth through geological, botanical, and zoological reports. By 1850 every state and some territories had initiated a geological survey, primarily for the purpose of locating mineral resources. The race to the West supported the accumulation of scientific data in the realm of natural history and the development of the sciences and scientists in the fields of geology, botany, zoology, paleontology, and to some extent, chemistry.

The transportation revolution inspired by the competitive race to the West nurtured the technological development of the railroad and everything connected with it: steam energy, civil and mechanical engineering, and the iron and steel industry. The first phase of this boom collapsed in 1837. The depression of 1837–1840 burst the speculative bubble; and state repudiations of foreign debts very nearly shut off all sources of capital to Americans. The effect on the promotion of science and scientific institutions were disastrous. The near collapse of the American Philosophical Society was one example.

Another scientific project almost wrecked by the depression was the United States Exploring Expedition to Antarctica of 1838–1842, headed by the outspoken young Lt. John Wilkes. The Expedition materialized out of the patriotism and scientific curiosity of a master promoter, Jeremiah Reynolds. Reynolds, an Ohio lawyer, caught the vision of a great national expedition in 1829 while with a private group exploring the wonders of the southern seas. By 1836 Reynolds managed to sell Congress on supporting such an expedition to Antarctica, arguing the great commercial benefits, such as discovery of new whaling and sealing grounds. But greater still, he pointed out in flamboyant terms, would be the honors and prestige America would gain by leading the world in exploration of these little-known lands. Both politics and economy cut into the scientific corps of the Wilkes Expedition, and although it did manage to sail in August, 1838, Wilkes fought for nearly twenty years to gain funds for adequate storage, classification of materials accumulated by the expedition, and publication of the voluminous reports.

Although the United States continued to suffer from periodic economic slumps after the Civil War, the nationalizing effects of the Union victory on the political structure of the country increased the credit of the federal government. It began to use its new position to bolster flagging regional and independent enterprises. But much more dramatic was the appearance of a new species of philanthropist. In the second half of the century the tremendous prosperity of manufacturing industries, as well as transportation and banking concerns, funneled unprecedented fortunes into the hands of a few entrepreneurs, who in turn not infrequently diverted a large part of their gains to the arts and sciences. Philanthropy of this kind was a major support of scientific education and research through World War I.

After the war, with a tangible record of achievement in military technology, the physical sciences stood high in American esteem. Industry and private foundations began to lavish funds in increasing amounts to support research institutes and laboratories employing scientists full time. The federal and state governments employed scientists in a variety of bureaus, which included laboratories to carry on independent work. Government support, decreasing in the 1920's, increased again in the 1930's during the depths of depression. The phenomenal increase of scientific personnel began. Chemists, geologists, mineralogists, filled the ranks of the expanding Bureau of Mines and the various bureaus of the Department of Agriculture dealing with mineral resources and conservation; mathematicians, economists, and statisticians entered the government through the Bureau of the Budget and the Census Bureau; physiologists and biologists were drawn into the expanded Public Health Service, through the National Institutes of Health. Scientists also benefited by the establishment of the Naval Research Laboratory in 1923, the National Research Fund in 1926, the Science Advisory Board for the Tennessee Valley in 1933, the Agricultural Research Center in 1934, and the massive study financed by Congress in 1935 under the National Resources Committee. Finally, the government, in a report on the results of a long-term study, recognized the need for basic research with the publication in 1938 of *Research—A National Resource.*

The outbreak of World War II in 1939 diverted the course of development, concentrating scientific efforts on the problems of war. The great achievements of wartime science culminated in the atomic explosions at Hiroshima and Nagasaki, not only ending the war but guaranteeing the physical sciences a major place in the postwar world. In 1950 Congress gave financial security to science with a huge endowment fund, administered by the National Science Foundation. Despite this apparent major victory for science, large numbers of scientists displayed their idealogical and moral insecurity in public debates over their responsibility for the use of the atomic bomb and further development of nuclear weapons. Such discussions show the increased awareness on the part of scientists of the intricate web of relationships that constitute the involvement of science with society.

Scientific Institutions

Science in America can be studied through the histories of the societies and institutions within which it progressed. Many community leaders served as officers and contributing members for a variety of organizations, from historical societies to medical societies. Large numbers of Americans contributed to the promotion of science in the belief that, like education, it was essential to the progress, prosperity, and spread of democracy. Statements expressing this faith are included in the announced objectives of a bewildering variety of local and state organizations for the promotion of knowledge.

The development of most cultural and educational organizations from 1785 to 1865 is strikingly similar, regardless of the particular fields of interest. Almost any population center with ambition was the birthplace of one or more learned societies. Between 1785 and 1845, 107 scientific and philosophical societies or academies were founded, mainly on the east coast. In the decade from 1845 to 1855, 141 were founded, still showing a heavy concentration along the Atlantic coastal states, but also a marked move into the old Northwest Territory. In spite of the four years of Civil War, 177 societies were founded during the decade 1855–1865. Eighteenth-century organizations were general in scope, modeled on the royal societies and academies of Europe. No one yet has examined their role in the general history of American culture and in the development of American science.

Periodicals, like Benjamin Silliman's *American Journal of Science and Art*, established in 1818, aimed at a general literate audience rather than a particular group. A large proportion of the papers published by these periodicals were descriptive or theoretical in content; yet all of the societies continued and even increased their emphasis on the utilitarian nature of science.

While the constitutions and objectives of local cultural agencies proclaimed the sincerity of their pursuit of knowledge, they were, nevertheless, often the product of an intense competition between major port cities and later the cities of the West for cultural preeminence. The origin of the American Academy of Arts and Science, for example, is very largely due to John Adams' jealously for the reputation of his native state and Boston. None of these societies, however, not even the few supported by the federal government, gained the kind of national position enjoyed by their European counterparts. A number of Americans strove mightily to organize such national institutions. Peter Force formed the American Historical Society in 1837, but it failed to be more than a Washington organization and publishing outlet for Force. In 1840 Congress set up the National Institution for the Promotion of Science, but even it was national in name rather than in reality. Membership rolls were dominated by local residents. Great distances militated against nonresident participation in meetings.

It is true that communications from corresponding members were read, but these were limited in number. The absence of any nationally recognized institutional capstone in the arts, sciences, or literature left a void conducive to free-ranging imagination and inquiry, but at the price of rampant charlatanism and competition. The competitors for cultural dominance—Boston, New York, Philadelphia, Baltimore, Washington, D.C., Charleston, and New Orleans—vied with one another but failed to lift themselves out of a narrow localism.

Several other types of institutions founded during this period helped mold the development and character of science in America. The first of these was the mechanics' institute, a widespread movement represented and to a large degree initiated by the founding in 1842 of the Franklin Institute of the State of Pennsylvania for the Promotion of the Mechanic Arts. The objective of the mechanics' institute was to encourage manufactures through popular lectures, prizes, and the publication of journals. The mechanics' institutes were geared to a lay public with no special education. Baltimore established the Maryland Institute for Promotion of Mechanic Arts in 1825, the same year in which a group organized the Middlesex Mechanic Association at Lowell, Massachusetts. Just over a decade later, the movement reached westward with the appearance of the Mechanics' Institute of Chicago.

Three other concurrent movements contributed in different ways to educating the public. The public school movement gathered momentum in the 1820's, dramatized in the 1830's by the organizing skill and evangelical zeal of such leaders as Horace Mann, Henry Barnard, and Caleb Wiley in the South. This movement culminated in the establishment in most states of tax-supported, free public schools, normal schools, teachers' societies and school journals. Public schools with trained teachers not only raised the literacy of the country but nurtured the national quest for learning and self-improvement. The library movement spurred on establishment of public and school libraries. The publishing industry aggressively sought employment for the enormously increased capacity of its rotary and steam presses. Publishing houses multiplied and spread the literature of science, both European and American, through popular books and textbooks.

The Lyceum movement, initially launched in 1800 by Dr. George Birkbeck, a professor of chemistry at the University of Glasgow, gained international recognition. The Lyceum had behind it the London Mechanics Institution and *Mechanics Magazine*. Birkbeck, sponsored by Lord Henry Brougham, could boast in 1824 of an enrollment of 1,000 workmen (at 20 shillings a head) in courses of lectures on mechanics, chemistry, geometry, hydrostatics, and the application of chemistry to the arts, astronomy and electricity. The Lyceum in the United States was initiated in 1826 by a former laboratory assistant of Benjamin Silliman, Josiah Holbrook. Under Holbrook's direction, the Lyceum sponsored traveling lecturers for local organizations, tied together in a loose national lecture circuit between 1846 and 1860.

The profusion, decentralization, and popularity of these local societies for the promotion and diffusion of knowledge were an integral part of the development of American science and scientific pursuits. The exceedingly small number of men devoting their lives to scientific research in the United States could hardly have done so without the backing of these organizations, which furnished forums for popular lectures and often organized popular financial support for scientific projects. For instance, in Cincinnati a young mathematics professor, railroad engineer, and graduate of West Point, Ormsby McKnight Mitchell, gave an exceedingly popular series of slide lectures on astronomy, which ended with a plea for support for an observatory. The lectures were successful enough to send Mitchell to Europe in 1843 to buy the finest telescope available. Many people who could not contribute cash demonstrated their interest by helping to building the observatory for the telescope. Amos Eaton (1776–1842), a New York lawyer, after attending one of Benjamin Silliman's popular lectures on geology, was so intrigued that at the age of forty he gave up the law to lecture on science and in 1824 gained the financial backing of Stephen Van Rensselaer for the Rensselaer Polytechnic Institute.

Local organizations issued publications and thus furnished an outlet for scientific papers and a means of obtaining by exchange whole libraries of similar publications from other states and from Europe. This kind of popular community support and invidual philanthropic endowment played an important role in the arts too. Academies of fine arts supported artists and established museums, while cities, states, and the federal government purchased art work and encouraged competition through prize awards. The traveling exhibit and lecture which developed from Charles Wilson Peale's continuous mural for eight sides of a cupola at Annapolis became a mainstay of the lecture circuit. Philadelphians founded the Pennsylvania Academy of Fine Arts in 1805 to promote the "cultivation of the fine arts in the U.S.A." In the same year, New York businessmen organized the New York Academy of Fine Arts, and by 1812 Cincinnati had its own academy.

Historical societies proliferated in equal proportion to the scientific and artistic societies.

The proliferation of organizations before the Civil War not only belies the facile generalization that Americans did not support culture, but is evidence of a vigorous and unique national culture which displayed a frustrated ambivalence: on the one hand a distrust of all products of the older monarchies, and on the other hand a desperate desire for European recognition to be won by competing on European terms. America and the New World continents, since their discovery, have made their most significant contributions to knowledge through forcing European philosophers and theorists to adjust to empirical data. Nathaniel Bowditch modestly made important corrections of errors in LaPlace's *Celestial Mechanics*, as well as adding necessary mathematical proofs and full explanations. Simon Newcomb not only corrected but extended Hansen's Tables for the variations in the motions of the moon. American paleontologists Edward C. Cope, O. C. Marsh, and Joseph Leidy managed to supply extensive evidence which deflated early theories of the recent creation of the New World continents. Later, Albert A. Michelson and Edward W. Morley, in the course of performing "the most famous experiment that failed," disproved the existence of ether and left a major gap in the unity of Newtonian physics. These, of course, are but a few of the most famous examples.

Economic and social theories, too, found their testing grounds in the backwoods utopias of the New World. Anthropological descriptions of the American Indians forced recognition that man in a "state of nature" was not necessarily freer, happier, or better. All great ideas, as well as fads, eventually migrated to America; and if the sojourn was not fatal, none escaped unchanged by the experience.

In the 1830's and 1840's there was a marked drive toward a greater degree of specialization among the sciences, but efforts to organize along these lines generally failed, because the model remained the European national society or academy. From the beginning, plans for establishing a professional community of scientists rested on expectations of federal support, which were consistently disappointed as scientists ran afoul of local jealousies and federal politics. Another obstacle confronting this early movement toward professional organization was the low degree of specialization and small number of professional men. Most of the professional scientists had universal interests, making it difficult for them to categorize themselves as chemists, geologists, physicists, astronomers, or mathematicians. The exact number of professionally-minded men is shrouded in the haze of contemporary rhetoric of assertive patriotism demanding an American science and literature, within which it is difficult to discern the sincere cries to unite "the real working men . . . of science" in order to establish standards and set themselves off from "mere inventors," "charlatans," and amateurs.

Some semblance of national organization did appear in the form of the American Association for the Advancement of Science. Yet, even with its inclusive membership and peripatetic meetings, it still represented the European ideal of embracing all "philosophy" in one national society. The ideal was even more nearly realized in 1863, when a group of Harvard professors and government scientists, led by Alexander Dallas Bache, succeeded in obtaining a charter from Congress creating a National Academy of Science. Although the motive was professional, the ostensible purpose of the academy was to mobilize science for the Union war effort. This organization, too, failed in the end to gain federal appropriations or to exert the kind of influence that its European counterparts enjoyed. It became, as one critic said, an organization whose only contribution was to publish obituaries of its honored dead.

After the Civil War the development of institutions within which scientists could function took an entirely different course. Scientists found a new base of support in the developing university and graduate school system. They were able to pursue highly specialized interests in fields that now had fairly well-defined conceptual boundaries. Therefore, the tendency was to organize along the lines defined by their teaching and research fields. The rapid accumulation of highly technical and empirical data in ever more highly specialized fields not only made advanced training a prerequisite to original scientific work but hastened the disengagement of science from general education in the colleges. One or two men teaching natural philosophy could not hope to understand, let alone teach, all science; yet when men sought to specialize teaching and research, they either ran into opposition from the proponents of general education or were isolated when students shunned their lectures. Colleagues, once able to communicate on the common ground of Newtonian mechanics or natural history, neither understood nor cared about the discoveries of Faraday, Helmholtz, Lord Kelvin, or Maxwell.

Meanwhile, more and more need was felt for advanced, specialized training not available in the United States. Partly in answer to this need, the number of young men traveling to European universities for advanced degrees or training increased in the decade of the 1850's. One thousand went to German universities, and the number nearly doubled after the Civil War. At home, state and private universities expanded rapidly between 1868 and 1892. Utilizing government subsidies under the Morrill Land-Grant Act of 1862, many states founded agricultural and mechanical colleges or further subsidized existing state institutions. Cornell University opened its doors in 1868 with the combined support of the state, the federal government, and the private benefaction of Ezra Cornell, whose fortune was based on the telegraph. The presidents of the new universities had themselves been trained in European universities in the 1850's; once given the mandate, they sought to revolutionize American higher education on European models. They emphasized graduate training and research and placed technical education on a par with the classical curriculum. The ambitions of state and local culture now centered on the university, and the measure of excellence became the number of highly trained specialists on the faculty, preferably with advanced degrees —meaning, until the end of the nineteenth century, degrees from European universities, particularly the highly successful German institutions.

The young men returning from Europe to academic positions in the United States were not content with learned societies which included amateurs as well as professionals. They often found the older publication outlets closed to their work or the work of their students, as for instance did James Joseph Sylvester, the great English mathematician at the Johns Hopkins University. Sylvester launched the Johns Hopkins series of mathematical monographs and was in 1894 the prime mover in turning the New York Mathematical Society, a local organization, into the American Mathematical Society, a national and professional group.

The reorganization of the American Association for the Advancement of Science in 1874 into a number of new sections under a new constitution was an effort to recognize the interests of specialists and avert disintegration. But the change was not sufficient to halt the movement toward associations of specialists. The chemists had indeed threatened a national chemical organization during the same year at the Priestly Centennial Celebration at Northumberland, Pennsylvania, and this was curtailed by the action of the Association. Two years later, however, chemists organized the American Chemical Society in New York City, and so began the formation of other local organiza-

tions, which joined under national charter in 1891. Physicians who
were engaged in research in the medical schools formed the American
Physiological Society in 1887. The Association of American Anatomists followed the next year. Then came the American Society of
Zoologists, 1890; The Botanical Society of America, 1894; American
Astronomical Society, 1897; American Society for Microbiology,
1899; followed by the American Physical Society and other professional organizations of specialists too numerous to list.

The development of national professional organizations reveals a
consistent pattern. Almost all were organized by young, professionally-
trained men who were rebellious against some element of the established order. They had in common the need to establish their own
identity as scientists, a forum for meeting and reading of papers, and
a means for publishing their work and that of their students. Often
elder statesmen with national reputations, although amateurs, served
as presidents of the new organizations. The first twenty years of such
a society's life usually served to establish its structural pattern, and
usually produced its most original work. All officers and work done
were on a voluntary basis. Hence, the men most concerned in organizing the society took on most of the work, serving many years in
office and forming an establishment or orthodoxy of their own.

Meanwhile, amateurs were forced out by the nature of the papers
and interests of the professionals, rather than by any exclusive membership policies. The election of a professionally trained and research-
oriented scholar as president can be seen as a sign of professional
security. Each of the new organizations rapidly became too general
for the growing number of specialties within its jurisdiction. In turn,
new organizations with more specialized publications were created,
and the worst fears of the old school seemed to be coming true. Increasing specialization and multiple independent organizations isolated
scientists one from another.

Actually, only during a short period from the 1870's to the 1890's
did scientific fields, such as chemistry, physics, astronomy, geology,
and biology seem clearly defined by conceptual boundaries. The splin-
tering action of specialization has generally resulted from a composite
of knowledge and techniques of several fields, making the new workers
half-breeds, unwelcome in any established society and forced into a
separate organization. For instance, Mendel's theory of inherited characteristics was not "lost," but resisted, partially because he applied
statistics to botany; and in 1901 Karl Pearson and Francis Galton
founded the journal, *Biometrika*, in response to the Royal Society's

decree that "mathematics should be kept apart from biological applications." In 1906 the American Physiological Society (1887) gave birth to the American Society of Biological Chemists, and in 1925 Leonard Bloomfield, finding no place in philology or anthropology for his studies of spoken language, founded the Linguistic Society of America.

Since World War II, although the trend continues, there is a widening recognition of the interrelatedness of knowledge in all fields and the necessity for opening lines of communication between specialties. Evidence of an emerging ecumenical movement to reunite the sciences, if not the whole culture, may be found in the work of James Bryant Conant, the popular discussions of C. P. Snow's *The Two Cultures*, and in 1963, the organization of the Scientists' Institute for Public Information. Such a movement, however, faces enormous problems of specialized language, techniques, concepts, and handling of the massive information explosion.

Even before 1900, a handful of perceptive men in the United States began to doubt the ultimate value of the sciences, even though science seemed to go from one success to another. The pessimism about science of Mark Twain and Henry Adams, for example, can be traced directly to their somewhat random and often faulty knowledge of science. The materialistic determinism of nineteenth-century science implied that the moral "progress" of mankind was an illusion, and scientific "progress" a directionless amassing of knowledge. The disenchantment gathered momentum with the impact of Freudian psychology, with Einstein's theory of relativity, and finally Werner Heisenberg's uncertainty principle. The distress of the nonscientist scholar was summed up in 1928 in Joseph Wood Krutch's book, *The Modern Temper*. Yet in the same year the physicist and Nobel laureate Robert A. Millikan asserted, with all seriousness, a naïve faith in progress, as scientific knowledge continued to accumulate in a steady assault on ignorance and superstition. Deploring the pessimistic tendencies of his contemporaries in literature and the arts, Millikan insisted that modern literature had become infested with emotional, destructive, oversexed, and neurotic influences. Therefore, since the humanists were ignorant in regard to scientific progress and corrupted by modern trends in literature and art, the scientists remained the real humanists, bringing order into our conception of the physical world and making man the master of his own fate.

The calm faith in the rightness of scientific progress exemplified by Millikan was described in the early 1930's by the Columbia University sociologist Robert Merton as the "ethos of science." Since World War II and the tragic consequences at Hiroshima and Nagasaki, the scientific world itself has been divided. The question of Henry James about the moral direction of scientific activity, a question which once seemed totally irrelevant to science, has now come after all to be a vital concern to many of the highest-ranking scientists. To their credit, scientists have not in general taken the traditional escape route of American business—one morality for the market place and one for citizenship. But on the other hand, they have not yet been able to find means to recapture the kind of rapport with modern society and a place in its culture that science had in less complicated times. The problem of the scientist's responsibility for his acts perplexes the scientific community at precisely the time when it has won economic and political support beyond the wildest dreams of John Adams and Thomas Jefferson. The present-day exaltation of science has been accompanied by the realization that scientific activity cannot be dissociated from its social, political, and economic environment, and that the growth of science cannot be separated from the mainstream of history, any more than the main flow of history can be complete without taking account of the science of its time.

Science in American Industry

Kendall A. Birr*

The impact of science on American industry in the second third of the twentieth century is so obvious and so omnipresent that we need to be reminded that it was not always so. Indeed, a technology dependent upon, or a branch of, applied science is a relatively recent development. For most of human history, science and technology were separate enterprises with differing objectives and conducted by different individuals and even different classes of people.

SEPARATION OF SCIENCE AND TECHNOLOGY

The roots of technology are hidden in prehistory. But from very early times, man learned to construct tools and manipulate nature for his own purposes. Agricultural techniques, pottery, textiles, various kinds of metalworking, building construction, printing, development of various nonhuman sources of power—including domestic animals, the waterwheel and the windmill—and even primitive chemical techniques, most notably those that produced dyes and gunpowder, were all products of artisans and manufacturers unacquainted with science. The improvement of industrial techniques was generally attributable to the innovations of skilled and imaginative craftsmen. Innovations become part of the established techniques of the craft—for a variety of reasons, most of which can be summarized by saying that they were economically desirable under the industrial conditions of a particular

* KENDALL A. BIRR was born in Wheaton, Illinois, in 1924. He received his B.A. degree from Cornell College and his M.S. and Ph.D. degrees from the University of Wisconsin. He has taught at the University of California at Berkeley and at Amherst College and is presently Professor of History and Chairman of the Division of Social Science at the State University of New York at Albany. He is the author (with Merle Curti) of *Prelude to Point Four* (Madison, 1954) and of *Pioneering in Industrial Research* (Washington, D.C., 1957); of articles in the *Mississippi Valley Historical Review*, *Isis*, and other journals; and of numerous reviews in scholarly journals.

time and place. The methods and techniques were transmitted from generation to generation, a pattern of technical education which was formalized, beginning in the Middle Ages, in the apprenticeship system. The source of technological knowledge was empiricism, the motivation was utilitarian, the innovator and conservator of technology was the craftsman.

The roots of science are similarly hidden in prehistory. Yet, by its very nature, we know more about the origins of science than of technology. For science is something more than observed phenomena; it is "the rational correlated knowledge of natural phenomena . . . a consistent discipline with experiment and observation as its sanctions and mathematics as its logic. . . ."[1] Such knowledge was produced by the relatively well-educated classes and preserved and transmitted in writing. Science as we know it is largely the product of an aristocratic class, and its discoveries have, from an early date, become part of the written record of human society.

Until sometime in the nineteenth century, science and technology led separate careers. There were several reasons for this. The most obvious was that before the nineteenth century, science had, for the most part, not produced generalizations that were of any clear use to industry. The history of science is replete with examples of scientific investigations which ultimately explained a long-practiced technology. Brewing, for example, was an ancient and much-appreciated art; yet scientists did not understand the processes involved until Pasteur's investigations into yeast in the 1860's.[2] Factors other than the lag of scientific knowledge help explain this separation. Class differences were also involved. Science was the product of a literate, educated aristocracy; technology belonged to the lower and middle classes. Class barriers were often difficult to cross, particularly when the educated aristocracies often disdained handicrafts and ignored the utilitarian.[3]

The history of the impact of science on American industry is largely a history of the coming together of these two traditions—science and

---

[1] A. R. Hall, "The Scientific Movement and Its Influence on Thought and Material Development," *The New Cambridge Modern History*, 12 vols. in progress, ed., J. P. T. Bury (Cambridge, Eng., 1957–), X, 49.

[2] T. K. Derry and Trevor I. Williams, *A Short History of Technology* (New York and Oxford, 1961), p. 695.

[3] For brief discussions of the separation of science and technology, see J. D. Bernal, *The Social Function of Science* (New York, 1939), chap. ii, and Robert P. Multhauf, "The Scientist and the 'Improver' of Technology," *Technology and Culture*, I (Winter 1959), 38–47.

technology. However, the story of that courtship and marriage is not a simple one. In part, it involves the history of the maturation of science and its infusion into existing technology. More often, as we shall see, science and technology have been involved in a complex interrelationship, each feeding upon the other. In addition, it is both parochial and misleading to discuss the relations between American science and industry alone, for both science and technology have shown scant respect for political boundaries. For much of its history, the United States has been a cultural province of a larger European society, and any discussion of the impact of science on American industry inevitably involves a discussion of the introduction of European scientific and technological ideas into American practice. Only occasionally before the twentieth century was there a reverse flow.

The separation of science and technology in early American society is apparent if one looks at the technology that underlay American manufacturing in the seventeenth and eighteenth centuries. Even a brief survey demonstrates that most industry was based on relatively primitive technologies, that these technologies changed only slowly, and that they were dependent only to a minor degree upon science.[4] Two illustrations must suffice.

First, a large proportion of manufacturing before the nineteenth century was conducted in relatively small craft shops. The key figure in these shops was the skilled artisan, inheritor of centuries of empirically derived skills, trained in his family or in an apprenticeship system. The number and variety of these craftsmen is astonishing. York, Pennsylvania, had 39 separate trades represented among its taxpayers in 1779. A complete list of the skilled craftsmen in the eighteenth century would doubtless number even more. Of their skill there is little doubt; the products of some of the eighteenth-century silversmiths and joiners and cabinetmakers are highly prized today. Yet, with one or two exceptions to be noted, it is difficult to find any evidence of science in their skills.[5]

Second, beyond the shops of the skilled artisans were larger organizations of industrial production, the mill and furnace industries. These manufacturing establishments generally required power-driven machinery or other expensive equipment that necessitated moderate-sized organizations involving capital investment and numbers of employees

---

[4] See Victor S. Clark, *History of Manufactures in the United States*, 3 vols. (New York, 1929), I, 161–81, and Curtis P. Nettels, *The Emergence of a National Economy, 1775–1815* (New York, 1962), chap. xiii.

[5] Carl Bridenbaugh, *The Colonial Craftsman* (New York, 1950).

considerably beyond the characteristic craft shop. Some of the larger enterprises, in 1815, employed 150 people and represented an investment of close to $200,000.[6] Among the more important of the mill and furnace industries was iron. Blessed with excellent supplies of crucial raw materials, particularly wood for charcoal, Americans were turning out one-seventh of the world's annual iron production by the eve of the American Revolution. Scattered throughout the colonies were bloomeries, primitive blast furnaces, casting facilities, small steel works, refining forges, and slitting mills. The technology was primitive. The bloomeries were little more than enlarged blacksmith's forges; blast furnaces used only a single tuyère for applying a cold blast; and the power used was confined generally to oxen-operated bellows or primitive waterpower installations. Nothing was known of the chemistry of the blast furnace operation in pre-Lavoisier days, and it is doubtful if the elementary understanding of iron metallurgy developed by Réaumur in 1722 was known in America. Equally important, the industry gave many signs of technological stagnation; American iron men stuck to charcoal in preference to coal, preferred the waterwheel to the steam engine, and were generally slow to introduce the new iron technology developing in eighteenth-century England.[7]

Yet it would not be accurate to emphasize the separation of science and technology in the eighteenth century without pointing out some of the points of juncture between the two traditions that foreshadowed future developments. Most of these junctures were examples of tentative aid offered one tradition by the other, not serious mergers of science and technology. Probably the most significant aid to science from the technological tradition was in the realm of scientific instruments; improved methods of making optical glass made possible the early telescopes and microscopes which opened whole new areas of scientific knowledge. Almost as important, problems posed by the operation of pumps in seventeenth-century mines motivated studies of the vacuum and air pressure with momentous results for the developing discipline of physics.

For its part, science provided insight useful to practical men of affairs. The needs of navigation motivated much work in astronomy and provided the main impetus for the development of the chronometer, essential for the determination of longitude. Similarly, astronomical knowledge and mathematics made possible accurate land meas-

---

[6] Nettels, p. 264.

[7] *Ibid.*, pp. 272–73; Bridenbaugh, p. 61; Clark, I, 169–75.

urement; without a doubt, surveying became one of the most widely used branches of applied science in eighteenth-century America. The new mechanics of the seventeenth century were quickly applied to problems of ballistics.[8] The role of science in the development of the steam engine is a moot question, but one can at least argue that scientific knowledge of atmospheric pressures was important in the development of the Newcomen engine, while a recent author has asserted that Watt approached the problem of improving the steam engine by analyzing what was initially a laboratory instrument and the physical processes involved in its operations.[9]

If only a few men managed to combine science and technology in their work, many others in Europe and America aspired to. One of the cardinal assumptions of eighteenth-century enlightened thought held that the principles of science could be applied to the improvement of man's material conditions. Many of the scientific societies of the eighteenth century took on a marked utilitarian cast. Both scientists and industrialists discussed technical problems in organizations such as the Lunar Society of Birmingham, the Manchester Literary and Philosophical Society, and the American Philosophical Society. Nowhere was this utilitarian emphasis more in evidence than in America. Devotees of science in this country attempted to drum up popular support for science by emphasizing its utility. If the immediate fruits of this faith were meager, the faith remained as a guarantee that the possibilities of productive interplay between science and technology would not be overlooked when it became more feasible.[10]

In colonial America no man exemplified the growing relations between science and technology better than Benjamin Franklin. Devoted to both, he was convinced that the two were mutually helpful. If Franklin's most important contribution to science was his theory of electricity, it was a theory that led to an eminently practical device, the lightning rod. The man who could advance a wave theory of light

---

[8] Stephen F. Mason, *A History of the Sciences*, rev. ed. (New York, 1962), pp. 243–55, 269–71; R. J. Forbes, *Man the Maker: A History of Technology and Engineering* (New York, 1950), pp. 140–44; G. N. Clark, *Science and Social Welfare in the Age of Newton*, 2nd ed. (Oxford, 1947), pp. 20–29, 76–78; Derry and Williams, p. 703.

[9] Milton Kerker, "Science and the Steam Engine," *Technology and Culture*, II (Fall 1961), 381–90.

[10] Mason, pp. 285–87; Brooke Hindle, *The Pursuit of Science in Revolutionary America, 1735–1789* (Chapel Hill, N.C., 1956), pp. 190–94; John C. Greene, "Science and the Public in the Age of Jefferson," *Isis*, XLIX (March 1958), 22–25.

also applied his talents to the invention of bifocals and the development of an improved stove.[11]

Yet these promising examples of collaboration between science and industry were not to multiply and bear fruit, even in the early stages of what historians conventionally refer to as the "Industrial Revolution." Historians still argue over precisely what the Industrial Revolution was, but nearly all agree that it was a complex socioeconomic development characterized in part by an increase in the rate of technological change.[12] A survey of the major technological changes associated with the early nineteenth century reveals quite readily how little these changes depended on scientific knowledge. Nearly all represented significant improvements in traditional craft techniques. At best, the contributions of science to these innovations were ancillary rather than central.

The great symbol of the Industrial Revolution was the steam engine. Newcomen's early machines and Watt's improvements in the eighteenth century involved, as we have noted, some interchange between scientists and engineers. Yet the basic principles of thermodynamics underlying the operation of any steam engine were not established until the middle of the nineteenth century. In the United States, the chief contributor to the improvement of the steam engine was Oliver Evans, a protean technological figure, who developed a relatively efficient high-pressure engine. Evans had no formal scientific training; he attended a country school until age fourteen and was then apprenticed to a wagonmaker. While he used all of his leisure moments to read books on mathematics and mechanics, his improvements were the product of exceptional mechanical skill rather than of scientific knowledge. Characteristically, his chief publication was *The Young Mill-Wright & Miller's Guide* (1795), which went through numerous editions and became a standard guide to young American mechanics.[13] There is little evidence to suggest that the host of engi-

---

[11] There are contrasting interpretations of Franklin's relationship to science in Carl Becker, "Benjamin Franklin," *Dictionary of American Biography*, 22 vols., ed., Allen Johnson *et al.* (New York, 1927–1958), VI, 588–89, 597–98 (hereafter cited as *DAB*), and Daniel J. Boorstin, *The Americans: The Colonial Experience* (New York, 1964), pp. 251–59. See also I. B. Cohen, ed., *Benjamin Franklin's Experiments* (Cambridge, Mass., 1941); I. B. Cohen, *Franklin and Newton* (Philadelphia, 1956); and Hindle, pp. 74–79.

[12] See Eric Lampard, *Industrial Revolution: Interpretations and Perspectives* (Washington, D.C., 1957) for an intelligent discussion of the whole problem.

[13] Derry and Williams, pp. 340–42; Carl W. Mitman, "Oliver Evans," *DAB*, VI, 208–9; Greville and Dorothy Bathe, *Oliver Evans, A Chronicle of Early American Engineering* (Philadelphia, 1935).

neers who applied steam power to factories, boats, and railroads drew on scientific knowledge to any extent greater than Evans did.

If the steam engine was the symbolic machine of the early Industrial Revolution, iron was its material. Without cheap iron the machinery revolution would have been impossible. The iron industry had undergone major changes in eighteenth-century England. Blast furnaces increased in size; steam-driven pumps increased the force of the blast and enabled English ironmasters to make the crucial shift from charcoal to coal. By 1828, the Scotsman James Neilson was heating the blast. Equally as important, the puddling process, combined with rolling mills, made possible the production of large amounts of relatively cheap wrought iron.

These innovations were based on empirical knowledge rather than on scientific understanding. On the whole, American ironmasters were slow to adopt the newer innovations, sometimes for valid economic reasons, often from ignorance. But the general picture of the American iron industry in the early nineteenth century is of one dominated by practical men who frowned on scientific "theorists." There were, to be sure, some exceptions. Abram Hewitt made a point of familiarizing himself with the growing literature on metallurgy but found it of only limited usefulness. John Fritz, one of America's most eminent nineteenth-century steel plant engineers, recalled in later life the puzzling problems of quality control that vexed ironmasters in the 1840's when they lacked satisfactory methods of chemical analysis. Before the Civil War, Victor Clark concluded, "Scientific study of the structure and composition of iron had little influence on manufacturing procedure even abroad, and American furnace-men were prejudiced strongly against theorists meddling in their industry."[14]

The ability to construct machines either of wood or of metal depended on the mechanic's ability to shape these materials. This is the basic function of machine tools, and striking improvements in such tools constituted one of the major technological achievements of the early Industrial Revolution. The basic tools involved were very old, and the late eighteenth- and early nineteenth-century makers of machine tools introduced striking improvements rather than completely new devices. Yet these improvements were crucial; for the first time

---

[14] Allan Nevins, *Abram S. Hewitt* (New York, 1935), pp. 137–40; John Fritz, *The Autobiography of John Fritz* (New York, 1912), pp. 50–52, 55–56; V. S. Clark, I, 415; W. Paul Strassmann, *Risk and Technological Innovation: American Manufacturing Methods during the Nineteenth Century* (Ithaca, 1959), pp. 22–32, 46–47.

in history, manufacturers and mechanics were able to shape metal parts with considerable precision and at relatively small cost. Most of the major innovations were made in England, but Americans contributed substantially, particularly in the development of slide and turret lathes, milling machines, and gear cutters.

The new machine tools so improved precision in shaping materials as to make possible the manufacture of interchangeable parts and that rationalization of manufacturing processes that we call mass production. The small-arms industry in America was the scene of the development of some of the most creative ideas in mass production; Eli Whitney and Simeon North at the beginning of the century and Samuel Colt and Elisha Root toward the middle of the century made the most striking contributions. But before the Civil War, the basic principle was applied to the manufacture of clocks and watches, locks, agricultural implements, and sewing machines. While Americans were not exclusively responsible for these developments, they were among the leaders.

The improvement of machine tools and the development of mass production methods based on interchangeable parts were the work of master mechanics, not of scientists. One looks in vain for evidence of innovators with formal scientific training applying scientific principles to the improvement of these tools. Machine tools and interchangeable parts were the purview of those master mechanics of legendary skill such as the local American blacksmith who, John Fritz assures us, was capable of constructing a six-horsepower steam engine using only the most primitive kinds of machine tools. Mechanical engineering was to remain an empirical art well into the second half of the nineteenth century.[15]

The development of steam and the improvement of waterpower combined with the availability of inexpensive iron and improved machine tools made possible the creation of a wide variety of new machines in industry. None were more characteristic of the early stages of the Industrial Revolution than the textile machines. Their names —the flying shuttle, the spinning jenny, the water frame, the mule—

---

[15] There are good accounts of the development of machine tools in Abbot P. Usher, *A History of Mechanical Inventions* (New York, 1929), chap. xii; K. R. Gilbert, "Machine-Tools," *A History of Technology*, 5 vols., ed., Charles Singer *et al.*, (New York and London, 1954–1958), IV, chap. xiv; D. F. Galloway, "Machine-Tools," *ibid.*, V, chap. xxvi; and Strassmann, chap. iv. See also Jeannette Mirsky and Allan Nevins, *The World of Eli Whitney* (New York, 1952), esp. chap. xiii; Robert S. Woodbury, "The Legend of Eli Whitney and Interchangeable Parts," *Technology and Culture*, I (Summer 1960), 235–53; and Fritz, p. 33.

are familiar to even the most casual student of the Industrial Revolution, even if their principles are not. While the basic innovations were English or French, Americans made significant contributions in the nineteenth century toward making the new machines faster and more automatic. The important point is that the key innovations were not dependent on scientific information or training but represented new and ingenious ways of performing long-understood operations. It is no denigration of the contributions of these inventors to point out that they were skilled mechanics rather than trained scientists.[16]

The same generalization holds for other areas of industry that were transformed by technological innovations in the early nineteenth century. The manufacture of clothing and of boots and shoes was revolutionized by the sewing machine. The hat industry and paper-making were mechanized to some degree. Canning processes and vulcanization of rubber were developed with no understanding of the bacteriological and chemical principles involved. On the American scene, no device was more characteristic of the empirical ingenuity of these inventors than Oliver Evans' highly mechanized flour mill of 1785. He improved existing mill machinery, introducing elevators, conveyors, hoppers, and other mechanical devices, completely mechanizing the process of converting grain into meal and flour. In such a mill, six men could annually convert 100,000 bushels of grain into flour in what one historian cautiously observes "may have been the first instance of an uninterrupted process of mechanical manufacturing . . . in the history of industry."[17] The mill was a marvel of mechanized materials handling. It was a triumph of mechanical ingenuity, not of science.

SCIENCE AND INDUSTRY INTERACT

By the middle of the nineteenth century, a profound change started to take place as the scientific and technological traditions began to interact in several areas. The fundamental prerequisite for this development was the growth of scientific knowledge to a point at which applied science became both a possibility and a reality. Evidence that this was occurring in the nineteenth century would constitute a catalog

---

[16] Usher, chap. ix, has a good brief account of the development of textile machinery; see also Strassmann, chap. iii.

[17] V. S. Clark, I, 179. Roger Burlingame, *March of the Iron Men* (New York, 1943) provides a semipopular account of many of these inventions on the American scene.

of the century's scientific discoveries. Most obvious, perhaps, were the establishment of chemistry, both organic and inorganic, on a sound theoretical basis and the development of certain areas of physics, notably electricity and heat. The development of the biological sciences was to be more important for medicine and agriculture than for industry, but the establishment of generally accepted principles of interpreting geological data was to have important implications for the mining industry. Clearly, the proliferation of scientific knowledge and the establishment of basic systems of interpreting the data had by mid-nineteenth century removed one of the great barriers to the development of applied science.

It was more difficult, however, to persuade manufacturers and mechanics to make use of scientific knowledge and to convince scientists that technological problems were important, partly because of overt hostility. Many nineteenth-century mechanics and craftsmen sneered at mere scientific "theorizing." Similarly, there is no doubt that a good many scientists denigrated the importance of applying their new scientific knowledge and techniques. But perhaps more important was the simple difficulty in getting representatives of both the technological and scientific traditions to concern themselves with each other. Craftsmen and mechanics were absorbed in the elaboration of their own techniques. Similarly, scientists turned more naturally to the problems suggested by the logic of the evolution of scientific knowledge than to those arising out of economic and technological activity.

While such matters are almost impossible to measure, it seems likely that these particular barriers were more easily overcome in the United States than in Western Europe. The tradition of "pure" science was never as strong in this country as abroad, while most Americans shared to an extraordinary degree in the hope of the Enlightenment that science could and would be applied to the improvement of man's material welfare. In the 1830's, Alexis de Tocqueville could assert with confidence that while pure science, applied science, and technology could be "separately cultivated . . . reason and experience prove that no one of them can prosper long if it is absolutely cut off from the two others."[18] And when he analyzed the American scene, De Tocqueville was less concerned with demonstrating the pervasive American concern with applied science than he was with explaining it.

---

[18] Alexis de Tocqueville, *Democracy in America*, 2 vols., ed., Phillips Bradley (New York, 1954), II, 43; see II, First Book, chap. x, "Why the Americans Are More Addicted to Practical than to Theoretical Science."

The result in nineteenth-century America was the differential application of science to industry. Initially, science came as an aid rather than a system. Individual industrial firms made effective use of particular scientific techniques or special pieces of scientific information without absorbing the scientific method or seeing the traditional technology assimilated to emerging applied science. Thus, American ironmasters hired chemists to make analyses of their operations long before there was thorough understanding of the scientific processes involved. The result was that some industries were hardly affected by science in the nineteenth century or at best were affected only in ancillary ways. But there were a few industries which from the beginning were science-based, and these provided the most spectacular examples of the marriage of science and technology.

Science and the Electrical Industry

The electrical industry was one of the most striking examples of an industry which from its origins was based, not on a craft tradition, but upon scientific discovery. Electricity had long been an object of curiosity. The ancient world knew something of magnetism, and some unknown medieval men introduced the compass into common use. But systematic investigation of the phenomenon began only with William Gilbert's *De Magnete* (1600). The eighteenth century saw the development of the first electrostatic machines and early attempts to devise theories to explain rapidly mounting collections of data. In America, as we have noted, Franklin contributed significantly to these developments. Experimenters in the eighteenth century were handicapped in their work, however, by the lack of a reliable source of electric current; this problem was resolved by Alessandro Volta, who in 1799 devised the first electric cell. Subsequently, Ampère and Ohm worked out the relationship between potential, current, and resistance in an electrical circuit.

The really crucial discoveries of the early nineteenth century, however, were those linking electric current with magnetism. In 1820, Hans Christian Oersted demonstrated that a wire carrying an electric current would rotate round a magnetic pole and that, conversely, a magnet tended to move around a stationary wire carrying a current. In England, Michael Faraday, and in the United States, Joseph Henry, discovered electromagnetic induction, thereby linking electric currents, magnetism, and general mechanical motion. These discoveries provided the basic ideas necessary for the development of the electrical industry of the nineteenth century: electromagnets, electrical circuits, motors, and generators were all implied in these early discoveries.[19]

While Henry had experimented in Albany in 1831 with a primitive telegraph, like many scientists he was not particularly interested in developing practical applications of some of his discoveries. But others were. By the early 1830's, all the theoretical ingredients for a successful telegraph were at hand: a steady sources of current from the battery, conductors that would carry current over considerable distances, and the electromagnet which could be used to detect signal impulses. A good many inventors rushed forward, and several produced workable designs. The major credit for developing a practical device, however, must go to an English anatomist, William Cooke, and an American painter, Samuel F. B. Morse. Neither was a scientist; both, however, turned for assistance to trained scientists, Cooke to the eminent English physicist, Charles Wheatstone, Morse to a New York chemist, Leonard D. Gale. The development of extensive telegraph networks and the ultimate laying of an Atlantic cable were more the work of persistent entrepreneurs and self-taught technicians than of scientists. The most rapid technical progress and the most sophisticated parts of the system were concerned with methods of detecting the signals, a part of the system which required little scientific knowledge and to which ingenious workmen could apply themselves with success. By contrast, batteries which provided the all-important current source were improved only slowly, chiefly because of limitations in knowledge of electrochemistry and the disinterest of scientists in this particular technical problem. The fact that the new industry depended on certain scientific discoveries did not immediately insure the application of scientific knowledge or research methods to the improvement of the early telegraph systems. The liaison between science and technology was limited; it is interesting to speculate on what the history of the telegraph industry would have been had more scientific talent been applied to the improvement of component parts of the system.[20]

Some of the talent involved in the improvement of the telegraph inevitably attacked the problem of transmitting the voice electrically.

---

[19] For a brief discussion of these developments, see Mason, chap. xxxviii. On Henry's work, see Thomas Coulson, *Joseph Henry, His Life & Work* (Princeton, 1950), chaps. ii–iii.

[20] See Harold I. Sharlin, *The Making of the Electrical Age* (New York, 1963), chap. i; Oliver W. Larkin, *Samuel F. B. Morse and American Democratic Art* (Boston, 1954), chaps. vii–ix; Robert Luther Thompson, *Wiring a Continent: The History of the Telegraph Industry in the United States 1832–1866* (Princeton, 1947).

While a number of inventors produced significant and to some degree workable devices, Alexander Graham Bell, after long litigation, was judged the inventor. The process by which he developed the telephone is instructive. Bell's background was scientific, but it was in speech, not electricity. As early as 1865, he became aware of some related work performed by the eminent German physicist, Helmholtz, work which turned Bell's attention to the telegraph, and along the way he gained valuable encouragement from the then venerable Joseph Henry. Bell's invention was not a mere gadget; it was grounded on a thorough understanding of the physical principles involved. He used a flexible diaphragm to actuate an electromagnet and thereby induce in a wire an undulatory current which corresponded to the sound vibrations. It was an ingenious application of a basic electrical principle established more than four decades earlier by Faraday.

The subsequent improvement of Bell's device and its elaboration into a massive communications network by World War I reveal a mixture of scientific principle and practical ingenuity. Thomas A. Edison and Emile Berliner, both ingenious engineers with limited scientific backgrounds, significantly improved the microphone. Both men appear to have operated with experimental, cut-and-try methods; their inventions were not the practical applications of scientific theory.

The development of effective switching mechanisms and long-distance telephone lines were problems that yielded to rather different kinds of attack. The earliest switchboards were completely manual, but growing numbers of telephones called for faster and more flexible switching systems. The inventor of the first successful automatic telephone system was Almon B. Strowger of Kansas City, who was neither an electrical engineer nor connected with the telephone industry except as an irate user. It was an ingenious device but not one founded on the developing physical sciences. Automatic switching systems made possible the extension of service to larger numbers of customers, but transmission of telephone conversations over long distances was seriously handicapped by the attenuation of the signal. Here, theoretical physicists came to the rescue. Oliver Heaviside, the eminent German mathematical physicist, demonstrated in 1893 that the difficulty was due to the capacitance of long lines, and that the problem could be resolved by increasing the line's inductance. Heaviside, however, did not see his idea through to its practical application. That was the work of Michael Pupin, one of America's first electrical engineers with a sound grounding in mathematical physics; in 1899, he discovered how to space the inductances so as to cancel effectively the capacitance effect of the cable. In the next two decades, the problems of long-lines communication were to be further resolved by the development of repeaters based on yet another line of development, the electron tube.[21]

The development of sources of electrical power, of systems of distribution, and of devices to utilize that power similarly showed the changing relationships between science and technology in the nineteenth century. Three facets of these developments are particularly interesting. First, the basic scientific principles on which the generators, motors, power distribution systems, and electric lights were to be based were discovered in the first third of the century by men such as Davy, Faraday, and Henry. Yet the industry itself did not become significant until the last two decades of the century. As one observer has commented, "Electrical engineering has, unlike civil and mechanical engineering, consistently been preceded by its allied science,"[22] but there was a striking half-century lag between the discovery of scientific principles and their application to engineering. Second, while some of the most important innovations occurred in Europe, the American industry developed rapidly, and American engineers made striking contributions to the growth of the industry.

Third, many of the Americans who made such contributions had considerable formal scientific training. Elihu Thomson, one of the founders of General Electric, was largely self-taught but himself taught science for several years in a Philadelphia high school. Henry Rowland, long-time professor of physics at the The Johns Hopkins University, was frequently employed as a consultant on electrical projects, most notably the Niagara Falls power project. Indeed, Michael Pupin, himself a highly trained and creative scientist, suggested that:

> Thomson . . . was the American Siemens, and Rowland was the American Helmholtz of the new era in the history of American industries —the era of close cooperation between abstract science and engineering. . . . The scientific spirit of Rowland's laboratory and lecture room was felt everywhere in the electrical industries. . . .[23]

Nikola Tesla, inventor of the A.C. motor, was a graduate of European

---

[21] Sharlin, chap. ii; William Chauncy Langdon, "Alexander Graham Bell," *DAB*, II, 148–52; Roger Burlingame, "Emile Berliner," *DAB*, XXI, 75–76; Matthew Josephson, *Edison* (New York, 1959), pp. 138–55; Michael Pupin, *From Immigrant to Inventor* (New York, 1926), pp. 329–40.

[22] Sharlin, p. 135.

[23] Pupin, p. 289.

technical schools, while Charles F. Brush, developer of the arc lamp, had a B.S. in chemistry from the University of Michigan and worked for some years as a consulting chemist. Frank Sprague, developer of electric traction systems, was a graduate of the U.S. Naval Academy, and at age twenty-five served as secretary of an award jury at the Crystal Palace Electrical Exhibition of London. Charles Steinmetz, protean student of hysteresis losses, A.C. circuits, and transient phenomena, nearly completed a Ph.D. at Breslau before fleeing the country for political reasons. And the electrical industry was among the first to establish scientific research laboratories. In few industries were trained scientists more readily welcomed or more profitably used in the last decades of the nineteenth century.

Fundamental to the growth of the electrical industry was the development of an adequate source of power. The battery, essentially a device for producing electricity from a chemical reaction, had been substantially improved until it became a convenient and reliable source of power for the telegraph. But batteries were heavy and could produce only limited voltages. The future was to belong to electromechanical methods of producing power. Faraday, in a classic paper to the Royal Society in 1831, established the basic principles of the generator, and within a year such machines were being demonstrated, by an American, Joseph Saxton, among others. It was another 40 years, however, before practical devices capable of generating substantial amounts of power became generally available. Americans made their contributions. Moses Farmer, in 1866, independently discovered the principle of self-exciting electromagnets, while Henry Rowland in 1873 and afterward established some of the basic principles of magnetic circuits crucial to proper generator design. It was another American, Charles P. Steinmetz, who in the 1890's explored hysteresis losses in such equipment. By the 1890's American firms were producing generators fully the equal or in advance of the best European models. When a group of entrepreneurs sought to harness Niagara Falls for electrical power, it turned to the Westinghouse Electric Company to build the generators.

One of the great virtues of electrical power was the flexibility of its distribution. Power from a single generating source could be sent over considerable distances and expeditiously subdivided and delivered to various electrical devices. Indeed, one of Edison's chief contributions to the electrical industry was the development of a commercially practical system for distributing power, measuring its use, and billing its users. The problems of power distribution posed one of the critical questions to be resolved by the industry in its early years: were electrical systems to be based on alternating or direct current? There were merits to each system; alternating current clearly had the advantage of more efficient transmission. The issue was fought over both in Europe and the United States, but the critical turning point came in the 1890's when the Niagara Falls generating project selected A.C. and chose Westinghouse, which had early committted itself to alternating current, to build the generators.

One of the chief arguments for a direct current system had been the fact that nearly all motors developed up to 1888 had used direct current. The conversion of electrical energy into mechanical energy had been implicit in Faraday's classic experiment of 1831, and, indeed, Joseph Henry in this country had experimented with an electric motor and encouraged other Americans to do the same. Yet the development of such motors proceeded slowly, in part because of the inadequacy of battery power, in part because the economic position of steam power in industry seemed unassailable. The real impetus to motor development came in the 1880's when Siemens and Halske in Germany and Frank Sprague in the United States applied electric power to street railways. Sprague in 1888 built the first commercially successful electric street railway in Richmond, Virginia, and in the subsequent decade electric power spread to most major urban transportation systems. Concurrently, Nikola Tesla, a Hungarian-born electrical engineer working in New York, in 1888 developed a successful alternating current motor, which was developed by, and integrated into, the Westinghouse A.C. system. By the end of the century, electricity was being widely used for traction purposes, and an efficient A.C. transmission system made both D.C. and A.C. motors competitive sources of power in industry and elsewhere. American engineers and manufacturing firms had been leaders in this development.

For most people, however, the most visible facet of the new electrical age was the electric lamp. Sir Humphry Davy in 1802 had observed that certain materials could be heated to incandescence by passing an electric current through them, and in 1808 he demonstrated a primitive arc lamp. However, it was a half century or more before either device became commercially practicable. Arc lamps, which used relatively high voltages, had to await the development of adequate generators. In the 1870's, they were being commercially exploited in Europe beginning with lighthouses. In the late 1870's and early 1880's, Charles F. Brush and the Thomson-Houston firm began producing systems in this country. The arc lamp made substantial commercial progress in the field of street lighting, but its high voltages, brilliancy, and mechanical complexity made it virtually useless for interior lighting.

The incandescent lamp was slow to develop for two reasons: first, it took a long while to locate a suitable filament material, and second, satisfactory vacuum techniques had to be developed to prevent the filament from being quickly oxidized. The second of these problems was resolved with the development of the Sprengel mercury vacuum pump in England in 1865. The first problem was attacked by a large number of inventors including Moses Farmer, Hiram Maxim, William E. Sawyer, and Edison in this country and St. George Lane-Fox and Joseph W. Swan in England. Virtually all produced workable lamps; indeed, Swan received important British patents on his devices, and Europeans often consider him the inventor of the incandescent electric lamp. But Edison genuinely deserves the credit for the invention, for he saw more clearly than the others the basic character of the problem and produced a lamp which was integrated into a complete generating and distribution system.

The implications of this electrical revolution were profound. The incandescent electric lamp and electric traction were both crucial elements in the development of late nineteenth-century urbanism. The ability to transmit electric power over considerable distances and then use the power in a wide variety of electric motors was to give to American industry a kind of freedom and flexibility it had never before enjoyed. Industry was now no longer tied to the steam engine and its system of shafts and pulleys.

But perhaps most important, the electrical industry provided one of the first nineteenth-century examples of an industry founded on scientific generalizations and developed by engineers and inventors with at least some limited formal training in the emerging scientific principles. This did not mean that the principal innovators in the field were trained scientists; many, if not most, were not. In his limited scientific knowledge and his vigorously empirical approach to his technical problems, Edison is characteristic of the group. Yet Edison was quite willing to call on scientifically trained men for assistance; F. R. Upton, his mathematician, had done work at Princeton and in Helmholtz's laboratory in Europe. As we have seen, by the last decade of the century more and more technically trained men were entering the industry. In the twentieth century, Edison himself was to become obsolete because of his limited scientific background; improvements in electrical machinery and the electric lamp and innovations in such

fields as electron tubes and radio were to be made by men with substantial amounts of scientific training, many of them working in the
new organized industrial research laboratories which the electrical
industry was quick to develop.[24]

Science and the Chemical Industry

The revolution in the nineteenth-century chemical industry provides
a second example of the impact of science on industry in that era.
There had been, of course, substantial chemical industries based on
empirical principles long before the development of chemical theory.
Tanning, the manufacture of soap, pottery and glass, the bleaching
and dyeing of textiles, and the refinement of natural pharmaceuticals
were ancient crafts based on long-practiced but ill-understood chemical techniques and processes.[25]

The shift of the chemical industry from an empirical to a scientific
enterprise was dependent on the growth of chemical theory, and this
accelerated beginning in the eighteenth century. The contributions of
that century's "chemical revolution" were substantial. Investigators
developed an understanding of the nature of the relations between
acids, bases, and salts, and of the processes of oxidation and reduction.
By the end of the century, the chemical industry had at least a qualitative understanding of some of its fundamental processes. Further
advance depended on quantitative investigations, and the eighteenth
century provided these too. Shortly after the end of the century,
Dalton could present the beginnings of an acceptable atomic theory.
These discoveries were to provide the foundation for the rapid development of the inorganic chemical industry of the early nineteenth
century.

In the first quarter of the nineteenth century, chemists hastened to
explore some of the implications of Dalton's atomic theory, though
they were unable to agree upon a common theory. The next quarter
century saw relatively few significant theoretical advances. Data were
accumulated, analytical techniques were sharpened, chemists demon-

---

[24] There are good brief accounts of the rise of the electrical industry in
Sharlin, chaps. v–vii; Derry and Williams, chap. xxii; and Strassmann, chap. v.
Harold C. Passer, *The Electrical Manufacturers, 1875–1900* (Cambridge, Mass.,
1953) is a splendid account of its subject, concentrating on the role of business
entrepreneurs but giving adequate attention to scientific and technological
matters. On these topics, see also Josephson, chaps. x–xiv, xvii, and Arthur A.
Bright, Jr., *The Electric-Lamp Industry: Technological Change and Economic
Development from 1800 to 1947* (New York, 1949).

[25] See, for example, Derry and Williams, p. 259; F. Sherwood Taylor, *A History of Industrial Chemistry* (New York, 1957), pp. 12–13, 167, 333–34.

strated that organic synthesis was possible, and, in general, the scene was set for the explosive developments of the 1850's and 1860's. They were too numerous and complex to summarize briefly. Suffice it to say that in both organic and inorganic chemistry these advances were characterized by the firm establishment of the atomic theory as symbolized by Mendeleev's periodic table of 1869 and by the development of structural formulae in organic chemistry culminating in Kekulé's portrait of the benzene ring in 1865. These theories, along with increasingly sophisticated knowledge of chemical processes, made chemistry one of the intellectually most exciting areas of nineteenth century science.[26] As one historian has observed, "the whole world of chemical discovery opened" before the student of that day; "there was scarcely a research that he could undertake which would not yield substantial discoveries."[27]

To this great chemical revolution Americans made few contributions. There were, to be sure, chemists of distinction in America— Wolcott Gibbs at Harvard or Ira Remsen at Johns Hopkins, for example; but only Josiah Willard Gibbs of Yale ranked with the best of Europe's scientists, and his theories were neglected, both in this country and abroad, for some time.[28] Nor, with some exceptions to be noted, did American chemists make strikingly original contributions to applied chemistry. Instead, they devoted their time and talents to mastering and transferring to this country both the theoretical and applied aspects of their discipline. A large proportion of U.S. chemists, both academic and industrial, were trained abroad, generally in Scotland in the first third of the century and in Germany thereafter. Those unable or unwilling to go abroad for their chemical education had good opportunities in this country in the first and last quarters of the century; the mid-nineteenth century was a relatively barren period in U.S. chemical education.[29]

Trained chemists made their way into American industry at a surprisingly early date. James C. Booth, who studied with Wöhler in Germany, opened a laboratory in Philadelphia, the center of the U.S. chemical industry, in 1836; he taught there but also served as a consultant for a good many industries. The number of such laboratories

---

26 *Ibid.*, chaps. xiii, xv, xviii–xx; Mason, chaps. xxvi, xxxvi.

27 F. S. Taylor, p. 232.

28 Lynde Phelps Wheeler, *Josiah Willard Gibbs* (New Haven, 1951).

29 See, for example, L. F. Haber, *The Chemical Industry during the Nineteenth Century* (Oxford, 1958), pp. 36–37, 71, 78, and biographical sketches of nineteenth-century chemists in the *DAB*.

proliferated in the middle of the century.[30] Many of the early manufacturing chemists had formal academic training in chemistry. Eugene Grasselli, who founded the heavy chemical industry in the United States west of the Appalachians, came from an Italian family which had been chemists and druggists for generations, and he himself was educated at Strassburg and Heidelberg before coming to this country. Similarly, when the Mallinckrodts decided to begin their chemical enterprises in St. Louis near the end of the Civil War, both Edward and Otto were sent to Germany by the family, where they studied with Fresenius at Wiesbaden and gained practical experience in German chemical plants.[31] In some cases, chemists were hired by going concerns to analyze and improve their work. Samuel Luther Dana worked for the Merrimac Print Works, a major textile firm, from 1834 through 1868, improving their bleaching and dyeing processes. While Dana was an isolated example in the 1830's, such practices became much more common by the end of the century. Herbert Dow, himself a graduate of the Case Institute of Technology, hired several graduates and faculty members of that institution when he organized the Dow Chemical Company in the 1890's.[32] Of all the scientists in the nineteenth century, the chemists seemed most amenable to industrial work, appearing in a good many industries not normally associated with chemistry.[33]

The industry entered by the pioneer chemists of the early nineteenth century was limited in scope and empirical in approach. To be sure, in the 1820's the leading category of manufactures in American exports was chemicals, but most of these were pot and pearl ashes and soap, fundamentally by-products of the expansion of American agriculture. The demand for chemicals was limited in the pre-Civil War period, and production was consequently restricted to some of the commoner acids and salts, a few dyes and painters' colors, some fine

---

[30] Howard R. Bartlett, "The Development of Industrial Research in the United States," *Research—A National Resource*, 3 vols. (Washington, D.C., 1938–1941), II, 72. See also the sketches of James F. Babcock, Henry C. Bolton, Frederick A. Genth, Thomas B. Stillman, Francis H. Storer, and C. M. Wetherill in the *DAB*.

[31] Williams Haynes, *Chemical Pioneers: The Founders of the American Chemical Industry* (New York, 1939), pp. 89–93, 155–59.

[32] Bartlett, pp. 25–26; Haynes, *Chemical Pioneers*, pp. 259–64, 271–72; and the sketch of Dana in the *DAB*.

[33] Bartlett, pp. 26–29 provides some examples.

chemicals, and black powder. As the U.S. tariff was lowered in the 1830's and after, the industry suffered from English imports, particularly of alkalis and bleaching powders; as late as the 1880's, most of the soda used in this country was imported. Nevertheless, a start was made, with the industry centered in the Philadelphia area.[34]

The basis for any large chemical industry is heavy chemicals, that is, acids and alkalis. In the nineteenth century, sulfuric acid was far and away the most important of the acids, while soda in its various forms was the most widely produced alkali. Both sulfuric acid and soda were used, both in certain manufacturing processes and as raw materials in the production of other chemicals. Thus, sulfuric acid was widely used to treat phosphate rock to produce fertilizers, but it was also essential in the Leblanc process of soda production. In the nineteenth century, most sulfuric acid was made by the lead-chamber process developed by empirical investigators in the eighteenth century and introduced to the United States in 1793. The process itself was little changed until World War I. Modifications designed to make it more efficient were introduced only slowly in the United States; Gay-Lussac towers, designed in the late 1820's, were used in only about half of the U.S. acid works as late as 1890. When Americans introduced the contact process from Germany shortly after 1900, however, some of the American plants performed better than the German ones.

Soda production in this country was not common before the 1880's; early in the century Americans depended on potash from wood ashes, and, subsequently, British imports ruled the American market. When soda production began in the 1880's, however, Americans were quick to introduce new technical processes. The Leblanc process dominated soda production nearly everywhere in the nineteenth century, but in 1884 Americans imported complete drawings and some technicians to construct and operate under license a Solvay process plant in Syracuse, New York. In the following decade it was an American, Hamilton Young Castner, who revolutionized the alkali business by developing a commercially practicable electrolytic system for producing pure caustic soda. A pilot plant was operated initially at Saltville, Virginia, followed by a much larger works at Niagara Falls to take advantage of the inexpensive electric power there. Indeed, Americans made some of their most important contributions to applied chemistry in the rapidly growing area of electrochemistry at century's end, and

[34] V. S. Clark, II, 129–30, 499; Haber, pp. 52–54; George Rogers Taylor, *The Transportation Revolution* (New York, 1951), pp. 188–90.

in so doing they made this country largely self-sufficient in caustic soda and bleaching powder.[35]

Various parts of the chemical industry responded in various ways to the chemical revolution of the nineteenth century. Some of the older empirical industries such as tanning remained long unaffected by burgeoning chemical knowledge. The first tanner in the United States to regularly employ a chemist did so in 1855, but the chemist appears to have contributed nothing of importance, and as late as 1890, only about half-a-dozen American tanneries had chemists on their staffs. When the technical revolution did occur in the 1880's and 1890's, however, Americans were in the forefront. Martin Dennis, for example, in 1893 began producing a tanning solution using a chromium chloride liquor in a one-bath process, and the following year a German tanner, returning from the Chicago Exposition, reported that "The best machines in the tanning line are American inventions, the merit of introducing new and valuable tannages, as Dongola and chrome, is exclusively due to the Americans, and every day we hear of new startling improvements and gigantic transactions from over the water." By century's end, chemical control was being generally introduced into the industry.[36]

Another old empirical chemical industry, explosives, felt the effects of the chemical revolution of the nineteenth century. For some six hundred years, black powder, a mixture of charcoal, sulfur, and saltpeter, was the sole explosive available, and American firms such as Du Pont demonstrated skill in mastering the techniques of its manufacture. The industry was, however, revolutionized by new discoveries in the second half of the nineteenth century. The first of these was an American innovation, for in 1857, Lammot du Pont, a chemistry graduate of the University of Pennsylvania, produced an excellent blasting powder while replacing the traditional saltpeter (potassium nitrate) with less expensive South American sodium nitrate. More important, in Europe nitrated cotton (guncotton) and nitroglycerin were discovered and proved to be powerful if unmanageable explosives. The latter was domesticated in the 1860's as dynamite by Alfred Nobel, and its production was begun in this country in 1869.

---

[35] Derry and Williams, pp. 535, 538–40, 549–51; Haber, pp. 144–51; F. S. Taylor, pp. 182–91, 388–89; Williams Haynes, *American Chemical Industry: A History*, 6 vols. (New York, 1945–1954), I, 263–66, 386–87.

[36] Quoted in V. S. Clark, II, 465. See also *ibid.*, III, 225; Haynes, *American Chemical Pioneers*, pp. 197–208; Peter C. Welsh, "A Craft That Resisted Change: American Tanning Practices to 1850," *Technology and Culture*, IV (Summer 1963), 299–317.

Various experimenters in this country and abroad succeeded in the 1880's in using guncotton to produce a smokeless powder. The advent of high explosives provided both industry and the military with an array of stronger and more flexible explosives, and their production stimulated the heavy chemicals industry which produced the acids required for production. Some American firms such as Du Pont were reluctant to abandon black powder in favor of high explosives, but they eventually did so. After Du Pont's reorganization in 1902, it established the Eastern Laboratory at Repauno under a Heidelberg Ph.D. in chemistry named Charles L. Reese who was charged with the task of systematically improving Du Pont's high explosives.[37]

The changes in the dye industry were even more startling and swift. As one historian has put it, "in the 1850's manufacture had been empirical—by the end of the next decade it was becoming scientific."[38] Indeed, the revolution in the dye industry was one of the great showcases of the value of scientific research in industry. Synthetic dyes got their start in 1856, when William H. Perkin, a young English chemist working with the German organic chemist, August Wilhelm von Hofmann, discovered a brilliant mauve dye from aniline, a coal-tar derivative. Aided by the burgeoning understanding of organic compounds, other chemists developed other varieties of synthetic dyes, some of them syntheses of traditional natural dyes. The outstanding example of this was the practical synthesis of indigo, first performed by Adolf von Baeyer in 1880 but perfected only after seventeen years of research costing nearly $5 million by the German Badische Anilin- und Soda-Fabrik Gesellschaft. While early leadership in dye research and production rested with the English, the Germans rapidly came to the fore; by 1914 only 20 percent of the dyes used in Britain were of domestic manufacture. In the United States a few firms manufactured the dyes, but some of them used imported intermediates, and there are few indications of any significant American contributions to the field. German competition was too stiff, and raw materials were too expensive, given the reluctance of American industry to abandon beehive coke ovens and turn instead to by-product ovens.[39]

---

[37] Haynes, *American Chemical Industry*, I, 204–6, 365–69; William S. Dutton, *Du Pont: One Hundred and Forty Years*, 2nd ed. (New York, 1949), pp. 80–83, 128–39, 156–61, 184–85.

[38] Haber, p. 81.

[39] Derry and Williams, pp. 542–46; Haber, pp. 144–45. See also John Joseph Beer, *The Emergence of the German Dye Industry* (Urbana, Ill., 1959).

The chemical industry was just beginning in the nineteenth century to demonstrate its ability to produce new materials, but Americans made some contributions in this area. In plastics, John Wesley Hyatt, the printer son of a blacksmith, in 1863 noted an advertisement offering a $10,000 reward for a new material with which to make billiard balls. Rather by accident his attention was turned to collodion, and in 1870, he patented a process of combining collodion with camphor under heat and pressure; the result was "Celluloid," one of the earliest synthetic materials.[40] "Celluloid" pretty much had the field to itself until 1907, when Leo Baekeland, a Belgian scientist working in the United States, developed the first thermosetting plastic, Bakelite. Both its physical and electrical qualities made it an ideal insulator, and it was quickly taken up for use in the electrical industry.[41] Meanwhile European investigators had come up with the first semisynthetic fibers, viscose and cellulose acetate, both chemical modifications of natural cellulose. While some Americans demonstrated interest in them and made some modest improvements, manufacture was not begun until 1911.[42] Before World War I, the full potentialities of this phase of industrial chemistry were only dimly visible.

Pharmaceuticals were also only peripherally influenced by chemical research before World War I. To be sure, chemists had developed effective anesthetics and germicides and had chemically isolated and identified the active ingredients of some important natural pharmaceuticals. But the search for synthetic drugs could begin only when there was a sound basis in organic theory, and when such research did begin, it was closely related to the dye industry and concentrated in Germany. The results were limited. Aspirin was discovered and some of the barbiturates were prepared. American pharmaceutical firms scouted for natural drugs and hired chemists to watch over and improve their manufacturing processes. But it was characteristic of the American situation that although the Johns Hopkins chemist Ira Remsen first produced, in 1879, the artificial sweetener, saccharin, manufacturing processes were perfected in Germany. And when John Queeny set up Monsanto Chemical in 1902 to manufacture saccharin,

[40] Dutton, pp. 153–55.

[41] F. S. Taylor, p. 258; Maurice Holland and Henry F. Pringle, *Industrial Explorers* (New York, 1928), pp. 96–109; Haynes, *American Chemical Industry*, III, 378–81.

[42] F. S. Taylor, pp. 255–57; Haynes, *American Chemical Industry*, III, 372–76.

he bought intermediates from Swiss firms and hired a Swiss chemist to take charge of manufacturing operations.[43]

Two other industries, photography and petroleum, were either products of, or closely related to, the chemical revolution, and in both cases, Americans were intimately involved. Why photography was not invented before the nineteenth century is something of a mystery, for knowledge of both the optical and chemical principles on which it rested was widespread in the eighteenth century. But the early form of the daguerreotype was not generally available until 1839. Americans became interested in photography shortly after; John William Draper, a chemistry professor at City College of New York, took the first portrait with a modified Daguerre process in 1840. But it was George Eastman and his associates who revolutionized the industry, chiefly with the development of roll film in 1889 by Hannibal Goodwin of New York and Henry Reichenbach, one of Eastman's chemists. As was often the case in the nineteenth century, these developments resulted from a judicious mixture of science and practical ingenuity. Indeed, as late as 1950, a major authority commented that "the making of photographic materials is in advance of the understanding of the basic science of the subject."[44] Perhaps so. Yet Eastman constantly consulted trained chemists, and in 1912 his photographic firm was one of the first corporations in America to establish an industrial research laboratory staffed by trained men whose function was research, not simply analysis or quality control.[45]

The petroleum industry developed initially not as a consequence of new scientific knowledge but because of the discovery of vast new deposits of petroleum. In locating and processing this raw material, the industry both drew upon, and contributed to, geology and chemistry. It was the chemists who first became interested in petroleum, and Yale's chemistry professor, Benjamin Silliman, Jr., in 1855 prepared a thorough report on samples of Pennsylvania crude for the entrepreneurs who were preparing to drill for oil there. His encourag-

---

[43] F. S. Taylor, pp. 243 ff.; Arthur W. Slater, "Fine Chemicals," *A History of Technology*, ed., Singer *et al.*, V, 317–18; W. A. Noyes, "Ira Remsen," *DAB*, XV, 501; Haynes, *American Chemical Pioneers*, pp. 234–35; Haynes, *American Chemical Industry*, I, 319, 326 ff.; Bartlett, pp. 60–61.

[44] C. E. Kenneth Mees, "The Growth of Industrial Research," *American Ceramic Society Bulletin*, XXIX (December 1950), 449.

[45] Helmut and Alison Gernsheim, "The Photographic Arts: Photography," *A History of Technology*, ed., Singer *et al.*, V, 716, 729; Derry and Williams, pp. 651–59; Ellwood Hendrick, "John William Draper," *DAB*, V, 439–40; Bartlett, pp. 65–67.

ing report did much to stimulate activity, culminating in Colonel Edward Drake's first well at Titusville, Pennsylvania, in 1859.[46]

Drake's first well precipitated a scramble for additional wells, initially in Pennsylvania, subsequently in other parts of the United States and the world. In that search the services of professional geologists were initially both unavailable and useless. Lacking basic geological understanding, oilmen turned to divining rods, oil smellers, and individuals claiming occult powers. Intensive field work, however, accumulated information, and theories, first crude and then increasingly sophisticated, appeared. By the middle 1880's, theoretical discussions were appearing in the journals. By the end of the century, everyone knew that petroleum could exist only in certain geological formations, and wildcatters were turning to geologists and the geological information accumulated by both the various state surveys and the U.S. Geological Survey. In the first decade of the twentieth century, major oil companies began hiring geologists, and immediately following World War I important new geophysical techniques—the torsion balance, the diamond core drill, and the seismograph—were introduced to aid oilmen in their search for oil-bearing structures.[47]

Early refining techniques were empirical and crude; in general, knowledge of the chemistry of refining processes lagged behind practice. Petroleum is a complex mixture of hydrocarbons, and the chief problem of the late nineteenth century was to separate the marketable kerosene fraction, widely used as illuminating oil, from the rest of the crude. The methods were already at hand; fractional distillation techniques were well known and widely used in such industries as coal oil, alcohol, and tar. At a fairly early date, refiners did some "cracking," that is, using heat to split some of the larger and heavier hydrocarbon molecules into lighter ones in the kerosene range. Thus, when the French chemist Berthelot published in 1867 his basic researches into the action of heat on various hydrocarbons, he merely provided a basis for interpreting what was happening in practice in the oil in-

---

[46] Harold F. Williamson and Arnold R. Daum, *The American Petroleum Industry: The Age of Illumination, 1859–1899* (Evanston, 1959), pp. 68–72.

[47] *Ibid.*, pp. 89–91, 131–33; R. J. Forbes, "Petroleum," *A History of Technology*, ed., Singer *et al.*, V, 111–12; F. Garvin Davenport, "Early American Geologists and the Oil Industry," *Indiana Magazine of History*, XLVII (March 1951), 21–36; George Sweet Gibb and Evelyn H. Knowlton, *The Resurgent Years, 1911–1927* (New York, 1956), pp. 57–58, 62–63, 301 ff., 318–21, 370, 373, 384–85, 389; Henrietta M. Larson and Kenneth Wiggins Porter, *History of Humble Oil and Refining Company* (New York, 1959), pp. 7, 15–16, 33, 75, 90, 112–17, 132–34, 139–41; Kendall Beaton, *Enterprise in Oil: A History of Shell in the United States* (New York, 1957), pp. 117, 164–66, 201–6.

dustry. Early refiners treated the distilled petroleum products with sulfuric acid and caustic soda to remove odors and improve colors; the treatment was effective and enlarged the markets of the heavy chemical manufacturers, but the chemistry of the treatment was obscure to those who used it. Most improvements in the refining process were the work of practical refiners rather than trained chemists. The most serious chemical problem facing refiners before the end of the century, the sulfur content of crude from the Lima, Ohio, fields, was solved by Herman Frasch, a German-born technician with only minimal formal training in chemistry. Similarly, early by-products such as mineral lubricating oils or "Vaseline," the first useful petroleum jelly, were developed by practical men rather than scientists.

Yet chemists slowly worked their way into the industry and demonstrated the value of systematic scientific knowledge. By 1882, Standard Oil was hiring trained chemists, primarily for analytical and control purposes. After the turn of the century, the numbers of such men increased. Dr. William Burton, who joined the staff of Indiana Standard in 1890, primarily in an analytical and control capacity, demonstrated the creative possibilities of trained chemists when, in 1913, he developed the first practical high-pressure, high-temperature cracking still and helped the industry meet the critical demand for one of the lightest of all petroleum fractions, gasoline. Subsequently, the company turned to outside consultants, including Ira Remsen of Johns Hopkins, in attempts to further improve the process. By the 1920's, most major oil companies were organizing research divisions, though it was often a struggle to overcome the prejudices of the "practical" men.[48]

The impact of science on the chemical industry, then, was rather different from its influence on the electrical industry. For one thing, the chemical industry had existed as a prescientific enterprise, and numerous nineteenth-century improvements came from men with minimal formal training in the discipline. For some time, chemical practice was in advance of theory and understanding, at least in some branches. For another, the chemical industries were far more complex and varied than the electrical. In some cases this permitted the continuation of industries such as tanning on a traditional empirical basis

---

[48] Williamson and Daum, pp. 51–53, 202–27, 242–46, 250–73, 480–81, 517, 599–618; Forbes, "Petroleum," pp. 112–16; Ralph W. and Muriel E. Hidy, *Pioneering in Big Business, 1882–1911* (New York, 1955), pp. 98–100, 157–61, 422–28, 437–42; Gibb and Knowlton, pp. 113–21, 520–31, 536–39; Beaton, pp. 502 ff.

long after other branches of chemicals had come under scientific influence. In other cases, however, developments in one branch of the industry had repercussions in others. Developments in petroleum refining and high explosives, for example, stimulated heavy chemicals by increasing demand for sulfuric acid. Furthermore, the chemical industry was dependent on Europe longer and to a greater degree for both innovations and materials than was the electrical industry.

Yet chemists slowly worked their way into industry, and the United States moved toward parity with the more advanced chemical industry of Germany. Initially, trained chemists served as consultants or were hired by firms to analyze raw materials and help control processes. By the 1870's and 1880's, they were beginning to exercise some technical independence and initiative, and by the end of the century, most chemical plants had a chemist or two and a laboratory of sorts on the premises.[49]

Yet it took World War I to bring home to both industrial leaders and the general public the importance of the industry and the degree to which we had become dependent on foreign, particularly German, technology and chemicals. Wartime demands for chemicals zoomed, while foreign supplies were cut off. Sharp shortages of potash, nitrogen, and coal-tar medicines and dyes resulted. Yet the industry responded remarkably well; in a very real sense the war marked the establishment of the modern American chemical industry. Equally important, the experience persuaded American industry in general of the importance of scientific research. After 1915, the movement of scientists into industry became an irresistible tide.[50]

Science and Engineering

The history of both the electrical and the chemical industries demonstrates the way in which the scientific revolution could generate previously unknown technologies, and the history of the latter shows the way in which traditional technologies could both resist and ultimately be transformed by scientific knowledge. Few other examples could show these processes so well. Yet other branches of technology were profoundly influenced by the new scientific knowledge. Take civil engineering, for example. The great nineteenth-century railroad bridges and train stations became technological symbols of their age, equivalent to Roman aqueducts or medieval cathedrals, and they

---

[49] Haynes, *American Chemical Industry*, I, 391, 395–96.

[50] Haynes, *American Chemical Industry*, II and III, covers the story in great detail. See particularly, III, chaps. xxiv and xxvi.

were, appropriately enough, influenced by the transformation of civil engineering from an art to a science.

Engineering was inevitably a conservative discipline. Traditions were ancient and well established; engineers were unlikely to innovate, for the costs of failure, both economic and human, were great. Yet, in the final analysis, it was economics that made inevitable the convergence of science and engineering, for the application of scientific methods made it possible for the engineer to build with increased safety, economy, and assurance. Safety margins could be calculated with greater precision with resultant savings in materials. The gross overbuilding in the interests of safety so characteristic of empirical construction could be abandoned.

The economics of American construction in the nineteenth century did not make for American technological leadership, for in the United States, throughout most of its early history, trained manpower was scarce and expensive while materials were plentiful and cheap. There is a good deal of evidence, then, that the convergence of science and engineering in this country lagged behind Europe. Yet, by the second half of the century, American engineers, particularly in the growing engineering schools, were learning to apply mathematical methods and scientific analysis of materials to their tasks, and even earlier, some Americans had made significant contributions to the development of scientific engineering.[51]

The theoretical and practical bases for a science of strength of materials were laid in the seventeenth and eighteenth centuries; as early as 1729 the Dutch scientist van'sGravesande designed and demonstrated machines to measure the strength of different materials such as wood, glass, and metals. By early in the nineteenth century, scientists, engineers, and manufacturers were cooperating in an effort to determine allowable stresses on chains for ships' anchors and wire or chains for suspension bridges, the stability of cast-iron columns, and the strength of railway rails and riveted joints in boilers. Equally important was the application of mathematical analysis to stresses in beams and various kinds of structures, and by the mid-nineteenth century, the results of these investigations were being embodied in manuals used by construction engineers.

Americans made few original contributions to these developments. However, by mid-century such men as Squire Whipple, a prominent

[51] James Kip Finch, *Engineering and Western Civilization* (New York, 1951), pp. 89–96; Richard Shelton Kirby, Sidney Withington, Arthur Burr Darling, Frederick Gridley Kilgour, *Engineering in History* (New York, 1956), pp. 327–29, 510–11.

New York engineer, and Herman Haupt, professor of engineering at Pennsylvania (now Gettysburg) College, were publishing manuals on bridge construction which involved analysis of stresses in the bridge members. By 1870, large-scale machines designed in Europe became available in this country to test large beams and other bridge elements. The contrast between the old and the new methods can be seen in two bridges. In 1801, James Finley built a suspension bridge and described in detail his empirical methods for locating the suspenders and for determining the proper length for each hanger and the curve of his suspension cable. "I know," he commented, "the young mathematician, with mind half matured, would smile at my mode of testing the relative force and effect of the several ties and bracings of any piece of framing: but the well informed, will not so lightly treat any information obtained or supposed to be obtained by actual experiment." Sixty-nine years later, when James B. Eads built his famous steel arch bridge across the Mississippi at St. Louis, he not only pioneered in the use of caissons to lay the foundation for his towers but also hired William Chauvenet, a mathematician and chancellor of Washington University in St. Louis, to help him calculate the stresses in the parabolic arches and used machines to test the steel members in the bridge.[52]

Science and Metallurgy

The iron industry of the early nineteenth century, as we have noted, was almost completely unaffected by the scientific revolution. The second half of the century saw profound changes in the industry, as first the Bessemer process, and then the open hearth furnace, converted what had been an iron industry into a steel industry. The scale of operations increased phenomenally as did the variety of products turned out. Yet, for the most part, these innovations were the work of shrewd empiricists, not of trained scientists. Indeed, the lack of chemical knowledge was a serious handicap and often spelled the difference between success and failure of a particular innovation.[53]

---

[52] Forbes, *Man the Maker*, pp. 179, 241; Kirby *et al.*, pp. 188–90, 229–33, 303; S. B. Hamilton, "Building Materials and Techniques," *A History of Technology*, ed., Singer *et al.*, V, 491–96; H. Shirley Smith, "Bridges and Tunnels," *ibid.*, V, 500–503, 510–11; Carl W. Condit, *American Building Art: The Nineteenth Century* (New York, 1960), pp. 4–9, 185–90.

[53] Kirby *et al.*, pp. 291–96, provides a clear discussion of the major technical innovations. Strassmann, pp. 32 ff. and 51–54 emphasizes the lack of chemical knowledge. See also the interesting brief discussion in Frank T. Sisco, "Research in the Iron and Steel Industry," *Research—A National Resource*, II, 158–59.

Some trained scientists, chiefly chemists, began entering the industry in the 1860's, initially for analytical and control work. Andrew Carnegie boasted that he was the first steelmaster to employ a trained chemist, but such was becoming commonplace by 1870, when Carnegie employed his man, and some played important roles in making new processes work.[54] As early as 1863, a chemical laboratory was attached to a metallurgical works at Wyandotte, Michigan, which was experimenting with the Bessemer process. However, few steel firms developed research facilities before World War I.[55] The experience of Albert Sauveur was instructive. A graduate of the Ecole des Mines in Liège and of M.I.T., he was hired in 1889 by the Pennsylvania Steel Company and in 1891 by the South Chicago works of the Illinois Steel Company. The works manager at South Chicago was sympathetic to Sauveur's ambitions to do research and provided him with a microscope and a room to work in. There he began his classic analysis of the microstructure of iron and steel that was to establish him as one of the world's leading metallographers. However, in 1897, a new general manager abolished his laboratory, and Sauveur, for two years, established his own testing laboratory before taking refuge in Harvard in 1899.[56]

The Industrial Revolution had sharply increased the demand for metals, and this rising demand sparked a worldwide search for new deposits. By and large, as one authority puts it, "The great new discoveries of mineral deposits . . . seem to have been due more to chance than to any new techniques suggested by geological theory."[57] Yet, as in the case of petroleum, the search for metals saw increasing use of geologists. State and federal geological surveys provided ever more useful data, and prospecting was converted from a glamorous, if often disheartening, adventure into a scientific enterprise. Mining engineers trained at the Freiberg Bergakadamie or at the Columbia School of Mines, established in 1864, entered the field in increasing numbers and brought with them more efficient methods of reaching metals at

---

[54] Nevins, p. 243; James Howard Bridge, *The Inside History of the Carnegie Steel Company* (New York, 1903), p. 65; sketches of William Metcalf, John Barnard Swett Pearse, Robert Woolston Hunt, Alfred Ephraim Hunt in *DAB*; John W. Oliver, *History of American Technology* (New York, 1956), p. 322; Strassmann, pp. 38–39, 52–53, 60–61.

[55] V. S. Clark, II, 70; Sisco, pp. 157–62; Bartlett, pp. 58–59.

[56] H. H. Lester, "Albert Sauveur," *DAB*, XXII, 594–95.

[57] Derry and Williams, p. 491.

a considerable depth and more effective means of processing the ores as well.[58]

Probably the most important science-based innovations in mining and metallurgy in the late nineteenth century resulted from the application of electrical and chemical knowledge. For example, by the end of the century, electromagnets were being used to separate ores of different magnetic qualities. In the early twentieth century, the flotation process was found to be the most efficient method of concentrating most ores. Most striking of all was the application of electrochemistry to metallurgy. The outstanding development here was Charles Hall's success in the 1880's at producing aluminum from its oxide by electrolytic means. But of nearly equal importance was electrolytic refining of copper; without the new refining method it would have been almost impossible to have produced copper of sufficient purity to meet the needs of the electrical industry. There are few better examples of the wide-ranging influence of the scientific revolutions in electricity and chemistry.[59]

THE TWENTIETH CENTURY: THE VICTORY OF ORGANIZED RESEARCH

The effective application of science to industry depended, as we have already noted, on the development of science to a point at which it could be effectively used. But the use of scientific knowledge was not automatic. It came only because businessmen became convinced that scientific knowledge and skills could be profitable and because men trained in science were willing, and found opportunity, to apply their knowledge. Only slowly did applied science became an integral part of the structure of American industry.

The potential usefulness of science became increasingly visible in the nineteenth century as more and more Americans gained a solid scientific education, first abroad, particularly in Germany, but increasingly at home with the organization of technical and engineering

---

[58] Edward C. Kirkland, *Industry Comes of Age* (New York, 1961), pp. 143–48; Rodman Wilson Paul, "Colorado as a Pioneer of Science in the Mining West," *Mississippi Valley Historical Review*, XLVII (June 1960), 34–50; William B. Gates, *Michigan Copper and Boston Dollars* (Cambridge, Mass., 1951), pp. 1–6, 22–30, 56–60.

[59] R. Chadwick, "New Extraction Processes for Metals," *A History of Technology*, ed., Singer *et al.*, V, 74–76, 84–85, 90–93; Harry N. Holmes, "Charles Martin Hall," *DAB*, VIII, 122–23.

schools and the establishment of graduate study and research in science at American universities in the last third of the century. Scientists were quick to organize, too, for the promotion of their disciplines. When the American Association for the Advancement of Science first met in 1848, it asserted that one of its objectives was "to procure for the labours of scientific men, increased facilities and wider usefulness."[60] In the final quarter of the century, most of the major engineering and scientific organizations were founded, many of them to promote the cause of applied science. The proliferation of journals, both professional and semipopular, also brought to the attention of industrialists the most recent innovations in applied science and technology.[61] As the century wore on, simple ignorance was less and less an excuse for technical backwardness.

Men of scientific bent and training slowly moved into industry, as we have already seen. They did so in various ways. Some were individual "engineer-entrepreneurs," that is, individual inventors who in the structure of nineteenth-century technology were obliged to commercialize their discoveries.[62] Others were called upon either as consultants or as full-time employees to assist in some development. The consultant was a characteristic figure of what W. David Lewis has characterized as the "putting out" stage of American industrial research. He was widely used in the nineteenth century, particularly as the value of scientific expertise became more obvious. The consultants for the Niagara Falls hydroelectric project, near the end of the century, for example, constituted almost a "Who's Who" of science and engineering.[63] The earliest scientists in industry generally played ancillary roles in what was still a largely empirical technology. The characteristic role of the chemist in the iron and steel industry, for example, was to analyze ores or other materials used in steelmaking. The earlier industrial laboratories, both corporate and consultant, were analytical laboratories. Yet their importance should not be underestimated. Scientifically trained men were often able to provide valuable technological shortcuts, to criticize existing processes, or in

---

[60] Ralph S. Bates, *Scientific Societies in the United States* (New York, 1945), p. 75.

[61] Merle Curti, *The Growth of American Thought*, 3rd ed. (New York, 1964), chap. xxiii discusses both the organization and the popularization of scientific scholarship in the late nineteenth century.

[62] Passer, pp. 356 ff. and *passim*.

[63] Strassmann, p. 220.

other ways to cut the costs of existing processes or the risks of proposed innovations.[64]

By the end of the century, many American industrial firms were using scientifically trained men; their inventions were being exploited by industry, scientists were widely employed to analyze and control existing processes, and they were frequently called on as consultants. The time was ripe for the introduction of the modern industrial research laboratory, that is, a group of scientifically trained men engaged in a cooperative search for new ideas. The industrial research laboratory had first appeared in the German chemical industry in the final third of the nineteenth century, particularly in firms producing coal-tar dyes. Stiff competition, rapidly changing technology, a good supply of trained chemists, and the traditions of German graduate scientific instruction apparently encouraged this development.[65] In this country Edison's laboratory, established at Menlo Park in 1876, provided a striking example of an organized research establishment; its head casually informed a friend one day that he proposed to turn out "a minor invention every ten days and a big thing every six months or so."[66] Few others, however, were able to finance such "invention factories" as Edison was out of profits from previous inventions. It was left to the large corporations developing everywhere on the American scene at the end of the century to introduce organized industrial research.

Major industrial research laboratories began appearing in American industry shortly after 1900. General Electric founded its Research Laboratory in 1900 under the direction of a German-trained chemist, Willis R. Whitney, who joined G.E. from M.I.T. As we have noted Du Pont in 1902 established its Eastern Laboratory under Charles L. Reese, a Heidelberg graduate. American Telephone and Telegraph began research work in this decade also, and in 1912, Eastman Kodak brought in C. E. Kenneth Mees from an English subsidiary to begin its organized research. Most of the early laboratories appeared in industries such as electricity or chemicals where there were large firms with sufficient financial resources and stability to support the laboratories and where there was a rapidly changing, competitive technology which made successful research imperative for the sponsoring firm.

---

[64] *Ibid.*, pp. 201–3.

[65] John J. Beer, "Coal-Tar Dye Manufacture and the Origins of the Modern Industrial Research Laboratory," *Isis*, XLIX (June 1958), 123–31.

[66] Josephson, pp. 133–34. See also Passer, pp. 78–79.

Many of the early laboratory heads were trained abroad, but in subsequent decades, American graduate schools turned out men of sufficient quality and numbers to obviate the necessity of looking abroad.

If the industrial research laboratory had its beginnings in the first decade of the twentieth century, it was not firmly established in this country until after World War I. The impact of that conflict on industrial research was profound. Shortages of dyes, other chemicals, and optical glass made many Americans aware of their previous dependence on German research. Primitive governmental attempts to harness science to the war effort and the yeoman service of some of the existing research laboratories persuaded others that research was essential. The result was a ferment of discussion and activity that bore fruit in the postwar years.[67]

The period between the two wars saw a steady growth of industrial research, only slightly inhibited by the depression of the 1930's. In 1927, the first year for which we have reasonably accurate figures, there were approximately 1,000 industrial research laboratories employing about 19,000 people. By 1938, there were 1,769 employing about 44,300. World War II brought a comprehensive attempt to organize scientific research in support of the war effort; as a result the number of employees in industrial research laboratories rose from about 44,300 to 133,000 between 1938 and 1946.[68] The cold war and concomitant government support for research brought further expansion. By 1962, over 300,000 scientists and engineers were engaged in research and development work in industry; total expenditures for 1962–63 for such work in industry were estimated at $11.56 billion with about 58 percent of the funds coming from federal sources.[69]

Organized industrial research has been carried on in a wide variety of institutions and in many different industries since its beginnings over a half century ago. Most of the work in such laboratories has been applied research and development rather than basic research;

[67] A. Hunter Dupree, *Science in the Federal Government* (Cambridge, Mass., 1957), chap. xvi; Bartlett, pp. 35–37; Kendall Birr, *Pioneering in Industrial Research* (Washington, D.C., 1957), pp. 63–65.

[68] Statistics compiled from *Industrial Research Laboratories*, a directory published by the National Research Council periodically beginning in 1920. On industrial research in World War II, see James Phinney Baxter, 3rd, *Scientists Against Time* (Boston, 1946).

[69] Growing concern with scientific research in the United States has led to more sophisticated statistical data; the figures cited are from the U.S. Bureau of the Census, *Statistical Abstract of the United States: 1964* (Washington, D.C., 1964), pp. 540–54.

most of it has been carried on in large laboratories and by large firms. While research activity has tended to spread into almost every industry, the contrasts between industries are startling. Research activity is far heavier in electrical machinery, communications, aircraft, and chemicals and its allied branches such as pharmaceuticals and petrochemicals, than in primary metals, mining, textiles, or food processing. While most industrial research activity has centered in company-owned laboratories, industry has been served also by an array of cooperative research efforts, nonprofit research institutes (such as the Mellon Institute of Pittsburgh and the Battelle Memorial Institute of Columbus, Ohio), independent commercial laboratories (of which the oldest, largest, and most successful is Arthur D. Little, Inc.), and fellowship arrangements with universities.[70]

To explore the full impact of such research and development on American technology and industry would require volumes. All we can do here is to indicate some of the directions it has taken and suggest some of the problems it has raised. That it has been of profound significance no one could deny. In the mid-1950's one student of the problem estimated that research had contributed one quarter to one half of the annual U.S. productivity increase, and estimated that $40 to 80 billion of the 1953 gross national product of $365 billion could be attributed to research and development performed over the previous quarter century.[71]

Whatever the validity of such estimates, the results of research and development in the twentieth century are readily visible almost everywhere. Applied science has diffused through most of American industry from its early foci in the electrical and chemical industries. The electrical industry, for example, has seen a flood of scientifically inspired technological innovations since its late nineteenth-century beginnings. Edison's incandescent lamp was radically modified, first by the use of the tungsten filament, then with the introduction of lamps filled with inert gases. In the twenties and thirties, enough was learned about electric-discharge and fluorescent phenomena to make possible the commercialization of the fluorescent lamp.[72]

---

[70] Birr, pp. 16–26; John Jewkes, David Sawers, Richard Stillerman, *The Sources of Invention* (New York, 1958), chap. vii.

[71] Raymond Ewell, cited in Francis Bello, "Industrial Research: Geniuses Now Welcome," *Fortune*, LIII (January 1956), 99.

[72] See Bright, *passim*.

Perhaps more important, a whole new industry—radio and television—has grown out of certain electrical investigations. In 1864, the great English physicist James Clerk Maxwell described the properties of electromagnetic waves; 22 years later, in Germany, Heinrich Hertz demonstrated experimentally the existence of such waves and laid the foundation for radio. By the end of the century, Marconi had demonstrated the practicability of transmitting radio signals great distances. But it was the discovery of the electron tube by Ambrose Fleming and Lee de Forest and its improvement by Irving Langmuir and Harold Arnold, the latter two scientists working in industrial research laboratories, that established radio on a firm basis. By the twenties, radio was technologically well developed and burgeoned suddenly and unexpectedly into the form of mass communication we are familiar with today. The basic scientific and technological problems associated with television were solved in the thirties, again with considerable aid from organized industrial research laboratories; its commercialization in the post-World War II period further enlarged the scope of mass communications. Meanwhile, scientists working at the Bell Telephone Laboratories investigated in the thirties the general area of solid state physics and in particular semiconductors. The result, in 1948, was the transistor, a new device for controlling the flow of electrons which has permitted the miniaturization of electron circuits and the development of such diverse end products as cheap portable radios and sophisticated electronic equipment for space vehicles.[73]

The spectacular new discoveries in lighting and electron tubes should not, however, obscure the cumulative economic importance of continuing research to improve the generation and transmission of electric power. Electric power stations at the turn of the century used about six pounds of coal per kilowatt-hour generated; by 1950, the average had fallen to about 1.19 pounds and the best plants were using only 0.74 pounds.[74]

---

[73] W. Rupert Maclaurin, *Invention and Innovation in the Radio Industry* (New York, 1949); Francis Bello, "The Transistor," *The Mighty Force of Research*, Editors of Fortune (New York, c. 1953–1956), pp. 234–47; Leonard S. Silk, *The Research Revolution* (New York, 1960), chap. iv.

[74] Richard J. Lund, "Demands for Energy," *Centennial of Engineering*, ed., Lenox R. Lohr (Chicago, 1953), pp. 849–50; see also Raymond C. Miller, *Kilowatts at Work: A History of the Detroit Edison Company* (Detroit, 1957), chap. xix, for a discussion of the experience of one large utility.

The chemical industry, too, has expanded phenomenally under the impact of successive scientific discoveries and technological innovations. Since World War I, it has been one of the fastest growing industries in the country. It has shared with the electrical industry leadership in industrial research since World War I, and the result has been both a steady flow of new products and processes and the gradual chemicalization of many areas of American industry. The production of basic chemicals has been revolutionized with the development of the contact process of making sulfuric acid and the direct fixation of nitrogen. Most spectacular has been the continued growth of organic chemistry, particularly of organic polymers or materials with long-chain molecules. These developments were most visible to the layman in the form of end products such as synthetic varnishes and lacquers (introduced to the automobile industry in the 1920's), synthetic fibers, and a wide variety of plastics ranging from Lucite to polyvinyl films and synthetic rubbers.

The synthesis and production of the first truly synthetic fiber, Nylon, is one of the most frequently cited examples of successful industrial research in the twentieth century. It had its origins in Du Pont's decision, in 1927, to begin basic as well as applied research. One of its new chemists, Wallace H. Carothers, selected as his problem the synthesis of polymers or long-chain molecules, a subject of interest to Du Pont, which was already involved with semisynthetic fibers, viscose, and acetate. Carothers, over a period of years, produced a large number of both polyesters and polyamides, but only in 1935 did he come up with a series of polyamides, one of which, Nylon "66," showed real possibilities. Even then it took another four years, the work of some 230 technicians, and some $20 million to learn how to produce the raw materials on a commercial scale, solve other production problems, devise new methods of converting Nylon into commercially acceptable fabrics, and get it through the pilot-plant stage.[75]

Equally impressive were the results of research in pharmaceuticals. The introduction of the sulfa drugs in the thirties and the antibiotics after World War II provided the most spectacular examples of successful antibacterial agents, but the products of the industry ranged far beyond such items. The rate of technical change has been very high. A survey made in 1947 revealed that over half the drugs then

---

[75] Jewkes *et al.*, pp. 21–23; "Du Pont: How to Win at Research," *Fortune*, XLII (October 1950), 124–26, 129; "Du Pont: Orlon: Case History of a New Fiber," *ibid.*, pp. 110–11.

in use were unknown a decade earlier, and it is not unusual for a firm to discover that a substantial proportion of its sales are in products only recently developed and marketed. Both a cause and consequence of these extremely rapid changes has been the high level of research; pharmaceutical firms have consistently spent a larger percentage of annual sales for research than any other American industry.

The scientific revolution in petroleum, just getting under way about World War I, has expanded remarkably, and with it research activity. Standard of Indiana's research staff, which numbered 13 in 1920, grew to about 450 in 1951. The results were to be seen in many areas. Petroleum refining has become a highly sophisticated techno-logical process involving both thermal and catalytic cracking and synthesis of heavier hydrocarbons. The resultant fuels have been up-graded with various additives beginning with the discovery of tetra-ethyl lead in 1921. Lubricants, too, have been produced in a much wider range and with a more sophisticated knowledge of their com-position and operation. Perhaps most important, however, was the development of a whole new industry, petrochemicals, designed to exploit the raw materials found in petroleum and natural gas. Indeed, the historian of the American chemical industry characterized this development as "a scientific and economic triumph outshining the establishment of the vaunted, better publicized German coal-tar chem-ical industry."[76]

The continuing chemicalization of industry could be seen in two other areas as well, rubber and agriculture. Rubber had developed as an empirical industry in the nineteenth century around the discoveries of Charles Goodyear, but it first found a major niche for itself with the development of the automobile and the pneumatic tire. The appli-cation of scientific research in the twentieth century brought both a clearer understanding of the complex chemistry of natural rubber and the development of synthetic rubbers, an important economic factor in the industry in World War II and after. Significantly, the major American research on synthetic rubber was done initially by Du Pont and Standard Oil of New Jersey rather than by the rubber companies.

Agriculture had earlier played a role in the growth of the chemical industry with the development of superphosphate fertilizers in the nineteenth century. But this was only the first step in the chemical revolution of agriculture which has occurred in the past three decades with the development of sophisticated arrays of pesticides, herbicides,

---

[76] Haynes, *American Chemical Industry*, V, 208.

fungicides, fertilizers, hormones, and soil conditioners. The result has been a startling growth in agricultural productivity, higher in recent years than in manufacturing or other sectors of the economy.[77]

Even metallurgy, long a stronghold of empirical knowledge, is being increasingly influenced by scientific research. In recent years, it has tended to become a branch of both physics and chemistry. The application of the phase rule to alloys, the development of X-ray crystallography, the emergence of new nonferrous metals, frequently from chemical producers, and the whole development of solid state physics have tended to put metallurgy on something resembling a sound scientific basis. Metals, like virtually all industrial materials, are coming under scientific control and analysis.[78]

But perhaps more exciting and significant than the steady diffusion of scientific knowledge and techniques into various areas of industry has been the convergence of several lines of scientific development in the creation of a new industry or industrial process. Three have been particularly striking in the twentieth century. The first is aeronautics and space sciences. Here the basic scientific work essential for a successful aerodynamic design was performed in nineteenth-century Europe, particularly by Sir George Cayley. The invention of the airplane was essentially an engineering task involving the selection of the correct ingredients from among the large number of alternatives available. This the Wright brothers did.

For the four decades after the Wrights' initial flight the chief task for research was the improvement and application of existing aerodynamic knowledge until the advent of jet engines and supersonic speeds posed a new set of problems. The scientific and technical problems of rocket-powered space vehicles are radically different from

---

[77] Haynes, *American Chemical Industry*, IV and V, discusses the history of the chemical industry between the wars in great detail. Volume VI contains useful historical sketches of most of the firms in the industry up to 1948. On pharmaceuticals, see also Ernest H. Volwiler, "The Pharmaceutical Industry," *Industrial Science: President and Future*, ed., Ruth C. Christman (Washington, D.C., 1952), pp. 58–67. For petroleum, see Robert E. Wilson, "Competitive and Co-Operative Research in the American Petroleum Industry," *Journal of the Institute of Petroleum*, XXXVII (August 1951), 410 ff.; Beaton, chap. ix, gives a good account of research in one of the leaders in the development of petrochemicals. Ralph F. Wolf, "Eighty-eight Years of Synthetic Rubber," *Scientific Monthly*, LXVI (March 1948), 221–31, provides a good popular survey of that subject. On the chemical revolution in agriculture, see Eric Hodgins, "Farming's Chemical Age," *The Mighty Force of Research*, pp. 150–71.

[78] Cyril Stanley Smith, "Pure and Applied Science in American Metallurgy," *Metal Progress*, LXI (January 1952), 51–54; Sisco, pp. 157–68; Lawrence P. Lessing, "The New Metals Age," *The Mighty Force of Research*, pp. 217–33.

those of conventional aircraft. While the experience gained through airframe construction has proved valuable, aerospace engineers have had to turn to a wide variety of scientists previously of only minor importance to aviation. Electronics, for example, plays a crucial role in communications, control, and guidance systems, while the chemical industry has furnished fuels, propulsion units, and a host of metals and other materials crucial for one or another part of a complex space vehicle. For the first time since the seventeenth century, astronomy has surged forward as an important branch of applied science. The sense of urgency with which aerospace problems have been attacked in recent years has made the industry one of the chief recipients of research support in this country.[79]

The development of nuclear energy provides a second example of the convergence of various lines of pure and applied science on a new industry. The scientific roots of nuclear energy lay in the exploration of the character of the atom culminating in 1939 in the discovery of the fission of uranium. But the conversion of that piece of scientific information into first nuclear weapons and subsequently nuclear power plants required the close cooperation of virtually every variety of scientist and engineer developed in a complex twentieth-century scientific environment. The work of theoretical physicists, of course, lay at the heart of such developments. But it was Du Pont which built and operated plutonium production facilities, Union Carbide which did the same for the gaseous-diffusion plant for separating U-235 from U-238, and a subsidiary of Eastman Kodak which operated equipment supplied by Westinghouse and General Electric in the electromagnetic isotope separation scheme. Few projects better displayed the crumbling boundaries between physics and chemistry, between science and engineering.[80]

A third example of the convergence of scientific and technological disciplines to create new industries is provided by the development of computers and of automation. The basic idea of some kind of

---

[79] For brief discussions of aeronautical research, see Peter W. Brooks, "Aeronautics," *A History of Technology*, ed., Singer *et al.*, V, 405–12; Hugh L. Dryden, "A Half Century of Aeronautical Research," *Proceedings of the American Philosophical Society*, XCVIII (April 15, 1954), 115–20; Jerome C. Hunsaker, "A Half Century of Aeronautical Development," *ibid.*, pp. 121–30. *Technology and Culture*, IV (Fall 1963), 377 ff. is devoted to a series of articles on the history of rocket technology.

[80] Richard G. Hewlett and Oscar E. Anderson, Jr., *The New World, 1939/ 1946* (University Park, Pa., 1962), the first volume in a history of the United States Atomic Energy Commission, provides a highly reliable and readable account of the development of nuclear energy.

mechanized computational system is very old; indeed, Charles Bab-
bage, an English mathematician, designed theoretically sound devices
in the early nineteenth century, but he was ultimately frustrated in
his attempts to build such machines by mechanical limitations inherent
in the technology of his time. Success was finally achieved with the
application first of electron tubes and relays, subsequently of transis-
tors to such devices. The result has been a fruitful union of mathematics and logic on the one hand and electronics and electrical engineering on the other to produce extremely high-speed computational
equipment capable of receiving and storing information, retrieving it,
and performing many kinds of logical operations on it.

Many of the elements of automation are similarly quite old. There
is a long history to the mechanization and rationalization of industrial
processes. As we have noted earlier, Oliver Evans, as early as 1785,
was able to devise a highly mechanized flour mill, and similar methods
were used to develop efficient production in areas ranging from clocks
and watches in the mid-nineteenth century to automobile assembly
lines in the twentieth. The unique element in automation is the introduction of automatic analysis and control of the process. Once again,
electronics and electrical engineering have played crucial roles, first
in providing instruments to collect information about the state of a
process, second in providing computers to receive and analyze this
information, and third in developing the control devices which, acting
on commands received from computers, automatically modify or correct the process. These developments are so new that their implications are not yet fully visible, but few would deny that their long-term
effects are likely to be of revolutionary significance.[81]

This review of the relations between science and American industry
has made certain things fairly clear. First, while science on the one
hand and technology and industry on the other were long semiauton-
omous activities, they are no longer. Beginning with the electrical
industry, the chemical industries, and civil engineering, scientific methods and processes have come to play an ever more important role
in the technology of modern industry. To be sure, the infusion of
science into technology has been a long and complex process not yet
completed. Empirical methods continue to play a significant role in

---

[81] See Sharlin, pp. 219–26; Edmund C. Berkeley, *The Computer Revolution*
(Garden City, N.Y., 1962) and Walter Buckingham, *Automation* (New York,
c. 1961) provide reliable nontechnical discussions of these two subjects and
some of their implications.

many industries, and many firms conduct little or no research and development work. Yet the trend is clear. At the worst a firm which refuses to engage in such work risks technological obsolescence; at best it will have to cope with the sneers of its more research-minded and more fashionable competitors.

Second, the marriage of science and technology has produced abundant offspring. There is no doubt that the rate of technological innovation has risen over the past two centuries, though the questions of the rate of increase and the proportion of that increase due to science are subject to much dispute. Innovations have doubtless contributed to rising American productivity,[82] and we have become increasingly aware in recent years of the importance of rising productivity in maintaining economic growth. For more than a generation, too, we have been concerned with the problems of social adjustment to rapid technological change. At the same time, nuclear energy and space sciences have made abundantly clear the importance of technological change for the very nature of international relations. Suddenly, science and technology have been elevated to positions of national concern.

Third, while throughout most of the nineteenth century the United States was a net importer of scientific and technological ideas, the position has been reversed in the twentieth century, particularly in the past three or four decades. This is no place to discuss in detail the question of international scientific leadership. Suffice it to say that the close relationship between science and technology in this country combined with internal developments in both Germany and England in the twentieth century have enabled the United States to seize world leadership in applied science. Despite the challenge of Soviet technology, it seems likely that the United States will continue to maintain a prominent position in the international trade in scientific and technical ideas for a long while.

These developments have also wrought a revolution in industry itself and have posed new problems both of public policy and of private action. For example, in recent years scientific research and development have become a "good thing," a matter of national concern. We watch the statistics of research expenditures, hovering between

---

[82] However, Francis Bello, "The Technology behind Productivity," *Automation and Technological Change*, The American Assembly (Englewood Cliffs, N.J., 1962), pp. 153–68, argues that too little research goes into improving productivity.

pride and satisfaction in their spectacular growth and anxiety lest the research effort be too small. We discuss with passion the question of the proper location of research activity; how much responsibility for the national research and development effort should be borne by the federal government, the universities, or the industrial research laboratories? How should our research effort be distributed between basic research, applied research, or technological development? What kind of protection and encouragement ought we to give scientists and inventors, either in research funds or in patent protection? Nor have we come to any firm conclusions about the relationship between legitimate patent protection, industrial research, and the antitrust laws. Yet these are problems that must and are being daily resolved through a congeries of individual decisions. From them no coherent national policy on the encouragement and control of technological innovation has arisen. Perhaps it is just as well, for we know so little about the process of innovation that, as one recent group of analysts concluded,

> . . . it becomes almost an impertinence to speculate concerning the conditions and institutions which may foster or destroy it . . . in seeking to provide a social framework conducive to innovation, there are great virtues in eclecticism.[83]

The advent of applied science has also posed new managerial problems for the leaders of American industry. On the one hand, rapid technological change has forced the entrepreneur to cope with a whole new set of problems virtually nonexistent in a technologically stagnant industry. On the other hand, applied science has actually lowered the risks in technological innovation, giving the entrepreneur greater assurance of technical success than he ever possessed in the era of unbridled empiricism.[84] In any event, the entrepreneur in a technologically changing industry must decide whether or not to engage in research. If he begins his own laboratory, he has to deal with the question of determining the level of support, recruiting a competent staff, providing it with adequate facilities, organizing the researchers, and choosing satisfactory research problems. Assuming that the research is productive, the industrialist must then decide which, if any, of the new products or processes he can profitably exploit. The in-

---

[83] Jewkes *et al.*, p. 246.

[84] Strassmann, *passim*, argues that American innovators have been cautious and that the use of applied science has cut the risks borne by the entrepreneur.

creasing technical sophistication of instruments, products, and processes means heavier capital investment and increasingly complex problems of depreciation and obsolescene. Yet it would not be entirely accurate to emphasize the problems that the new technology has brought; it has also provided some of its own solutions, particularly in the form of the computer and related methods of administration and decision making.[85]

And what of the worker? Technological innovation has through the ages made obsolete existing skills and displaced workers. The classic example, of course, is the mechanization of the textile industry in which unskilled workers tending machines displaced skilled spinners and weavers. The cumulative effect of nineteenth-century technological change was to destroy the demand for the old craft skills and elevate the economic importance of the unskilled laborer. In the late nineteenth and the early twentieth centuries, the rapid growth of white-collar and service jobs further increased the demand for unskilled or semiskilled workers. The tendency of some of the newer innovations, particularly automation, however, is to destroy the positions of many of the unskilled and semiskilled in industry. The automated engine-block factory, the computerized bookkeeping system, and automatic dialing systems for telephones are good examples. In the long run, of course, the technological innovations should generate sufficient economic growth to absorb the displaced workers, particularly if they possess the skills to manage or maintain the increasingly sophisticated industrial machines and processes. But as John Maynard Keynes once observed, in the long run we are all dead, and at mid-century the short-run dislocations of labor posed social problems of considerable urgency.[86]

In the past three centuries, scientific knowledge has grown at an exponential rate. In the past century, men of the Western world have

---

[85] The problems of administering industrial scientific research have already provoked a large literature. C. E. Kenneth Mees and John A. Leermakers, *The Organization of Industrial Scientific Research*, 2nd ed. (New York, 1950) was one of the earliest and best of the "how to" manuals and has the additional virtue of considerable historical data. Birr, chap. iv, discusses the policies of the General Electric Research Laboratory, while Robert N. Anthony, *Management Controls in Industrial Research* (Boston, 1952), provides a comprehensive survey of practice. Simon Marcson, *The Scientist in American Industry* (New York, 1960) is characteristic of a growing literature with a strong sociological orientation.

[86] See Buckingham, pp. 91 ff., and Ewan Clague and Leon Greenberg, "Employment," *Automation and Technological Change*, pp. 114–31.

learned to apply this knowledge to the control of their material environment. The character of the process by which this has occurred is only dimly seen and partially understood. But no one can at this point doubt its revolutionary results. If scientific discoveries have resolved some long-standing problems, they have uncovered others. Comprehending the full meaning of these developments poses problems which scientists, historians, and social scientists have only begun to attack.

Science and American Agriculture

Reynold M. Wik*

In 1942 Secretary of Agriculture Clinton R. Anderson summarized the revolution that science and technology had wrought in farming in the United States. No longer did the American farmer have to rely on sheer muscle. He now had tractors to pull heavy loads, dig holes, and grind feed and thus cultivate vast areas of land with a minimum of labor. Poultry scientists had shown him how to double egg production. Farmers now had strains of alfalfa, wheat, and oats that resisted plant diseases, thanks to the agronomists. Researchers had provided him with chemicals that killed weeds and fertilized the soil, and insecticides that sanitized farm buildings. Improved breeds of sheep, cattle, and hogs produced more wool, beef, and bacon. Airplanes hauled perishable produce to market, while new refrigerating processes kept it fresh and wholesome. Hybrid fruit trees and hybrid corn brought higher yields. Science could even convert corncobs to industrial uses. Agricultural research had revealed the mysteries of the good earth, and increased knowledge could make possible the abundant life for every family. In a sanguine mood, the Secretary promised that "more was yet to come."[1]

*REYNOLD M. WIK is May Treat Morrison Professor of American History and Chairman of the Social Science Division at Mills College. He is also an advisory editor of *Technology and Culture* and a member of the Advisory Council of the Society for the History of Technology. He received his B.A. from Sioux Falls College and his M.A. and Ph.D. from the University of Minnesota. He has written a number of articles, notably on technology and agricultural history, and was awarded the Albert J. Beveridge Memorial Prize by the American Historical Society in 1950 for the book, *Steam Power on the American Farm*. He is now completing a book on "Henry Ford's Rural America." The author received a grant from the American Philosophical Society to carry out this research.

[1] U.S. Department of Agriculture, *Science in Farming: The Yearbook of Agriculture, 1943–1947* (Washington, D.C.,), p. v.

Eighteen years later the *United States Census Reports* of 1960 showed that farm families possessed these modern conveniences: Of the farm families having electricity, 98 percent owned refrigerators, 90 percent used electric irons, 72 percent had vacuum cleaners, and 93 percent owned motor-driven washing machines. In addition, the farm population operated 4,685,000 tractors, 3,000,000 trucks and 4,260,000 automobiles. In fact, for seven million farm workers in the United States there were now seven million farm tractors and trucks.[2]

Yields per acre of crop land doubled between 1930 and 1960:

	1930	1960
Wheat (bushels per acre)	14	24
Corn " "	26	54
Cotton (pounds per acre)	171	440

Output per manhour more than quadrupled. A generation ago a man in the corn belt could till 80 acres. Today, with modern machinery he can handle 240. In 1940 a farmer fed 10 people; today he feeds 30.

These impressive achievements had a long background in American agricultural history. Traditionally, Americans approached their problems pragmatically. Throughout the entire colonization venture following the settlement in Jamestown in 1607, they employed trial and error methods to sustain life, to defend themselves, and to improve their status. In the process of adjustment they increased their knowledge, because they could not escape the observations of their own experience.

DISSEMINATION OF INFORMATION

Newly acquired agricultural information encouraged and enabled the colonists to plant tobacco and maize, to import the seed of hemp, flax, cotton, and indigo, and to introduce the mulberry trees for the feeding of silkworms. Meanwhile, George Washington imported improved cattle and horses from Europe, while Thomas Jefferson became the first American to design a moldboard plow on true mathematical principles.[3]

---

[2] U.S. Bureau of the Census, *United States Census of Agriculture*, V, *General Report, Statistics by Subjects* (Washington, D.C., 1959), 207. There were approximately 14 million people living on 4 million farms in the United States in 1960. Of these 14 million, 7 million are called farm workers, men who owned their farms or worked for wages.

[3] Percy W. Bidwell and John I. Falconer, *History of Agriculture in the Northern United States, 1620–1860* (Washington, D.C., 1925), p. 208.

Likewise, prominent Americans helped disseminate agricultural information through correspondence. Thomas Jefferson, after visiting England in 1786, wrote to his friend John Page saying that the most striking thing he had seen was the use of a steam engine to drive a gristmill. He expressed the opinion that steam power would be applied to farming practices in the future, because it represented the new developments in technology.[4] After Jared Eliot of Killingsworth, Connecticut, wrote some essays about farming in New England, Benjamin Franklin wrote numerous letters to the author in which he discussed such matters as the culture of flax, the price of linseed oil, the growing of hemp, and the making of potash. On one occasion, he praised John Bartram, the botanist, "well filled on the subjects of botany, fossils, husbandry and the first creation."[5]

Further spread of information came with the establishment of scientific agricultural societies by gentlemen farmers. The Philadelphia Society for the Promotion of Agriculture was founded in 1785, with George Washington as an honorary member. Six years later, a similar organization in New York announced it would collect information from all parts of the state and conduct experiments to seek improvement of exhausted land. Their officers circulated questionnaires asking such questions as: Have you made any experiments with marl? To what depth should land be plowed? Are oxen more serviceable than horses? Can wild turkeys be domesticated? What turns wheat to smut? What apples make the best cider? How can cattle be most easily relieved when choaked by apples or potatoes?[6]

These societies published *Transactions*, which periodically put before the public the best farming practices in Europe and America. In addition, they offered premiums for the discovery of ways to destroy insect pests and for methods of improving the quality of seeds and the fertility of the soil. However, the "dirt farmers" worked so hard to make a living that they had little time to read. Charles L. Flint claimed these publications "fell almost dead upon the people, who rejected book farming as impertinent and useless, and who knew as little of the chemistry of agriculture as the problems of astronomy."[7]

---

[4] H. A. Washington, ed., *The Writings of Thomas Jefferson* (New York, 1884), I, 548–51.

[5] T. Swann Harding, *Some Landmarks in the History of the Department of Agriculture* (Washington, D.C., January, 1942), p. 4.

[6] *Transactions of the Society for the Promotion of Agriculture, Arts, and Manufacturers* (Albany, N.Y., 1801), I, xi, xii, xiv.

[7] Thomas P. Kettell, ed., *Eighty Years Progress in the United States* (New York, 1861), I, 25.

Aware of the average farmer's indifference to published scientific journals, Elkanah Watson of Pittsfield, Massachusetts, in 1807 decided to shift rural education from the head to the heart by exhibiting two Merino sheep in the public square. Thus he founded the livestock fair in the United States, an institution destined to become one of the most popular mediums for spreading the latest scientific information among farm people.

Farm journalism began to improve with the publication, in 1819, of the *American Farmer*, edited by Stuart Skinner of Baltimore. This periodical set the standard for agricultural journalism, and it was followed by a number of similar journals, among them the *Farmer's Register* and the *Prairie Farmer*. The *American Farmer* emphasized livestock, the *Farmer's Register* stressed agricultural machinery, and the *Prairie Farmer* concentrated on common school education and farm machinery. Written primarily for practical farmers, these periodicals described the latest scientific farm practices and urged their readers to be receptive to innovation and change. The editor's major interests often dominated the news. Editorials stressed the advantage of deep plowing, drainage of wet soil, crop rotation, selective breeding of livestock, and the use of fertilizers. Fairs and agricultural tours were reported in detail, and British articles and translations of French articles were printed.[8]

MEAGERNESS OF EARLY INVENTION

The early Americans possessed an extraordinary amount of flexibility in adjusting to the life in the new world, but it is easy to overrate their achievements in science and technology. The widely held belief that our colonial forefathers were men of exceptional inventive ability is largely a myth. It is true that the early settlers were forced by necessity to be inventive in order to survive in a hostile wilderness. Ralph Waldo Emerson claimed the colonists "had the habit of invention in their brains."[9] Artemus Ward insisted Yankees could "invent, chop, swap, work, and fight if necessary."[10] Mark Twain's Connecticut Yankee bragged, "Why, I could make anything a body wanted—anything in the world, it didn't make any difference what: and if there

---

[8] Albert L Demaree, "The Farm Journals, Their Editors, and Their Public, 1830–1860," *Agricultural History*, XV (October 1941), 24.

[9] Ralph Waldo Emerson, "Resources," *Works of Ralph Waldo Emerson*, VIII, 137.

[10] Edmund Fuller, *Tinkers and Genius* (New York, 1955), p. 58.

wasn't any quick new-fangled way to make a thing, I could invent one—and do it as easy as rolling off a log."[11]

But, granted that the colonists were resourceful and clever with their hands, they were more inclined to be imitative than inventive. Since the period from 1607 to 1775 represents almost half of the total span of United States history, and since the conditions in the New World were such as should stimulate the creative imaginations of our forefathers, we would be entitled to expect the colonists to have produced some remarkable machines prior to the Revolutionary War. Unfortunately, however, evidence now suggests that the colonial people failed to invent *any* successful machines of any importance; at least historians fail to mention them.

The absence of mechanical inventions in early America frustrates scholars eager to praise the mechanical achievements of colonial days. The material available to them is exceedingly thin. Benjamin Franklin is often called America's first inventor with his improved stove, lightning rods, electrical devices, and his rocking chair with a built-in fan to keep off the flies. While these innovations were useful, none of them could properly be classified as a mechanical machine, as an apparatus of interrelated parts with separate functions and capable of performing some kind of work. Edmund Fuller, in *Tinkers and Genius*, tells the story of burgeoning Yankee inventiveness, but the only colonial machine mentioned is David Bushnell's one-man submarine, an oddity which failed in its initial use against British shipping in 1776.[12] Likewise, John Oliver, in *History of American Technology*, entitled his first chapter "Yankee Ingenuity" and then proceeded to demonstrate that every tool, farm implement, and machine in colonial America originated abroad.[13] Nothing was invented in colonial America to compare with the invention of the steam engine by James Watt, or the inventions in the textile industry in England, such as John Kay's flying shuttle, James Hargreave's spinning jenny, Richard Arkwright's spinning frame, Edmund Cartwright's power loom. All of these inventions appeared in Europe before the adoption of the American Constitution.

Hence, we must conclude that the stereotype of the New England Yankee as an inventive magician in colonial days is without a factual basis. He may have been influenced by a Calvinism which sanctified

---

11 Mark Twain, *The Connecticut Yankee* (New York, 1890), p. 15.

12 Fuller, *op. cit.*, p. xi.

13 John Oliver, *History of Technology* (New York, 1956), p. 1.

hard work, the poor land which forced him to eke out a livelihood by becoming a jack-of-all-trades, and the long winter nights may have been conducive to whittling or bundling, but that he possessed superior mechanical brains during this era may be dismissed as another bit of folklore. In fact, Samuel Morison, eminent Harvard University historian, recently concluded, "The scientific production of colonial New England was negligible, even compared with Mexico."[14] Victor S. Clark, in his study of manufacturing, points out that colonial patents were distinguished from those of a later period by being for process rather than machinery, and that aside from Roland Houghton's theodolite in 1735, there "appears not to have been a single mechanical device so protected in New England from the time of Jenkins to the Revolution."[15] Benjamin Butterworth presents 200 pages of evidence in *The Growth of Industrial Art*, published in 1892, but pictures or describes in his commentary[16] no machines invented in colonial days. Joseph Wickham Roe, industrial engineer of Yale University, insisted that inventors showed little activity until after the Revolutionary War.[17] Indeed, the most striking feature of colonial technology is its sterility, not its inventiveness. As Mitchell Wilson accurately states, "Yankee ingenuity and Yankee git-up-and-go did not exist in colonial days."[18]

Because of this paucity of inventions, writers rejoice, when, after scratching over the scanty technological crumbs of two centuries, they reach 1793, because now they have an honest-to-God American invention in Eli Whitney's cotton gin. It is no wonder that his name is immortal. Why reasonably well-educated colonists managed to live in an environment so desperately in need of mechanical innovations and still remained so uninventive remains an enigma. They seemed determined to prove that necessity had nothing to do with invention, and their failure to hit upon a significant new machine in 170 years of feverish activity is in itself one of the mysteries of American history.

---

[14] Samuel Morison, *The Intellectual Life of Colonial New England* (Ithaca, N.Y.), p. 241.

[15] Victor S. Clark, *History of Manufacturers in the United States*, I (New York, 1929), p. 48.

[16] Benjamin Butterworth, *The Growth of Industrial Art* (Washington, D.C., 1892), pp. 1–200.

[17] Richard Shelton Kirby, ed., *Inventors and Engineers of Old New Haven* (New Haven, 1939), p. 11.

[18] Mitchell Wilson, *American Science and Invention* (New York, 1954), p. 11.

Apparently the early farmers found it easier to be imitative than original. Walter P. Webb suggested that European migrants accustomed to a tree culture at home settled in a forested America where adaptation followed natural lines in the building of homes, farming, and home industries. Since their techniques for making a living worked, it seemed unnecessary to change them.[19] Thus European procedures prevailed in the new land. Houses of wood or brick were built rather than log cabins. English common law, language, and religion and habits and customs tended to be perpetuated in the New World.

Then, too, the dearth of mechanical inventions among the colonists may be explained in the same manner as the absence of good novels, great poetry, famous paintings, noted musical compositions, significant sculpture or drama. If these pioneers were too preoccupied with manual labor to make cultural achievements, it is conceivable that they were also too busy to invent machines. If cultural arts flourish only in a stable, affluent society which provides some leisure for contemplation, the same conditions must prevail to nurture the inventive spirit.

EARLY GOVERNMENT AID TO AGRICULTURE AND INDUSTRY

The student of scientific agriculture will notice that public funds were frequently used to foster improved conditions on the American farm. It would be misleading to assume that science took root in early America because our forefathers kept the government out of the affairs of the individual and rejected all aspects of the welfare state. On the contrary, the nation's early history reflected considerable economic pluralism rather than unadulterated laissez-faire capitalism.

The colonial governments subsidized a variety of projects. New Jersey, Pennsylvania and Massachusetts granted bounties for the establishment of iron foundries, while Virginia aided the textile manufacturers. Town officials of East Bridgewater, Massachusetts, hired several Scotsmen to come to America in 1786 to build Arkwright spinning machines.[20] In the following year, $14,000 was spent on a similar project in Beverly. Richard Morris, in *Government and Labor in Early America*, has pointed out that entrepreneurs in the seven-

---

[19] Walter P. Webb, *The Great Plains* (Austin, Texas, 1931), pp. 1–68.
[20] Holland Thompson, *The Age of Invention* (New Haven, 1921), p. 85.

teenth century were not free to carry on business as they saw fit, nor were workers always free to choose their vocations. At times, craftsmen in Virginia were forbidden to leave their work to take up farming. Men were required to work specified days each week in the harvest fields or on public works. Likewise, legislation frequently set wage and price ceilings and regulated the fees charged by lawyers and doctors. Physicians caring for the poor or treating men in the army were paid by the state. It appears that laissez-faire economics was far from the minds of the founding fathers.[21]

Because of the mixed economy, it seemed natural that government should encourage work in science and technology. During the Revolutionary War, military arms were produced in government armories as well as private firms. Congress made the Springfield Armory a national institution in 1794. Here Thomas Blanchard designed copying lathes for manufacturing standardized parts for rifles. The federal government also rescued Eli Whitney from financial ruin by offering him contracts for arms manufacture. By 1809 he had received $134,000 in Federal funds.[22] Samuel F. B. Morse accepted $30,000 from the federal treasury to help build a telegraph line from Baltimore to Washington.

The United States government encouraged scientific work by appropriating funds in 1794 for the training of engineers. An act of Congress stipulated that eight cadets were to be attached to the Army and authorized the President to appoint four teachers of the arts and sciences for their instruction. Later presidents Jefferson and Madison urged that more emphasis be placed on engineering studies at the Military Academy at West Point.[23] In addition, Congress established the Smithsonian Institution, in 1846, as a museum, research center, and publisher of scientific reports.

Since public funds were used for a variety of other purposes, it seemed logical to assume that government should finance agricultural projects as well. George Washington doubtless reflected the sentiment of his day when he stated in his last message to Congress on Decem-

---

[21] Richard B. Morris, *Government and Labor in Early America*, p. 11. See also *American State Papers, Military Affairs, Class V*, V, *Documents, Legislative and Executive of the United States* (Washington, D.C., 1860), 311–12.

[22] *American State Papers, Military Affairs, Class V*, IV, *Report of the Secretary of War* (Washington, D.C., 1831), 711.

[23] *American State Papers. Military Affairs, Class V*, V, *Documents, Legislative and Executive of the United States* (Washington, D.C., 1860), 312.

ber 7, 1796, that agriculture was of prime importance to the national welfare. He advocated the establishment of a Federal Board of Agriculture and insisted that:

> In proportion as nations advance in population and other circumstances of maturity, this truth becomes more apparent, and renders the cultivation of the soil more and more an object of public patronage. Institutions for promoting it grow up, supported by the public purse; and to what object can it be dedicated with greater propriety.[24]

Although the federal government hesitated to dole out money directly for agriculture, the several states did divert funds in this direction. New Hampshire, in 1810, subsidized several agricultural societies, while Massachusetts paid $115,800 from the state treasury to support similar organizations over a 15-year period. Massachusetts also paid farmers $27,000 in bounties from 1838 to 1840 to encourage the planting of wheat. In Maine $200,000 went as bounty to farmers for growing wheat and corn from 1837 to 1839.[25]

The first specific congressional appropriation for agriculture came in 1839, when the Patent Office was given $1,000 for the collection of farm statistics. Henry L. Ellsworth, the Patent Commissioner, urged Congress to increase these appropriations. Apparently he had Justus von Liebig's influential work, *Chemistry in Its Application to Agriculture and Physiology*, because he insisted that chemistry could be a boon to the farmer. "If the application of the sciences be yet further made to husbandry," he said, "what vast improvements may be anticipated."[26] He pointed out that chemistry had provided a way for western farmers to market oil, because now pork fat could be converted into stearine for candles. Chemistry also showed how 10 gallons of oil could be extracted from 100 bushels of corn meal. The Patent Office officials looked to the science of agriculture to make folklore yield to scientific analysis. Potato diseases could be eradicated, and the Hessian fly, so destructive to wheat, could be controlled. Experience had proved that every grain, vegetable, and fruit could be improved by scientific cultivation. Indeed, genius had stooped from its lofty height to lessen the farmer's burden.

---

[24] Harding, *op. cit.*, p. 4.

[25] Bidwell and Falconer, *op. cit.*, pp. 189–93.

[26] U.S. Department of Agriculture, *After a Hundred Years: The Yearbook of Agriculture* (Washington, D.C., 1962), p. 22.

When Dr. Daniel Lee joined the Patent Office to supervise the scientific work of the agency, he begged Congress to increase appropriations for agriculture to prevent universal impoverishment of the soil. "The prayers of generations had gone unheard," he asserted. "How could the appropriation of $1,000 restore the fertility of 100 million acres of land? . . . Agricultural schools should be established to teach young people the principles of soil-building science."[27] Thus the struggle to secure federal funds for agricultural education was intensified, and the battle was won when the Land-Grant College Act was passed in 1862.

Farm journals joined in the crusade for more federal aid to agriculture. *De Bow's Review*, in 1858, maintained that the nation had good soil, laborsaving machinery, and industrious workers, but the farmer lacked theoretical knowledge, inventive skills, and a system of science to make adequate progress. Above all:

> No species of human pursuit is more depending and more indebted to Chemistry than agriculture. Chemistry does not only give instruction to the farmer on everything there is, but teaches him what is wanting, and how it can be got. . . . If but a single series of such investigations would be undertaken on the part of the Federal or State Government, we do not for a moment doubt that the results would be looked upon with astonishment and hailed with delight by legislators, statesmen and personal agriculturists.[28]

In the face of mounting pressures, Congress abandoned its position that agriculture needed no direct financial aid and, in 1854, granted $35,000 for agricultural experimental work on a two-acre plot near Missouri Avenue in Washington, D.C. Glover Townsend, an entomologist, joined the Patent Office staff; a chemist and botanist were employed to do research; and arrangements were made to have the Smithsonian Institution publish meteorological statistics. Thus the same Congress that passed the Kansas-Nebraska Bill, which was destined to split the nation politically into two factions and lead to violence in "Bleeding Kansas," initiated the first major financial aid to agriculture. Henceforth the farmer was to receive some of the same consideration which had been bestowed on the businessman by the

---

[27] Harding, *op. cit.*, pp. 20–23.

[28] "Necessity of Agricultural Reform," *De Bow's Review*, XXV (1858), 158–63. See also A. Hunter Dupree, *Science and Emergence of Modern Americam, 1865–1916*, Berkeley Series (Chicago, 1963), pp. 30–50.

founding fathers of the Constitution and the administration of George Washington.

DEVELOPMENT OF MECHANICAL TECHNOLOGY

Perhaps the most significant progress in American agriculture resulted from the application of scientific knowledge to mechanical technology. The ability to use iron and steel in making machinery made obsolete the "Man with the Hoe" and ushered in the era of modern farming. The invention of iron plows made it possible to harness animal power more efficiently to prepare the seedbed; now farmers could plow more acres than they could harvest in a season. The advent of the horse-drawn seeder, cultivator, and reaper permitted farmers to harvest as much grain as they could plant. However, now they could raise more grain than they could thresh in the winter months. When horsepowered machines failed to provide adequate belt power for threshing and other belt work, the steam engine became essential. In this sense, machines plus adequate power created the agricultural revolution of the nineteenth century.

Although some American farmers were so conservative that they rejected mechanical innovations, others were eager to experiment with the new technology. The transition from horse power to mechanical power became one of the major achievements in modern farming.

Interestingly enough, scientific technology reached rural America at an early date. Historically, the farm engineers predated the railroad engineers. In England, George Stephenson's first locomotive ran in 1813; in the United States, the "Stourbridge Lion" made its first successful run in 1829. But in the meantime, steam engines had been installed on several southern plantations as early as 1807, the year in which Robert Fulton made his historic trip up the Hudson River in the "Claremont." While Stephenson and Fulton received world renown for bringing steam power to transportation and commerce, apparently no one noticed that rural Americans had already started a revolution of their own by applying steam power to agriculture. Levi Woodbury, Secretary of the Treasury, issued a report in 1838 indicating that it had become commonplace for planters to purchase stationary steam engines for threshing rice, sawing wood, ginning cotton, and grinding cane in the sugar mills.[29]

---

[29] *House Executive Documents* (25th Cong., 3rd sess.), II, No. 345, 1–472.

The first farm steam engineers worked in the South, where the rapidly expanding rural economy encouraged planters to purchase the most modern machinery on the market. Frederick Law Olmsted once described these plantation owners as "the most intelligent, enterprising and wealthy men of business in the United States."[30] When water, wind, and mule power proved inadequate, these men imported 16-horsepower Fawcett engines from Liverpool which cost $7,000 each. Bolted down to solid foundations and belted to line shafts, these engines furnished the power to drive the various plantation machines. Overseers and negro slaves both operated the engines. Thus the notion that all southern planters sat on the shaded porches of white mansions, reading Sir Walter Scott and drinking mint juleps, while all the slaves, in the image of *Uncle Tom's Cabin,* bent under the lash in the cotton fields needs revision. Planters made use of slave labor, it is true, but it should be remembered that they were also among the most mechanically and scientifically minded people in the nation. Eager to learn more about machinery, they introduced power farming to America, a move destined eventually to remove the backbreaking work for laborers in both North and South.

Subsequently, farmers in the northern states bought portable steam engines which were mounted on wheels and could be moved about with horses. These developed 10 to 20 horsepower and cost about $1,000. They were made self-propelled in the 1870's. Hence, the steam engine provided the first mechanical power for extensive use in agriculture, and laid the foundation for the present-day power farming.

In addition, the use of the steam engine encouraged large-scale farming. When threshing machines required twice as much power as furnished by the horse, the improved steam engine provided timely assistance. For example, Oliver Dalrymple, in 1884, used 30 steam engines to thresh 30,000 acres of wheat in the Red River Valley of Dakota.[31] Dr. Hugh J. Glenn owned a 66,000-acre farm in California, where his steam threshing outfit poured out 5,779 bushels of wheat on August 8, 1874.[32]

As power demands increased, a total of 3,600,000 steam horsepower served agriculture in 1910, an amount equal to the strength of

---

[30] Frederick Law Olmsted, *A Journey in the Seaboard Slave States* (New York, 1856), p. 669.

[31] U.S. Bureau of the Census, *United States Census of 1880*, III, *Report of the Production of Agriculture*, 75.

[32] *Michigan Farmer*, August 21, 1877, p. 2. See also *Pacific Rural Press*, May 6, 1876, pp. 1–2.

7 million horses.[33] At this time, approximately 100,000 farm engineers were operating these engines. They staged colorful performances with new machines glistening in new paint and shining brass. Some engines weighed 20 tons, developed 100 horsepower, and cost as much as $6,000. The Best and Holt engines on the Pacific Coast could outpull 40 mules,, and when attached to combines, they could harvest 100 acres a day.[34]

The farm engineers who operated steam engines had a scientific bent. They were familar with the principles of slide valves, injectors, steam pressures, lubrication oils, gear ratios, and boiler operations. They rejected their fathers' veneration of the horse and welcomed an opportunity to learn more about mechanics. They encouraged the building of better roads and the introduction of courses in mechanics in state agricultural colleges. In using steam power for plowing, threshing, and hauling freight, these men helped pave the way for the later introduction of the gasoline tractor and the Model T automobile.

To facilitate the spread of information about new technological developments, the manufacturing companies demonstrated their machinery at competive field trials and at county and state fairs. The McCormick reapers competed with rival machines in scores of contests both here and abroad. Plowing contests in midwestern states drew large crowds. During the South Dakota State Fair in 1913, over 160 acres of land were plowed as demonstrations during the Fair week. To prove how quickly a farm steam engine could be started, stopped, and reversed, the Huber Manufacturing Company ran the rear wheel of the engine over planks which teetered over a central fulcrum. The engine could be run forward and backward without causing the plank to touch the ground on either side of the center block. The Northwest Thresher Company of Stillwater, Minnesota, demonstrated the sensitive control of the throttle by running the rear wheel of the engine up against an egg with just enough force to crack but not crush it. Another stunt was to open the back of an open-faced watch and hang it on a post. Then the 20-ton engine was backed against the watch until the case snapped shut without the slightest damage to either the crystal or the watch. The Winnipeg Plowing trials, from 1908 to 1913, featured mammoth steam engines and

---

[33] William Hurst and Lillian Church, *Power and Machinery in Agriculture*, U.S. Department of Agriculture, Miscellaneous Bulletin No. 157 (Washington, D.C., April 1933), p. 7.

[34] Reynold M. Wik, *Steam Power on the American Farm* (Philadelphia, 1953), p. 94.

tractors engaged in contests, while college professors judged their performances. Prizes were awarded the winners. These contests made testing a regular part of the operation of every agricultural machinery factory. Testing made designing engineers more conscious of economy, ease of handling, and durability of engine parts. It also demonstrated rather convincingly that the gasoline tractor was destined to be the farm power unit of the future.[35]

Tractor shows were popular from 1915 to 1920, when demonstrations were held in many of the agricultural cities of the midwest. As many as 50,000 people attended some of these shows to tramp up and down the fields to see the tractors perform. One company sold 160 tractors during one demonstration. These demonstrations convinced many farmers that tractors were superior to horses for farming purposes.

. SCIENTIFIC STUDY OF AGRICULTURE

When Abraham Lincoln, on May 15, 1862, signed a bill establishing the Department of Agriculture, and on July 2, signed the Land-Grant College bill, the foundations were laid for scientific studies in agriculture for the next century. Isaac Newton, the first Commissioner of Agriculture, stated that his objectives would be to collect, arrange, and publish agricultural information; distribute seeds; answer farmers queries; institute chemical investigations; investigate cotton culture; seek to introduce silkworms from China; and promote the culture of flax and hemp as substitutes for cotton. He also proposed a chemical laboratory for analysis of soils, grains, fruits, plants, and vegetables and urged the establishment of professorships of botany and entomology. He wished to use science for the benefit of agriculture, but as A. Hunter Dupree has pointed out, "he had no specific ideas as to what problems could be solved or how they should be attacked."[36] During the first year, the Department consisted of a horticulturist, a chemist, an entomologist, a statistician, and 24 other staff members. Some experimental work was begun in a garden between Fourth and Sixth streets, and a larger area between Independence and Constitution avenues was used for an experimental farm when the Union army no longer needed it for a cattle yard.

Early scientific achievements included C. M. Wetherill's study of

---

[35] *Ibid.*, p. 186.

[36] A. Hunter Dupree, *Science in the Federal Government* (Cambridge, Mass., 1957), p. 152.

sugars and his report on the *Chemical Analysis of Grapes*. Later, Henri Erni reported on fermentation studies and made analyses of wines, coal, soils, asphalt, and guano. During Grant's administration, Commissioner Horace Capron attempted to investigate the cause of the Texas fever, which had proved fatal to many of the domesticated cattle which came in contact with the Texas longhorns being driven up from the South. However, the department seemed unable to carry out a long-term research project on this problem. Although cattlemen in the Southwest believed the disease was carried by ticks, the scientists in Washington, D.C., erroneously attributed the disease to a fungus growth.

Inadequate financing plagued the Department of Agriculture for the first 20 years of its existence. Appropriations for the Department were only $199,770 in 1864 and $199,500 in 1880.[37] However, the Department had a renaissance in the 1880's and 1890's, which continued into the twentieth century. The Hatch Act of 1887 established the Office of Experiment Stations in the Department. The federal government provided money for distribution to the state experiment stations for carrying out basic research. The Adams Act of 1906 provided additional funds for experiment stations engaged in research "bearing directly on the agricultural industry of the United States."

Increased prestige came to the Department in 1889, when Congress elevated it to Cabinet status. When the Army Signal Corps was transferred to the Department in 1891 and the Weather Bureau was established, the number employed by the Department reached 1,577. Besides, various commissions which had acted independently were now absorbed by the Department. For example, the United States Entomological Commission attempted to cope with the grasshopper plagues which swept the Midwest during the 1870's. In 1880 this agency became part of the Department of Agriculture, where its appropriations grew from $7,000 in 1880 to $42,000 in 1885. This division studied insects and attempted to prevent the introduction of pests from Europe and to control the spread of the boll weevil in the cotton states. After 1906 the Division became a Bureau in name, and under more aggressive leadership, field laboratories were set up in infested areas rather than waiting for farm problems to be brought to Washington. By securing grants for money for research in a general area instead of allocating it for specific purposes, the Department of Agriculture gained flexibility to shift programs as conditions warranted.

---

[37] *Ibid.*, p. 156.

The Department developed rapidly under the leadership of James Wilson of Iowa, who served as Secretary from 1897 to 1913. During these years he transformed his agency into an outstanding research, regulatory, educational, and custodial institution. In 1900 the Arlington Farm of 400 acres in Virginia was acquired for experimental work. The Bureau of Plant Industry used this land until 1941, when it was transferred to the War Department as a site for the Pentagon. Additional research facilities were secured for the Agricultural Research Center at Beltsville, Maryland.

During the depression of the 1930's, the Agricultural Adjustment Act established in the Department of Agriculture the Agricultural Adjustment Administration, which assumed responsibility for initiating programs for soil conservation, rural electrification, and research in the branches of economics and science. The AAA initiated, for instance, the Forest Products Laboratory near Madison, Wisconsin, as one of four regional laboratories dedicated to the work of developing industrial uses for farm products.

Although the Congress never established a national university, the federal government endeavored to meet the practical needs of rural Americans by passage of the Land-Grant College Act of 1862, which endowed state colleges with 11 million acres of land, equal in size to twice the area of Vermont. The legislation introduced the principle of federal grants-in-aid to the states. As a result of the Act, 68 institutions, sometimes referred to as "peoples colleges" or "cow colleges," were established. They provided education at a minimum cost. From these schools came large numbers dedicated to the ideal of a more scientific agriculture.

Iowa State University in Ames, Iowa, opened in 1869, became the first land-grant college in the nation. Its enrollment grew from a beginning student body of 173 to 10,776 in 1964. Initially, only a course in agriculture and one in mechanics were offered; today there are 80 disciplines in the five divisions of engineering, agriculture, home economics, veterinary medicine, and science and humanities. Iowa State's pioneering ventures include the first college curriculum for a degree of bachelor of science in dairy industry, initiated in 1897, and a course in agricultural journalism, first offered in 1905. To keep pace with the increased mechanization of agriculture, the college first offered a course in farm mechanics in 1902 and graduated its first farm engineer in 1910. In the 1930's, inbred lines of corn were developed at Ames which were almost exclusively Iowa hybrids.[38]

---

[38] *After a Hundred Years, op. cit.*, pp. 13–20.

Today, this work is typical of all the land-grant colleges and universities. These institutions enroll one fifth of the total college population, grant 40 percent of the doctoral degrees in all subjects and all of the doctoral degrees in agriculture. From these institutions flow scientific advances which have bettered the lot of all Americans.

WORK OF INDIVIDUAL SCIENTISTS IN THE DEPARTMENT OF AGRICULTURE

Some indication of the profound significance of science in American agriculture can be seen in the work of individual scientists in the Department of Agriculture. In 1883 livestock diseases received little attention from governmental agencies. At the time, hog cholera caused deaths amounting to the value of $30 million annually. Cattlemen feared the Texas fever and pleuropneumonia, anthrax and blackleg. The causes of these diseases were unknown or in dispute, and veterinary science had not been able to provide adequate treatment. Constant demands for assistance resulted in the act of Congress which established the Bureau of Animal Industry in 1884 and appropriated $150,000 to put the law into effect.

Farmers had long suspected that the cattle tick transmitted Texas fever. Theobald Smith, the Bureau's first pathologist, began experimenting with tick fever in 1888. He discovered that the cause of the disease was a protozoan parasite that multiplied in the blood of infected animals. Working with Cooper Curtice and F. L. Kilborne, Smith announced, in 1892, confirmation of the suspicion that infection could be carried from one animal to another by the tick. This was a momentous discovery—the first demonstration that disease-producing microorganisms could be transmitted by an insect carrier. The obvious cure was to get rid of the ticks, and this was achieved by a long-range eradication program. The original research cost $65,000, but the saving to cattlemen today amounts to $65 million a year. In addition, this discovery led others to scrutinize the mosquito as a possible disease carrier, thus paving the way for the understanding and control of such serious maladies as malaria, typhus, bubonic plague, and Rocky Mountain spotted fever.[39]

Again, when Marion Dorset joined the Department in 1894, he knew that hog cholera created losses of $65 million annually. The Bureau of Animal Industry thought the cause of the disease to be a bacterium and prepared a serum to combat it. However, Dorset found

---

[39] *Science in Farming, op. cit.,* pp. 1–2.

the serum to be ineffective against cholera and went on to demonstrate that the disease was caused by an ultramicroscopic virus rather than a bacterium. He also proved that hogs that recovered from the disease were immune for life. While conducting experiments in Iowa in 1903, his team of scientists found that the blood from immune hogs gave only temporary immunity to other hogs. Then Dorset began using two injections. The first was a serum from the blood of a pig which had survived the cholera. The second was an injection of the virus from an infected hog. Today, this double injection method provides protection against this dreaded disease.

Another scientist in the Department, S. Henry Ayers, contributed to the health of the American people by convincing them that the pasteurization of milk was desirable. Physicians and public officials had opposed pasteurization, because they believed that the process destroyed the lactic acid bacteria in milk, causing it to sour. Besides, they thought that the method produced toxins making it unfit for human consumption. Ayers ran thousands of tests, and his report, published in 1910, convinced people that the pasteurized milk was safer than raw milk.

Still another Department scientist, Dr. Harvey W. Wiley, conducted research that contributed to better health. He spent 21 years investigating the adulteration of food products on the market. His analyses showed that cottonseed oil was commonly used as an adulterant in making butter. Poisonous dyes were often used to color food, while foreign matter contaminated much of the foodstuffs. His findings contributed to the passage of the Pure Food and Drug Act of 1906.

In 1890 Professor S. M. Babcock of the University of Wisconsin came to the aid of housewives by devising a test for butterfat in milk and cream. He showed that by adding a bit of sulfuric acid to a measured sample of milk and whirling it for a few minutes in a graduated container, one could read the percentage of butterfat at a glance. This percentage multiplied by the total weight of the milk gave the amount of butterfat in a can of milk. The Babcock test gave dairy farmers a better way to measure the value of their cows. This led to official testing of dairy herds by the members of the Dairy Herd Improvement Association, in which over 40,000 dairy farmers keep production records on more than a half-million cows. The test provided a method to check the legal requirements for butterfat in every bottle of milk sold in the market, to the benefit of the consumer.

In the field of plant industry, it is known that 30,000 different diseases attack plants in the United States with a cost of $3 billion a year.[40] Agricultural pathology gained new impetus from Louis Pasteur's discovery that bacteria produced some animal diseases. Following Pasteur's lead Professor T. J. Burrill of Illinois, in 1878, proved bacteria to be the cause of "fire blight," a devasting disease which swept through apple and pear orchards. The discovery led to a whole new theory of plant disease. Dr. Erwin F. Smith and his associates of the United States Department of Agriculture carried the work forward. Smith summarized his findings in *Bacterial Disease*, published in 1920. Today, there are 170 known kinds of bacteria which attack plant life. In addition, more than 200 plant viruses have been isolated since 1900. Among these are "curly top," which injures sugar beets, tomatoes, and beans, and tristeza, which attacks orange groves.

To cope with these types of diseases, William A. Orton, a plant pathologist in the Department, concentrated on the wilt which damaged cotton crops. He used experimental plots to breed a new variety of cotton which would not wilt. This became a landmark in agricultural research because it pioneered in breeding plants which were resistant to disease.

Likewise, Dr. E. C. Stakman of the University of Minnesota became concerned about rust, which often ruined the wheat crops. He confirmed earlier work done in Sweden which indicated that there were several types of stem rust. He proved that rust was not produced by a single organism; several closely related organisms could produce the disease. These he called "pathogenic races." This variation in strains explained why a variety of wheat which was resistant to one form of stem rust for years suddenly succumbed to another. Apparently the rust causing the trouble was one better adapted to the environment. When a new variety of wheat is planted, it may become diseased because another variety of the rust multiplies to infest the crop. The problem continues, since there is no wheat strain which is resistant to all varieties of stem rust.

Since the quest for improved plants never ceases, the Department of Agriculture, in 1898, set up an agency to introduce new plants into the United States from other countries. As a result, there have been more than 275,000 plant introductions from all parts of the world.[41] Frank Nicholas Meyer, a horticulturist, spent 13 years collecting plant life in the Far East. In 1906 he walked 1,800 miles through

---

[40] U.S. Department of Agriculture, *Plant Diseases: The Yearbook of Agriculture, 1953* (Washington, D.C.), p. 3.

[41] *After a Hundred Years, op. cit.,* p. 102.

China collecting seeds of grapes, fruit, cabbage, rice, and soybeans. He tasted produce in the markets of Manchuria, Korea, and Siberia and wrote reports on his findings. Today these introductions continue, with tests of adaptability being made at state experimental stations. Seeds thought to be essential for the needs of crop breeders in the future are preserved in the National Seed Laboratory in Fort Collins, Colorado.

In this tradition, Mark Alfred Carleton conducted exploration of wheat varieties in Russia from 1894 to 1918. Through his efforts, hard red winter and Durum wheats became widely accepted in the United States. During subsequent years, the Department of Agriculture has preserved the wheat germ plasm, the hereditary material in the wheat kernel. This collection, now numbering 16,000 accessions of wheat varieties, is used for research in pedigree selection, hybridization, and crossbreeding.

WORK OF LAYMEN IN IMPROVING AGRICULTURE

Yet, not all of the scientific efforts made to improve agriculture were made by highly trained experts. Most farmers engaged in selective breeding activities by picking out the best ears of corn for seed and by selecting the best-quality livestock for breeding stock. They knew from experience that the weak begat weak and the strong begat strong. In this manner, Wendelin Grimm, a German farmer who emigrated to Minnesota in 1857, experimented with alfalfa seeds he had brought with him from Germany. Each year he planted the seeds of the plants which had survived the winter, until he finally got an ecotype that could survive the severe Minnesota winters. The Grimm alfalfa continued to be an important crop in the Midwest until recent years, when it has been largely replaced by wilt-resistant alfalfas such as Buffalo, Caliverde, Vernal, Ranger, and Cody.

Over the years, businessmen and private corporations have contributed to scientific knowledge of American agriculture. Henry Ford and the company he founded in 1903 furnish a good example. The Ford Model T "Tin Lizzy" became the first automobile owned by millions of farmers, because its reliability, ruggedness, and low cost made it especially useful in rural areas. It forced the farmers to learn something about mechanics, electrical systems, and gasoline motors. They learned to clean spark plugs, grind the valves, tighten the rods, apply blowout patches, and change the transmission bands. At times they attached pulleys to the crankshaft or rear wheels to use the car's

20 horsepower for grinding feed, sawing wood, shearing sheep, pumping water, churning butter, elevating grain, and shelling corn. The Model T put America on wheels, and according to Denis Brogan, this feat became the greatest sociological phenomenon of the first half of the twentieth century.[42]

One of Henry Ford's scientific efforts to improve agriculture consisted in experiments to produce alcohol as a motor fuel by distilling it from farm crops. During the 1920's and 1930's, he attempted to convert potatoes, corn, and other farm crops into industrial alcohol, but with limited success. In 1923 he joined with Harvey Firestone and Thomas Edison in a project to produce rubber from 70 different plants. Even though the goldenrod yielded some rubber in the laboratory at Ways Station, Georgia, the meager results and the advent of the Great Depression led Ford to abandon the experiment in the United States.

However, it was the soybean which gave Ford the best chance to apply science to farming practices. The "Ford and the Beanstalk" program originated as a technique to fight the depression. If industry could be encouraged to use more farm products, this demand would raise the prices of farm crops. Since by-products were often going to waste, chemists should discover ways to convert wheat, corn, straw, and corn cobs into articles of commercial value.

After some experimentation in Dearborn in 1930, Ford chemists chose the soybean as the most promising raw material. The company spent over a million dollars in soybean research during the next two years.[43] Three hundred varieties of beans were planted on 8,000 acres of land. In the laboratory, the oil from the soybeans was extracted by a distillation process. This oil made superior enamel for painting automobiles and yielded a fluid suitable for shock absorbers. The residue soybean meal contained protein which could be molded into horn buttons, distributor cases, and electric light assemblies. The window trim on the Ford cars utilized 144,000 bushels of soybeans annually. Ford chemists also, by the way, encouraged the use of soybeans for food as an ingredient in breakfast foods, candy, and baking products.

During the Great Depression, Henry Ford joined with Francis P. Garvin to found the National Farm Chemurgic Council, which was

---

[42] Denis Brogan, "Unnoticed Changes in America," *Harper's Magazine*, February, 1957, p. 29.

[43] "Fair Lane Papers" (Ford Motor Company Archives, Dearborn, Mich.), manuscript for press release (no author), 1934.

designed to increase the industrial uses of farm products. Aided by 25 state chemurgic councils, a million dollars were raised for this type of research. Efforts were made to convert pine trees into paper pulp, to extract starch from sweet potatoes, to secure industrial alcohol from farm crops. A plant in Atchinson, Kansas, produced a blend of alcohol and gasoline which burned well in motors, but the product could not compete with petroleum products. Other research work made use of soybeans for making glycerine, linoleum, oleomargarine, soap, varnish, and paint. These developments help explain why the soybean acreage in the United States jumped from one million acres in 1934 to 12 million in 1944.[44]

PRESENT-DAY RESEARCH

Today the focal point for scientific studies conducted by the Department of Agriculture is the Agricultural Research Center near Beltsville, Maryland. Here 5,000 scientists are engaged in 3,000 research projects costing approximately $135 million a year. The Center includes 1,160 buildings, 35 greenhouses, 10,500 acres of land, 3,000 head of livestock, and 10,000 in poultry. The National Fungus Collection contains 665,00 specimens of fungi and plant disease organisms, and another collection includes 60,000 lots of parasites which effect animal life.[45]

Since the Center employs so many specialists, it is easy for them to consult one another on mutual problems dealing with the life sciences, physical sciences, and social sciences. Here an agronomist who studies weeds may readily confer with botanists, hydrologists, and soil scientists, while an investigation of anaplasmosis in cattle would bring together physiologists, pathologists, entomologists, and chemists. In recent years, work has been extended to basic research in investigating life processes, the changes in living cells, and the physiology of virology. Sixteen of the laboratories carrying on this work are at Beltsville, while others are located in Peoria, New Orleans, Washington, and Albany, and Berkeley in California and Wyndmoor near Philadelphia.

A visit to the Albany laboratory would reveal 200 professional people making various types of analyses of food. One project meas-

---

[44] U.S. Bureau of the Census, *Statistical Abstract of the United States: 1955* (Washington, D.C.), p. 664.

[45] *After a Hundred Years, op. cit.*, p. 38.

ures the effect of temperature on color, texture, flavor, and vitamin content of frozen foods. A new technique called gas-liquid-partition chromatography is so sensitive that the expert can make an analysis of flavors and aromas which are too subtle to be detected by the human nose. The pharmacologists run safety checks on foods to spot toxic and allergenic substances present in some farm crops. Tests are made on growth-promoting or growth-inhibiting substances to aid the feeders of livestock and poultry.

In recent years, engineering research conducted by land-grant universities and private corporations has greatly improved farm machinery. The modern tractor can deliver 13 horsepower from one gallon of gasoline, whereas the tractor of 1920 could develop only 5 horsepower from the same amount of fuel. To provide more comfort for the operator, tractors can be equipped with power steering, foam rubber seats, umbrellas, air-conditioned cabs with windshields and radios. At the University of Nebraska in 1956 a tractor was driven by remote control. A radio device started the motor, stopped it, shifted gears. and guided the machine across the field. An automatic pilot was activated by feelers which sensed the position of the row crops being cultivated.

In addition, mechanical innovations have led to the manufacture of self-propelled grain combines, corn pickers, sugar beet harvesters, and cotton pickers. Mechanization has reduced the time required to produce an acre of cotton from 150 hours to 30 hours. The new cotton pickers can do more work in a day than 50 men. Various hydraulic and electrical equipment makes the tractor versatile enough to perform virtually every job encountered on the farm.

Airplanes were first used for farm purposes in 1921 near Dayton, Ohio, when they were employed to spray fruit trees infested with the larvae of the catalpa sphinx, which were defoliating the trees. The following year, airplanes were used to spray calcium arsenate to control the boll weevil in the cotton fields. During World War II, the discovery of DDT provided an insecticide which was ten times more potent than earlier sprays. In 1960 over 60 million acres of farmland were sprayed from the air. Planes are also used to spread fertilizers, to seed lakes with fish, to reseed forest terrain, and to fight forest fires. Today thousands of farmers own their own planes for business and recreation. The Ohio State University, in 1964, introduced a course in aerial application, which gives instruction in the use of aircraft for agricultural purposes. Prerequisites include 500 hours of flying time and a commercial pilot's rating.

Similarly, the miracles of science become evident in all phases of farm life. Although the field of genetics is only about 70 years old, it had already influenced agricultural practices. One of the most spectacular developments has been the hybridization of corn, a discovery which provided a key to all scientific breeding. In addition, plant hormones are used to regulate plant growth, either to accelerate growth or retard it. For instance, if only a speck, one-millionth of an ounce of dichlorophenoxyacetic acid is put on one side side of the stem of a bean seedling, the cells along the treated side grow faster than those on the untreated side, thus bending the plant in a direction away from the treated surface. Also, by using chemicals, chrysanthemums can be made to grow on a prescribed schedule.

Developmental research has created thousands of new products such as cellulose, rayon, plastics, caesin wool fiber, and other synthetic articles. Marketing research has replaced the corner store with the supermarket, while engineering techniques have provided 200 different uses of electrical power on the modern farm.

SOME PROBLEMS RESULTING FROM TECHNOLOGICAL CHANGE

Yet, the sciences of biology, chemistry, and metallurgy have endowed agriculture with a new productivity which has exceeded by far the consuming capacity of the nation and has created technological unemployment. Overproduction has glutted the farmer's markets since the Civil War, until the present surpluses baffle the minds of our most competent leaders. In this sense, the physical and natural sciences have outrun the social sciences. This situation may suggest that crash programs of the future should be in the fields of human behavior instead of in the area of production of consumer products. If 7 million farm workers can produce more than 200 million Americans can consume, how are the energies of rural people going to be directed into purposeful work which gives dignity to the individual? If improved efficiency is to abolish the small family farm and create the gigantic corporation farm with all hands working for wages, is this fostering a collective enterprise which closely resembles the collective farms in the Iron Curtain countries?

Then, too, the burgeoning scientific complex challenges at some points man's ethical and philosophic creeds. For example, livestock breeders in increasing numbers are using artificial insemination to improve their dairy and beef cattle. This process has been under investigation since 1780, when Lazaro Spallanzani, an Italian, artificially inseminated a dog to prove that semen so introduced could start a normal pregnancy. The Russian, Elie Inavov, set up in 1919 an experimental station in Moscow to further similar research. By 1936, six dairy associations in the United States were using artificial insemination methods. At present, one bull can be used to impregnate 1,000 cows each year, thus making it possible for a large number of livestock breeders to share in the advantages of superior stock. Semen can be kept at low temperature for as long as five years.[46] Needless to say, this raises the question of whether Americans are more concerned about the genetic improvement of animals than they are about the improvement of people. Will science challenge the moral basis of the genetics of the human family?

To the serious student of American civilization, it seems clear that a definitive interpretation of this nation's science and technology is virtually impossible because studies of the subject are too limited. Thus far there have been few honest attempts to explain the scientific and technological processes which have made the growth of American agriculture one of the marvels of the world. Did this growth stem from a wealth of natural resources and favorable geography? If so, why did the colonists with similar advantages in the New World fail to achieve similar success? Did stable government, a heterogeneous population, democracy, or capitalism provide the impetus for this phenomenal achievement?

Intuitively, the common man knows that the two dominant factors underlying this nation's strength are its democratic institutions and its scientific and technological capacity to produce abundant goods for peacetime living and wartime necessity. Yet, these two fundamental concepts have received unequal treatment by scholars doing research, writing, and teaching. As a result, university curriculums are crowded with courses in government, political parties, and behavioral studies, while courses in the history of science are relatively new and courses in the history of technology are given in less than a dozen institutions. This represents a feeble effort in a country which now looks to science and technology to save our collective hides in a cold war and at the same time land us on the moon.

---

[46] Ralph W. Phillips, "Artificial Breeding," *Science in Farming: Yearbook of Agriculture, 1943–1947*, pp. 113–21. See also *After a Hundred Years, op. cit.*, p. 303.

A sound interpretation of American scientific endeavor is still lacking despite the admonitions of Frederick Jackson Turner, who urged his colleagues to look beyond politics to explain our culture. Likewise, Guy Stanton Ford insisted that scholars should study science and invention because "these dwarf all instruments of government in their effects upon modern society."[47] However, such study is difficult because the source materials are scattered and sound scholary works are rare.

---

[47] Guy Stanton Ford, "Some Suggestions to American Historians," *American Historical Review*, XLIII (January 1938), 254.

Science and Medicine

John Duffy*

When William Harvey revealed his theory of the circulation of the blood in the seventeenth century and Anton van Leeuwenhoek discovered protozoa, bacteria, and red blood cells through his microscope, it might seem that medicine was indeed marching in the forefront of science. One might think that such major breakthroughs would lead immediately to better medical care and improved methods of preventing disease. Such, however, was not the case. The best minds in medicine became fascinated with new discoveries in physics, mathematics, and astronomy. Impressed by Newton's law of gravity, medical scientists hoped that they, too, could find one law of health or one fundamental cause of sickness. They turned too often to speculation and neglected the investigation and experimentation which alone could lead to advancement in medicine.

From the late seventeenth century through the first half of the nineteenth century, medical writers set forth their ideas with a firm and positive conviction. Their theories all too quickly crystallized into dogma, and the medical world was rent by violent clashes between the adherents of the many schools of medical thought. In the meantime, the average practitioner continued to base his therapy upon the age-old humoral thesis and to rely upon the traditional bleeding,

---

* JOHN DUFFY, Professor of the History of Medicine in the School of Medicine and Department of History of Tulane University, was born in Barrow-in-Furness, England, in 1915. He received his M.A. from Louisiana State University and his Ph.D. from the University of California, Los Angeles. He is the author of *Epidemics in Colonial America* (Baton Rouge, 1953); *Parson Clapp of the Strangers' Church of New Orleans* (Baton Rouge, 1957); *The Rudolph Matas History of Medicine in Louisiana* (2 vols., Baton Rouge, 1958–62); and the soon to be published *The Sword of Pestilence: The New Orleans Yellow Fever Epidemic* (Baton Rouge). He has written many articles in the fields of medicine and history. He has served on the Executive Councils of the Southern Historical Association and the American Association for the History of Medicine and has been Secretary of Western Pennsylvania Society for Medical History.

blistering, vomiting, purging, and sweating. Although the extent to which these drastic measures were used varied from physician to physician and from period to period, the nineteenth century was well advanced before any major change in medical practice took place.

Throughout the eighteenth century, medical philosophers remained preoccupied with their grand designs and paid little attention to experimental methods. Not until the Paris clinicians began, in the first half of the nineteenth century, to correlate clinical symptoms with the findings of the dissecting rooms was scientific methodology applied on any appreciable scale to the study of medicine. True scientific medicine did not come of age until the bacteriological revolution of the late nineteenth century. Probably the chief reason for the failure of medicine to utilize scientific methodology earlier lies in the baffling complexity of the human beings it hoped to treat. Aside from the involved principles of chemistry and physics implicit in the human body, there are many subtle and pervasive human factors which determine an individual's reaction to external shock, disease, or injury. In consequence, medicine became an art as well as a science. Moreover, a rising respect for human dignity in the Western World severely inhibited experimentation with human subjects. The pressing nature of medical problems, which involve suffering and death, also tended to force physicians to concentrate upon empirical practices which might bring quick relief. For example, a doctor who witnessed the death agonies of a hundred or more patients during recurrent epidemics could scarcely be expected to dedicate himself to the pursuit of pure knowledge and abstract truths in the medical area. It was only to be expected that the physicial sciences, which dealt largely with inanimate objects or the lesser forms of life, should progress more rapidly than the art of medicine—with all that the word "art" implies.

The factors which slowed the growth of scientific medicine in Western Europe also operated in America; even though out of the mainstream, the American colonists in the seventeenth century were essentially Europeans. In several of the colonies, notably Virginia and Plymouth, the early struggle for existence was so bitter that it occupied all attention. Even in areas such as Massachusetts and Maryland, where the grim experience of their predecessors had eased the path of settlement, endemic disorders and chronic dietetic ailments made sickness and death omnipresent, while the double threat of pestilence and famine was constantly at hand. Under the circumstances, there was little leisure for the objective search for knowledge, and the few physicians and surgeons were hard put to provide rudimentary medical care.

Doctors were in short supply throughout the colonial period. The profession of medicine in Europe was reserved for gentlemen, and the relatively few university trained physicians catered almost exclusively to the upper classes. The lower economic groups were compelled to rely upon bloodletters, bonesetters, midwives, apothecaries, and empirically trained surgeons or chirurgeons. Since only a few venturesome physicians embarked for the New World, colonial medical care rested largely in the hands of ship surgeons and other empirics. As late as the American Revolution, at a time when prosperous cities and a leisure class had emerged, the accepted estimate is that only 10 percent of colonial physicians held university degrees.[1] The rest had acquired their training through the apprenticeship system or else had simply laid claim to the title of "doctor."

In terms of medical practice, however, the lack of formally trained physicians was not quite so grave as it might appear. Medicine was taught in the universities largely from a theoretical standpoint. Indeed, the phrase "to read medicine" remained current almost to the twentieth century. Too frequently, physicians with university degrees were more concerned with treating their patients according to a particular medical doctrine or system than in dealing with them as individual cases. The empirically trained doctors, on the other hand, were far more likely to base their therapy upon observation and practical experience and to treat the patient rather than the disease.

The American milieu had one beneficial effect upon medical practice. In Europe the physicians maintained a sharp distinction between the gentlemanly art of medicine and the manual skill of surgery. In America the great demand for medical men and the mobility of colonial society made it virtually impossible to maintain such a caste system. Physicians were expected to let blood, set bones, and handle the limited surgery of the day. In the process, the physician-surgeon often became a better practitioner. Certainly, he became more venturesome and self-reliant, for boldness characterized much of early American surgery.

While no significant medical contributions could be expected in the Colonies during the seventeenth century, the fact that seven autopsies were performed there prior to 1690 indicates at least an interest

---

[1] Francis R. Packard, *History of Medicine in the United States* (New York and London, 1931), I, 273.

in medical matters.[2] One of these autopsies was done at the request of the Reverend Increase Mather, who sought to know why one of his children had died. In 1693 his son, the Reverend Cotton Mather, also witnessed an autopsy performed on one of his own children.[3] The role of the minister-physician is one of great antiquity, and ministers, usually the best-educated men in the community, were often called upon in colonial America for medical as well as spiritual aid. Cotton Mather was even better prepared for this role than most men of his calling. A speech impediment in his youth had made him apprehensive that he would not be able to follow in his father's footsteps. In consequence, he had studied medicine before overcoming this handicap and returning to his chosen field of theology. Throughout his life, Mather retained a keen interest in medicine and kept abreast of new developments. For example, when the early pioneers in microscopy discovered minute forms of life and the animalcular theory was postulated, *i.e.*, that little "animals" were the causal factors in disease, Mather was one of the few men to espouse this novel viewpoint.[4]

Apropos of the minister-physician, the first medical treatise published in North America was the work of Thomas Thacher, a Boston minister. It was a sound, common-sense broadside published in 1678 under the title, *A Brief Rule To Guide the Common-People of New-England How to Order Themselves and Theirs in the Small Pocks, or Measels*. Measles, a serious and often fatal disease in the Colonies, brought death to several members of Cotton Mather's immediate family, and led the redoubtable parson to issue a pamphlet which included an accurate description of the disease and some good advice for dealing with it. Living in a day when excessive medication and drastic purging, vomiting, and bleeding characterized medical practice, Mather wrote: "Let this Advice for the Sick, be principally attended to; *Don't Kill 'em!* That is to say, With mischievous Kindness. Indeed," he continued, "if we stopt here, and said no more, this were enough to save more *Lives* than our *Wars* have destroyed." He then urged ample rest, moderate diet, and minimum medication, and

---

[2] Albert Matthews, "Notes on Early Autopsies and Anatomical Lectures," *Colonial Society of Massachusetts Publications*, XIX (1916–1917), 273–90.

[3] Worthington Chauncey Ford, ed., *Diary of Cotton Mather, 1681–1708*, in *Massachusetts Historical Society Collections*, ser. 7, VII (Boston, 1911), 164.

[4] Otho T. Beall, Jr., and Richard H. Shryock, *Cotton Mather: First Significant Figure in American Medicine* (Baltimore, 1954), pp. 87–88.

warned his readers of the secondary infections which we recognize today as the sequelae of measles.[5]

The pragmatic American spirit about which Professor Daniel J. Boorstin has written so well in recent years is clearly shown in the colonial experience with smallpox inoculation.[6] Variolation or inoculation, a forerunner of vaccination, consisted of taking pus from the pustules of an active smallpox case and inserting it under the skin of a healthy individual. The inoculated person usually developed a relatively mild case of smallpox and thereby acquired an immunity to the disease. Although exact figures cannot be ascertained, the deaths from inoculation ranged from about 1 to 5 per 100. In terms of modern health statistics, inoculation would be a highly questionable practice, but smallpox is a terrible disease in which the case fatality rate, particularly at the beginning of an epidemic, can run higher than 80 percent.[7]

On the face of it, variolation had obvious advantages; its application, however, was not quite so simple. In the first place, the inoculated individual, while having only a mild case himself, was capable of passing on a deadly disease to all susceptible persons. Originally, those inoculated were carefully isolated, but as the practice became more common, people became careless and the indiscriminate use of variolation often did lead to epidemics of smallpox or intensified existing outbreaks. In the second place, many colonists argued with justice that it was foolish to infect oneself with a deadly pestilence when it was possible to escape merely by leaving the infected town or district. In fact, even the rumor of smallpox was enough to precipitate a mass exodus from colonial towns.

Cotton Mather was the first of the American colonists to recognize the merit in this smallpox preventive. On seeing the original articles in the *Transactions* of the Royal Society, he immediately urged the Boston doctors to give it a trial. Only one, Dr. Zabdiel Boyleston, was willing. In 1721 an outbreak of smallpox in the city provided the

---

[5] Cotton Mather, *A Letter about a Good Management under the Distemper of the Measles, etc.* (Boston, 1739); *Diary of Cotton Mather, 1709–1724, loc. cit.*, ser. 7, VIII (Boston, 1912), 255–61.

[6] Daniel J. Boorstin, *The Americans, the Colonial Experience* (New York, 1958).

[7] For a thorough discussion of inoculation, see John Duffy, *Epidemics in Colonial America* (Baton Rouge, La., 1953), pp. 23–42, and John B. Blake, *Public Health in the Town of Boston, 1630–1822* (Cambridge, Mass., 1959), pp. 52–74, 243–47.

two men with an opportunity, and Boyleston inoculated his and Mather's children. A tremendous furor was set off, and Mather in particular was bitterly denounced. Over and above the rational grounds for complaint against variolation, Mather was accused of opposing God's will, since smallpox, like other pestilences, was assumed to be a sign of God's displeasure. Using a method all too familiar to us today, someone hurled a "granado" or bomb through one of Mather's windows, attached to which was a note saying: "COTTON MATHER, You Dog, Dam you, I'll inoculate you with this, with a Pox to you." Fortunately for Mather—and for all of us —the bomb failed to explode; otherwise these immortal words might have been lost to posterity.[8]

Despite its stormy beginning, as the eighteenth century advanced, inoculation gradually gained favor in the Colonies and, within forty years from its introduction, the outbreak of a smallpox epidemic became the signal for mass inoculation. When the opening of the Revolutionary War spread smallpox throughout America, George Washington, at the suggestion of Dr. John Morgan, his physician-in-chief, ordered a general inoculation of all troops.[9] Without question, inoculation was a factor in reducing the danger from smallpox in eighteenth-century America. Its greater success in the Colonies than in England and on the Continent can be explained on two grounds. First, American medical care may have lacked some of the refinements of practice in Great Britain, but it was available to nearly all citizens. Second, Americans were a practical people, and once the value of inoculation had been demonstrated, they were quick to take advantage of it in times of threatened epidemics.

In the second half of the eighteenth century, notable strides were made in anatomy, pathology, and physiology. There was a growing recognition of diseases as distinct entities, and attempts were made to classify disorders on the basis of clinical symptoms. The most significant work in this respect had been done in the late seventeenth century by the great English physician, Thomas Sydenham (1624–1689). In this connection, colonial physicians contributed some classic descriptions of yellow fever, scarlet fever, and diphtheria. The real contributions from American physicians, however, came in the field of botany.

---

[8] *Diary of Cotton Mather*, VIII, 634, 657–59; Duffy, *Epidemics in Colonial America*, pp. 28–30.

[9] Packard, *History of Medicine in the United States*, I, 577–78.

English physicians and surgeons were prominent in the Royal Society, and European doctors were among the major supporters of every scientific organization. Since botanicals were the basic pharmaceuticals, medical training always included a formal course in this field, and it was only natural that physicians should be particularly interested in the subject. Moreover, the eighteenth century was one in which a vast amount of botanical information was pouring into Europe, and naturalists were preoccupied with classification and description. The New World seemed to be an unlimited storehouse of biological and botanical treasures, and European naturalists eagerly sought specimens and information. Thus colonial physicians, who were drawn to botany, soon developed close rapport with leading scientists in Europe.

Among the many colonial physicians contributing to botany and natural history, several stand out. Cadwallader Colden, a young Scottish physician who came to the Colonies in 1710, managed to find time for his scientific work by obtaining a governmental sinecure as surveyor-general of the Province of New York. Like the other American naturalists, he corresponded with, and was well known to, such figures as Carl Linnaeus, Peter Collinson, and John Frederick Gronovius. Colden was one of the first botanists to thoroughly understand the Linnaean system and to recognize the weakness of its method of sexual classification. Another colonial physician who made notable contributions in botany was Dr. Alexander Garden of Charleston. Like Colden, Garden described many new genera and was well enough versed to question some of Linnaeus' decisions, occasionally winning his point. His standing in the scientific world was such that when the Revolution forced him to return to England, he became a vice president of the Royal Society.

An American naturalist comparable to Garden was Dr. John Mitchell (1798–1858) of Urbana, Virginia. Mitchell, too, recognized the problems inherent in the Linnaean system and sought to modify certain aspects of it. As a botanist, he described twenty-one new genera, and, in addition, made significant observations in natural history. The only physician in New England with an active interest in botany and natural history was Dr. William Douglass. Like many medical graduates in the Colonies, Douglass received his medical training at Edinburgh and Leyden. He arrived in Boston in 1718 and promptly began collecting plants, mineral specimens, and data on meteorology. He was a man of wide-ranging interests, however, and, after becoming involved in the inoculation controversy which raged in Boston in the 1720's, his interest in botany lagged.[10]

Even in botany and natural history, colonial physicians played only a supporting role, and certainly in terms of the overall development of science, their contributions were negligible. It is significant, however, that despite their small numbers and isolation from Europe, they kept abreast of current thinking and, wherever possible, sought a practical application of any new discovery. The widespread use of inoculation, at least, clearly shows the American genius for large-scale application.

Since medicine was regarded as essentially a theoretical field which could be learned by reading, there were few educated men who did not at least dabble in it, and most of them were not averse to prescribing for their families and servants. Nor were they reluctant to pass judgment upon their family physicians or to take public issue with prominent medical men. The classic instance of Washington's final illness, in which he ordered his overseer to let some of his blood before calling a physician, was typical of plantation medicine down through the nineteenth century.

The most outstanding layman in American medical history was Benjamin Franklin (1706–1790), whose insatiable curiosity led him to explore nearly all avenues of human knowledge. Franklin's views on moderate eating and drinking, his emphasis upon fresh air, exercise, and bathing, and his invention of bifocal glasses mark him as an intelligent and practical man. So, too, does his espousal of inoculation. As early as 1730, he advocated its practice in the *Pennsylvania Gazette*, and, when his four-year old son died of smallpox in 1736, Franklin, on hearing a rumor that the child had died as a result of inoculation, publicly denied it in his newspaper and reasserted his faith in variolation.[11] A better illustration of Franklin's scientific approach to medical work can be found in his observations with respect to the use of electric shock therapy for paralytic patients. During the 1740's, dabbling with electricity became quite popular in England and on the Continent. Once this mysterious source of energy was discovered, both quacks and reputable physicians sought to use it for medical purposes.

---

[10] Brooke Hindle, *The Pursuit of Science in Revolutionary America, 1735–1789* (Chapel Hill, N.C., 1956), pp. 36–58.

[11] William Pepper, *The Medical Side of Benjamin Franklin* (Philadelphia, 1911), p. 15.

About the middle of the century, as stories began to appear in newspapers telling of miraculous cures achieved through electricity, many individuals appealed to Franklin for help in treating paralytic victims. In 1757 Franklin, at the request of the famous English army physician, Sir John Pringle (1707–1782), sent a detailed account of his experiences with these cases. Franklin reported that he first seated the patients in a chair on "an electric stool" and drew large sparks from all parts of the affected side or limb. "Then," he stated, "I fully charged two six gallon glass jars, each of which had about three square feet of surface coated, and I send the united shock of these through the affected limb or limbs, repeating the stroke commonly three times each day." The patients usually reported an immediate sensation of warmth and subsequent pricking in the paralyzed areas. Franklin added that the subjects generally showed some signs of progress during the first few days, but usually reached a plateau about the fifth day. In virtually all cases, he said, after the first enthusiasm, the patients, "finding the shocks pretty severe," became discouraged, returned home, and soon relapsed to their former state.

Unlike some of his contemporaries who were prone to jump to conclusions, Franklin objectively analyzed his experiences with electric therapy. He speculated that the temporary success was due either to the exercise associated with the journey to his house or else "from the spirits given by the hope of success. . . ." Whatever the case, he added, he had never achieved any permanent improvement. Recognizing that his technique may have been wrong, he did suggest that more benefit might have accrued if the "electric shocks had been accompanied with proper medicine and regimen, under the direction of a skillful physician." He admitted, too, that it might have been better to have given a series of small shocks rather than the larger ones which he administered. Recognizing the limited nature of his own experiments, the pragmatic Franklin did not rule out electrotherapy, but, he declared, he himself had seen no real benefit.[12]

In reviewing the medical side of Benjamin Franklin, one can say that there was scarcely an area of medicine and public health that he did not at least touch upon, and in every instance he exhibited a healthy skepticism and a logical, practical approach. Over and above his direct contributions, by assisting Drs. William Shippen, John Morgan, and Benjamin Rush to study abroad, Franklin helped lay the

---

[12] *Ibid.*, pp. 31–32.

basis for medical education in the Colonies. Without question, Franklin was the outstanding American medical scientist of the colonial period.

So long as colonial physicians were compelled to look abroad for their education, and their contacts with European scientific societies were restricted by slow and difficult communication, American medicine and science could make little progress. By 1760, American cities were becoming sufficiently large and prosperous to support their own medical schools, societies, and hospitals. Philadelphia led the way and held its preeminent position for many years, but New York and Boston did not lag too far behind. The chief impetus for establishing medical schools came from England and the Continent, where medical professors encouraged young colonials to promote medicine and science in their homeland. In addition to moral support, they gave money, books, and other gifts for educational purposes. For example, Dr. John Fothergill, an outstanding English physician, contributed a collection of anatomical drawings and casts, and a set of medical books.[13]

The first step toward establishing an effective American medical profession came with the founding of the Pennsylvania Hospital in Philadelphia.[14] The hospital, which first opened its doors in 1752, was the brain child of Dr. Thomas Bond, a well-known Philadelphia physician, but it was the support of Benjamin Franklin, who was a prime mover in its establishment, which made it a reality. The founding of the hospital facilitated the establishment of a medical school, since it was to this hospital that Dr. Fothergill gave his medical collection. In his letter informing the managers of the hospital of his gift, he stated that it was intended for teaching purposes and that he was recommending Dr. William Shippen as a lecturer in anatomy. He mentioned that Dr. Shippen would soon be followed by Dr. John Morgan, and that the two young physicians were qualified, "if suitably countenanced by the Legislature . . . to erect a school of physic among you that may draw students from various parts of America and the West Indies. . . ."[15]

Suffice it to say, the two protégés of Dr. Fothergill returned to Philadelphia and were responsible for starting the first medical school in the Colonies. In 1766, at the formal opening of this school, the

---

[13] Hindle, pp. 114–15.

[14] Richard H. Shryock, *Medicine and Society in America, 1660–1860* (New York, 1960), p. 22.

[15] Packard, *History of Medicine in the United States*, I, 222–24.

Medical School of the College of Philadelphia, Dr. John Morgan delivered a two-day address in which he stated his aims and objectives. He stressed the close connection between science and medicine, and asserted the necessity for medical practitioners to have a thorough understanding of anatomy and physiology. Reflecting the new spirit of the times, he declared: "Observation and physical experiments should blend their light to dissipate obscurity from medicine."[16] Laudable as were the aims of its founder, many years elapsed before they became a reality. From the start, the school attracted a great many students, and by the opening of the American Revolution, Philadelphia was without question the medical center of America.

The example set by Philadelphia was quickly followed by New York. Urged on by an able group of physicians, in 1768 the trustees of King's College opened a medical department. The presence of this medical school accentuated the lack of a hospital in the city, and, led by Dr. Samuel Bard (1742–1821), several faculty members campaigned to win government and private support for such an institution. Individual donations and public grants from the city and province were promptly forthcoming, but a succession of mishaps almost proved disastrous. The first building was destroyed by fire just at its completion, and the outbreak of the Revolution deferred the opening of the hospital for many more years.

The Revolution set back the cause of both science and medicine. The close personal ties with leading scientists in England were broken during the war years, and at the same time, the flow of medical and scientific writings was drastically reduced. The new patriotism engendered by the war, combined with the political, economic, and social readjustments which the new Republic faced, discouraged Americans from sending their sons to Europe for the completion of their education. Those American medical schools and hospitals which survived the disruption of the war were slow to recover. Only three more medical schools were established in America before the end of the eighteenth century: Harvard added a medical department in 1783; Dartmouth in 1798; and Transylvania University in Lexington, Kentucky, in 1799. Despite the intent of the founders to establish centers of scientific research and learning, by 1800 American medical schools were still small, struggling teaching institutions.[17] Almost a century

---

[16] Hindle, pp. 114–15.

[17] For a good history of early American medical education, see William F. Norwood, *Medical Education in the United States before the Civil War* (Philadelphia and London, 1944).

of growth was necessary before American medical schools would become real centers for scientific research and training.

In the first flush of enthusiasm following the Peace of Paris, dozens of medical and scientific societies blossomed, but, without adequate libraries, universities, museums, and laboratories and only a limited contact with European intellectuals, too many of them either withered away or remained essentially provincial in their outlook. On the credit side, the Revolutionary War did provide a stimulus to surgery. In addition to the practical experience which the war provided, Americans came in contact with English, French, and German surgeons and a certain amount of cross-fertilization occurred. The net balance, however, was decidedly unfavorable, and American medicine did not emerge from the doldrums until after the Civil War.

By the time the American Republic had solved its immediate domestic problems and made itself independent of Europe by fighting the War of 1812, a boisterous, exuberant nationalism caused Americans to look to themselves rather than to Europe for leadership. With a vast frontier beckoning, they became preoccupied with economic development and material progress. Under the circumstances, the search for knowledge for its own sake had little appeal. Medical schools, which might have provided leadership in scientific pursuits, were strictly teaching institutions, concerned with giving their graduates a rudimentary knowledge of anatomy, practice, and therapeutics.

In response to a burgeoning population and a rapidly expanding need for doctors, a host of proprietary medical schools opened their doors, many of them little more than diploma mills. Even legitimate schools often lacked adequately trained faculties and had neither clinical nor laboratory facilities. With most students interested only in obtaining a degree at the lowest possible cost, the responsible schools could scarcely raise their standards without destroying themselves. Not until the American Medical Association was organized in 1847 were any serious efforts made to improve the caliber of American medical education. Even then, progress was slow and medical education was not placed on a firm foundation until the Flexner report of 1909 virtually forced the closing of all substandard medical schools.[18]

The picture was not completely black. Individual physicians and surgeons managed to make some notable contributions in the years between the Revolution and the Civil War. In the postwar years, Dr. Benjamin Rush (1745–1813) was the outstanding American physi-

---

[18] Abraham Flexner, *Medical Education in the United States and Canada* (New York, 1910).

cian. He was an exponent of scientific methodology and strongly believed that medicine should be placed upon a scientific basis. A keen observer, as his descriptions of yellow fever, dengue, and cholera infantum reveal, he warned his students to be skeptical of all encompassing systems of medicine. On matters of social action Rush was progressive. Politically, he was an avowed democrat who undoubtedly took pleasure in signing his name to the Declaration of Independence. He advocated prison reform and public health measures, and fought against slavery and the brutal treatment of the insane.

Yet, he was too much a product of the eighteenth century to fulfill his own scientific objectives, and he fell into precisely the same trap which had ensnared his predecessors. His critical observations made him dubious of their theories, but, in dismissing them, he could not help filling the void with one of his own. In reality, he used the doctrines of William Cullen, John Brown, and Friedrich Hoffman as a basis for a medical system which asserted that vascular tension was the one fundamental sickness and that, since there was only one disease, treatment correspondingly could be simplified. Therapy, Rush believed, should be aimed at either stimulating bodily tension or else bringing about a relaxation. Bloodletting was indicated in nearly all instances, and it became one of his prime weapons in attacking disease.[19]

Unfortunately, Rush's drastic therapy won a far wider acceptance than his more sensible views on subjects such as the humane treatment for the insane. Excessive bleeding and the administration of drastic purgatives remained imbedded in American medical practice—particularly in the South and West—long after Rush's monistic theory of disease had been discredited. It should be pointed out that rigorous or "heroic" therapy was in no sense attributable solely to Rush. Its practice was already widespread; Rush merely accentuated certain aspects and gave them an impetus in the United States.

Benjamin Rush represented the passing of the old order, and it is significant that this medical theory, which made such a great impression upon his contemporaries, received short shrift at the hands of the succeeding generation. Not only were his medical writings derided, but even his pretensions to scientific medicine. Commenting with devastating effect upon Rush's statement that "Medicine is my wife and science my mistress," Dr. Oliver Wendell Holmes declared: "I do

---

[19] Richard H. Shryock, *The Development of Modern Medicine, an Interpretation of the Social and Scientific Factors Involved* (New York, 1947), pp. 29–31.

not think that the breach of the seventh commandment can be shown to have been of advantage to the legitimate owner of his affections."[20] Profound changes were in the making during the first half of the nineteenth century. Though American medical contributions to these changes were minimal, there was at least a recognition that a solid body of factual knowledge was needed and that without it, speculation in medicine was fruitless.

Benjamin Rush was a strong, flamboyant personality, whose medical ideas gained a hearing precisely because the author was such a public figure. From the standpoint of scientific medicine, an obscure military surgeon serving at an isolated army post left a far greater mark upon the pages of medical history. In 1822 Surgeon William Beaumont (1785–1853) of Fort Mackinac, Michigan, was summoned to the side of Alexis St. Martin, a young French-Canadian voyageur who had been wounded in the stomach by a shotgun blast. Although the case appeared to be hopeless, Beaumont carefully treated the injury. Despite his best efforts, St. Martin was slow in recovering, and the wall of his stomach adhered to the intercostal muscle, leaving him with a permanent gastric fistula.

After caring for St. Martin in his own home for over two years, Beaumont realized that the fistula, which gave ready access to the stomach, made St. Martin an ideal subject for studying the physiology of digestion. Prior to this time, little was known about the digestive process, although William Prout, an English chemist, had determined in 1824 that the gastric juice was largely hydrochloric acid. For many years, debates had raged as to whether food was digested mechanically or chemically and whether or not fermentation was involved. The answer was soon provided by Beaumont. He introduced samples into St. Martin's stomach by means of the fistula and, by frequently sampling its contents, he was able to explain the basic process of digestion.

Dr. Beaumont had no easy task, since St. Martin was an exceedingly reluctant subject, but by 1833 he was able to publish his classic study, *Experiments and Observations on the Gastric Juice and the Physiology of Digestion.* As Francis Packard states, Beaumont proved that digestion

> was truly a chemical process; that the gastric juice was not a mucous secretion macerating the food; that it contained hydrochloric acid; that its action was affected by mental or emotional disturbances; that it had a definite relation to the amount and nature of digested food; that the

[20] Fielding H. Garrison, *An Introduction to the History of Medicine* (Philadelphia and London, 1929), p. 379.

walls of the stomach were endowed with peristaltic motion, and that water disappeared from the stomach through the pylorus with remarkable rapidity.[21]

Beaumont's work met with immediate recognition both in America and Europe, but physiology was an abstruse subject, with seemingly little relationship to medical practice, and Beaumont returned to relative obscurity. Had his findings been directly related to the great epidemic diseases, the chief preoccupation of medicine in these years, Beaumont might have received the honors which were awarded to Edward Jenner. It was his misfortune to be pioneering in a little understood area.

Beaumont was certainly no dedicated scientist. By sheer chance a marvelous opportunity arose, and he was intelligent enough to seize upon it. As a young man, he had demonstrated that he was a careful and perceptive observer. While presenting clearly and lucidly the results of his experiments with St. Martin, Beaumont made no effort to speculate upon gastric physiology but let the results speak for themselves.

The second outstanding American contribution to medicine was the introduction of dental and surgical anesthesia. Although its discovery was largely empirical, rather than the product of scientific research, its impact was too profound to be overlooked. Efforts to relieve pain are age-old, and in the early nineteenth century everything conspired to bring anesthesia upon the scene. As early as 1799, Sir Humphrey Davy reported of nitrous oxide that since it "appears capable of destroying physical pain, it may probably be used with advantage on surgical operations. . . ."[22] The discovery in 1831 of chloroform added a third anesthetic agent to the two already in existence, nitrous oxide and sulphuric ether. The well-known properties of these gases had made "ether frolics" and "laughing gas" parties quite common among young people.

More significantly, as anatomical knowledge increased and the concept of local pathology, or the localization of disease, gained support, surgical intervention became more frequent. From the standpoint of both surgeon and patient, longer and more complicated operations increased the need to relieve pain. Probably the rising humanitarian spirit, which increased sensitivity to human suffering,

---

[21] Packard, *History of Medicine in the United States*, II, 1069–70.

[22] Louis H. Bauer, ed., *Seventy-Five Years of Medical Progress, 1878–1953* (Philadelphia, 1954), pp. 15–16.

was another contributing factor in creating a social milieu receptive to anesthesia. Certainly, in the early nineteenth century there appears to have been a greater resort to the use of alcohol and opium in preparing patients for surgery. When mesmerism or hypnotism was introduced into obstetrics and surgery in the 1830's, it won considerable approval. As Dr. George Rosen suggests, had it not been for the discovery of chemical anesthesia in 1846, hypnotism might well have assumed a far greater role in surgery and obstetrics.[23]

In America one other factor helped to precipitate the discovery of anesthesia; this was the rapidly developing field of dentistry. Just why America should have taken the lead in dentistry in the nineteenth century is not easy to explain, but the fact remains. Possibly because the problems of dentistry were immediate and mechanical, the nature of dental work appealed to Americans. In any event, in terms of building up their clientele and facilitating their work, dentists were anxious to find some sort of pain reliever. Hence it was no accident that the first experiments with anesthesia were performed by dentists, nor that they were the first to draw the attention of the medical profession to its possibilities.

In 1844 Horace Wells (1815–1848), a Connecticut dentist, began using nitrous oxide in the extraction of teeth. He tried to demonstrate his discovery at the Harvard Medical School, but his attempt failed. Subsequently, the death of one of his patients under anesthesia led him to give up the practice. Another dentist, William Thomas Green Morton (1819–1868), who was familiar with Well's efforts, inquired of one of his former professors, Dr. Charles T. Jackson, about substances other than nitrous oxide. At Jackson's suggestion, Morton tried sulphuric ether on his patients and found it quite successful. He then asked Dr. John Collins Warren, the famous Boston surgeon, to let him try this new agent on one of the doctor's surgical patients. On October 16, 1846, in the Massachusetts General Hospital, the celebrated operation took place. Almost immediately, anesthesia (a name suggested by Dr. Oliver Wendell Holmes) was hailed as a major medical triumph, and within a few months its use was spreading widely in the United States and Western Europe.

The immediate impact of anesthesia was to increase surgical intervention. In the first place, anesthesia removed one of the prime ob-

---

[23] George Rosen, "Mesmerism and Surgery, a Strange Chapter in the History of Anesthesia," *Journal of the History of Medicine and Allied Sciences,* I (October 1946), 543–46.

jections to surgery, for even the most callous surgeons could not be completely insensitive to the agony of their patients writhing in the straps of the operating table. In the second place, it provided the opportunity to perform more delicate surgery upon the quiescent patient. The greater number of operations, while they promoted surgical technique and emboldened surgeons to broaden their sphere of action, was not immediately beneficial to patients. In a day when cleanliness in hospitals was a fad adopted by only a few doctors, the net effect was to increase the so-called hospital fevers—gangrene, erysipelas, septicemia, and so forth. The operations were successful, but there was a sharp rise in the number of patients who died from supervening infections. Fortunately, the bacteriological revolution was close at hand. First antiseptic and then aseptic techniques were soon to place surgery upon a sound basis.

With respect to surgery, it might well be argued that it is essentially a matter of technique rather than of science. Should the surgeon who possesses a high degree of manual dexterity and a mechanical bent which enables him to devise new instruments be considered a scientist or a technician? The dividing line between science and technology or between pure and applied research is always a tenuous one, and this is especially the case with medicine. The surgeon who boldly undertakes a new form of surgical intervention presumably had diagnosed a medical problem, formed a hypothesis as to how it may be corrected, devised a technique, and then performed the experiment. Within the general meaning of science, surgical advances can be classified as part of the development of scientific medicine.

Individual American surgeons demonstrated both courage and initiative. For example, as early as 1759, John Bard successfully operated for extrauterine pregnancy and in 1818 John King, a South Carolina surgeon who duplicated this operation, published the first book on the subject. Probably a more celebrated feat was that of Ephraim McDowell, who in 1809 performed the first ovariotomy. This bold act, which took place in the frontier state of Kentucky, is often cited as an example of American frontier surgery, but, as Shryock points out, McDowell was educated in Edinburgh. The best American surgeons were usually to be found in the eastern cities.[24] It was in New York that men such as Wright Post and Valentine Mott were attacking the problem of major aneurisms by ligating or

---

[24] Shryock, *Medicine and Society in America*, p. 132.

tying off the greater blood vessels, thus steadily extending the field of vascular surgery. At the same time, other American surgeons were making notable progress with surgery of the long bones and joints.

Obstetrics and gynecology was another area in which Americans made substantial contributions. In addition to the operations for extrauterine pregnancy, American surgeons were responsible for a series of cesarean sections. The first was the work of Dr. Jesse Bennett, a rural practitioner in Virginia who operated on his wife in 1794. In the 1820's, a Louisiana surgeon, François Marie Prevost (1764–1842), performed a number of cesarean operations, and there is evidence to indicate that Prevost was not the only Louisiana surgeon to use this method of delivery. While Prevost practiced in a rural area, he had been a medical student in Paris at a time when a bitter wrangle was in process over the merits of the cesarean section versus the symphyseotomy, a more dangerous and complicated method of delivery.[25] Thus, Prevost, like McDowell, was a product of Old World medical training.

The next major step in gynecology was taken by another southerner, Dr. James Marion Sims (1813–1883). The dismayed remarks of Sims's father upon hearing of his son's intention to study medicine are a fine commentary upon the state of the profession in the 1830's. He declared emphatically that "it is a profession for which I have the utmost contempt. There is no science in it. There is no honor to be achieved . . . [and] no reputation to be made. . . ."[26] After taking a degree at the Medical College of South Carolina, the younger Sims began practicing in Montgomery, Alabama. He soon began encountering cases of vesicovaginal fistula, a painful and embarrassing condition which had long been the despair of surgeons. Determined to find some cure, he spent several years experimenting until finally, in the early summer of 1847, he devised a method for eliminating the fistula which involved the use of silver sutures.

He published an account of his operation in 1853, the same year that he moved to New York. Here he demonstrated his operation to the leading surgeons, only to find himself virtually excluded from gynecological surgery, since the New York doctors refused to help him obtain a hospital position. Unwilling to concede defeat, he managed to organize the Woman's Hospital in New York and soon estab-

---

[25] John Duffy, ed., *The Rudolph Matas History of Medicine in Louisiana*, 2 vols. (Baton Rouge, La., 1958–1962), I, 295–99; II, 72–75.

[26] Packard, *History of Medicine in the United States*, II, 1137.

lished himself as a leading gynecologist. Subsequently, he was invited to the European capitals to demonstrate his new technique. Overseas he was awarded honor after honor, but it was not until his return to New York in 1872 that he gained the recognition in America that was his due.[27]

Following the example of Sims, a number of southern surgeons moved into the area of gynecology, and, according to Garrison, literally dominated this branch of surgery during the post-Civil War years. As operative gynecology became more common, the field flourished, and "surgeons vied with one another in removing ovaries and uteri by the thousands. . . ." Like all fads, the passage of time and changing conditions eventually put an end to this wholesale and, in many instances, needless surgery.[28]

The nature of early surgery, which involved a high degree of manual dexterity and which could show immediate results, was more likely to appeal to Americans than the study of internal medicine. In consequence, American physicians added relatively little in this latter area. Before any real progress could be made in medicine, broad advances had to come in pathology, physiology, chemistry, and other related fields. But the connection between the discoveries in physiology and medical practice seemed very tenuous to the majority of American physicians. Few of them heeded the appeal of Dr. John D. Godman of Philadelphia, who urged American medical men, in 1824, to overcome the two-century lag in medical progress by undertaking basic research in morbid pathology.[29]

The very complexity of medicine made it difficult to devise a proper scientific methodology, and until this could be done, there was no way to attack the prevailing theories and traditional practices. The best work in this respect, as noted earlier, was being done by the Paris clinical school during the first half of the nineteenth century. Working in large hospitals, French clinicians were able to observe hundreds of patients and to keep accurate clinical records. Great numbers of autopsies were performed, and it was possible for the first time to correlate, on a mass scale, clinical symptoms with pathological lesions. These observations facilitated the differentiation of the many forms of disease. In light of the new findings, the old vague terminology—

27 *Ibid.*, II, 1136–41.

28 Fielding H. Garrison, "Medicine," in Charles A. Beard, ed., *A Century of Progress* (New York and London, 1933), pp. 336–37.

29 Shryock, *Medicine and Society in America*, p. 128.

hospital fever, bilious fever, flux, teething, and so forth—was gradually replaced with a more exact classification. Once the various disease entities could be identified and diagnosed with some precision, it was possible to test the effectiveness of many forms of therapy. In short order, bloodletting, purging, and vomiting, as well as calomel and a number of other drugs, were found to be of little value. The net effect was to lead the Paris school in the direction of therapeutic nihilism—the belief that nearly all medicines were useless.

The findings of the French clinicians coincided with those of better physicians generally. In America, while progress was slower, a similar trend was taking place. In part, it was the American public which forced physicians to modify the traditionally rigorous medical practices. Resentful of constant bloodletting and massive doses of calomel, the public turned away from the regulars and began to support a host of irregular medical sects. The successes achieved by many of the irregulars lay in their dependence upon the curative powers of nature. For example, the hydropaths advocated cold baths, moderate exercise and diet; the homeopaths prescribed infinitely small doses of medicine on the theory that the more minute the portion, the more effective its results; and the Thomsonians relied almost exclusively upon botanic remedies. However farfetched the rationale of these medical groups, the orthodox physicians in the United States were forced to recognize that patients of the irregulars often did as well, if not better, than their own. Consequently, a good part of useless medical paraphernalia was discarded, clearing the way for a new approach in medicine. By the time of the Civil War, American doctors had learned that, in dealing with communicable diseases, medical interference was rarely beneficial and often harmful. They had learned, too, that good nursing, moderate diet, and rest was usually the best therapy. The real development of scientific medicine, however, had to wait until universities became research centers.

Public health or preventive medicine, which is in essence the application of medical knowledge on a broad scale, can only operate within the framework of existing medical doctrines. In America, the basic public health concepts, like those of medicine, were derived largely from Great Britain, although colonial conditions often caused them to be modified. For example, smallpox, the colonists' most feared disease, was accepted as a normal childhood hazard in England and on the Continent, where it had long been endemic. On the other hand, the American settlements, isolated both from Europe and from each other, remained relatively free from the infection except for occasional violent outbreaks. Hence they had good reason for trying to stop the disease from gaining a foothold.

The medical profession might debate whether or not epidemic diseases were the product of meteorological conditions, vegetable and animal putrefaction, or even occult forces, but the public never doubted that these disorders were contagious. Starting in the seventeenth century, regulations passed by colonial legislatures and municipal authorities isolated cases of smallpox and other contagious disorders and at the same time provided for quarantines against infected towns and villages. The early laws were applied only in times of emergency, but as the eighteenth century advanced, the procedures became more formalized. Permanent port or health physicians were appointed to inspect incoming vessels, and pesthouses were established to isolate strangers and the sick poor whose diseases might threaten the town.[30]

The association of malaria, one of the most serious endemic disorders in the American colonies, with swampy, low-lying areas was long recognized. This association led to the miasmic thesis, the theory that the disease was due to some unknown gaseous substance emanating from the putrefying organic matter. This, in turn, induced the belief that foul or "noisome" odors might cause other diseases, too. The entire implications of the relationship between dirt and disease gained headway in the late eighteenth century and reached full momentum in the mid-nineteenth, when it provided much of the theoretical basis for the sanitary movement. However, even in the seventeenth century, towns such as Boston and New York passed laws regulating the erection and cleaning of privies and requiring property owners to clean their lots and the sections of the street adjacent to them.

While smallpox had supplied the chief impetus to the quarantine regulations, it was yellow fever which first made Americans conscious of the need for public health measures. A series of disastrous yellow fever epidemics struck the eastern seaboard ports from 1793 to 1805. The panic aroused by this frightening and deadly fever led to demands for governmental action. It was apparent to all observant medical men that yellow fever, which we now know is spread by the *Aedes aegypti* mosquito, was not contagious in the sense of smallpox. The failure of yellow fever to conform to the normal pattern stimulated a growing belief that epidemics were brought about by certain predisposing local conditions. The general public still continued to cling to contagionism,

---

[30] For a good discussion of early health laws, see Blake, *Public Health in the Town of Boston.*

but the medical profession split wide open on the issue. Contagion versus anticontagion or in practical terms, quarantine versus sanitation, continued to be the major issue in public health for most of the nineteenth century. The sanitationists, who advocated a relatively expensive program as compared to the fairly simple one of the quarantine faction, had one advantage in that they could appeal to civic-minded citizens on purely aesthetic grounds. Moreover, the failure of quarantine to keep yellow fever and Asiatic cholera out of American ports gave a strong impetus to the sanitation movement.

While yellow fever had supplied the initial stimulus to public health, it was Asiatic cholera which aroused Americans from their lethargy and awakened them to the need for ample supplies of pure water, effective programs of sanitation, and comprehensive drainage and sewage systems. Starting in 1832, cholera swept through North America three times in the nineteenth century, leaving thousands dead in its wake.[31] Each succeeding epidemic wave, however, strengthened the hands of the health boards, brought newer and more rigorous sanitary laws, and, temporarily, tightened the enforcement of existing ordinances. By the 1850's, the sanitary movement was in full swing, and the stage was set for the creation of permanent state and municipal boards of health. The Civil War may have delayed this step, but the experiences of the Union and Confederate armies demonstrated conclusively the value of sanitary measures in reducing sickness and death.

In glancing back over public health development prior to the Civil War, it is quite clear that the whole movement was largely empirical. Quarantine, inoculation, and sanitation scarcely belong under the rubric of scientific medicine. Yet the latter two were influenced by the emergence of quantification. In justifying the use of inoculation, its advocates in Europe and America collected case fatality statistics with respect to those who acquired the disease naturally and those who acquired it by inoculation. Epidemic diseases, which on occasions might literally decimate a town, further promoted the collection of bills of mortality. These published accounts of the monthly or annual number of deaths provided the humanitarian reformers of the late eighteenth and early nineteenth centuries with some insight into the condition of the lower social classes. The disclosure of the appalling death rates among the children of the poor was one factor in gaining support for the infant welfare movement of the eighteenth century.

---

[31] Charles E. Rosenberg, *The Cholera Years, The United States in 1832, 1849 and 1866* (Chicago, 1962).

Mortality statistics compiled by men such as Dr. Thomas Percival in Liverpool, around 1800, and Louis-René Villermé in France, around 1828, clearly demonstrated the relationship between death, disease, and poverty.

In America two New Englanders, Dr. Edward Jarvis and Lemuel Shattuck, took the lead in promoting the collection of vital statistics. Both men were active in the American Statistical Society (founded in 1838), and Shattuck was largely responsible for securing a Massachusetts law in 1842 improving the collection of vital statistics.[32] Subsequently, he was invited to assist with the census of 1850. By the mid-nineteenth century, in nearly every American city, reformers were accumulating statistical evidence to show the appalling morbidity rates among the working classes. Advocates of health reform, such as Shattuck and Jarvis in Massachusetts, Drs. John Griscom and Elisha Harris in New York, and Drs. J. C. Simonds and Edward H. Barton in Louisiana, all assiduously promoted this work.

At the same time, they urged their state and local governments to establish effective registration agencies for collecting vital statistics. The American Medical Association, founded shortly before the mid-century, consistently supported the movement, and local medical societies often added their voices to the appeal. Medical societies, however, represented only a small fraction of the practicing physicians, and progress was very slow. In 1870 Massachusetts, finally reacting to Shattuck's celebrated report of 1850, established the first adequate state system for registering vital statistics. Support from the federal government was provided when Dr. John Shaw Billings (1838–1913) of the Surgeon General's Office set up the Federal Registration Area in 1880, but even by 1900 only about 40 percent of the American population lived within areas having effective registration laws.[33] Incomplete as the data may have been, it supplied the public health reformers with ammunition.

The years from the Civil War to the end of the century were ones in which American doctors were slowly awakening to the demands of science. The center of interest for American students shifted from Paris to Germany, where the emphasis upon research and the extensive laboratory facilities was making German science and medicine preeminent. The only really important American contributions in these years were the governmental publications in the field of medical

---

[32] Dirk J. Struik, *Yankee Science in the Making* (Boston, 1948), pp. 232–33.
[33] Garrison, "Medicine," pp. 338–40.

literature and bibliography. In the postwar years, the publication of the six volumes of *The Medical and Surgical History of the War of the Rebellion, 1861–65* provided a wealth of information. Of even greater significance was the work of Dr. John S. Billings, who, starting with some surplus hospital funds, built up the Surgeon General's Library into the greatest medical library in the world. He was responsible, too, for establishing the *Index Medicus* in 1879 and initiating the publication of the volumes of the *Index Catalogue*.

Billings' influence ranged much further than the field of medical bibliography. As noted earlier, he actively promoted the gathering of vital statistics, and when American medical schools slowly turned toward a scientific orientation, Billings played a key role in the process. Led by Harvard in 1871, medical schools gradually lengthened and reformed their teaching programs, but the major change came in 1893 with the establishment of The Johns Hopkins Medical School. Here, under the leadership of Dr. William H. Welch (1850–1934) and his cohorts, medical education was associated with an effective research program. Significantly, it was Dr. Billings who planned The Johns Hopkins Hospital and designed the administrative program of the medical school.

Johns Hopkins, with its emphasis upon laboratory medicine and the basic sciences, set a pattern for American medical schools. Those schools which were unable or unwilling to face the realities of scientific medicine and measure up to the new standards soon found themselves ruthlessly weeded out. In 1905 the American Medical Association set up a Council or committee on medical education. After two years of study, the Council devised a system for inspecting and grading schools. Subsequently, the Carnegie Foundation financed a survey by Abraham Flexner. His findings, made known in the celebrated Flexner report of 1910, clearly showed the tremendous disparity between the best and the worst medical education. The widespread publicity given his findings combined with the financial aid which the Rockefeller Foundation gave to those schools which Flexner deemed salvageable eventually led to the elimination of substandard institutions. By the end of World War I, medical training and research had developed to a point where American doctors no longer needed to complete their education in European universities; henceforth the process was reversed, and American medical research centers began attracting students from abroad.

Paralleling the slow development of scientific research in connection with medical education were the tentative efforts of the United

States government to promote scientific work. After the Civil War, the Department of Agriculture began giving some support to biological and chemical research projects, and, through its interest in veterinary medicine, gradually moved into basic research. The short-lived National Board of Health, 1879–1883, while operating with only minimal funds, helped to establish the principle of governmental aid for university research. The United States Army, under the direction of Surgeon General George M. Sternberg, a pioneer bacteriologist, founded the Army Medical School in 1893, an institution which was designed both as a training and research center. In the meantime the United States Marine Hospital Service in 1887 began creating laboratories and promoting research in the area of infectious diseases. Congress, however, was still dubious of basic scientific investigation and was far more inclined to appropriate funds for research in agriculture, where the payoff was more tangible and immediate. At the local level, municipal health boards in the 1890's were beginning to appreciate the significance of science in relation to medicine. New York City, for example, began bacteriological work in the 1880's, and in 1893 established a diagnostic laboratory and started an active program of bacteriological research.

With the advent of the twentieth century the scope of governmental aid broadened, but it was private philanthropy which chiefly subsidized medical research during the first thirty years of the century. Beginning with the Rockefeller Institute for Medical Research in 1901, the John McCormick Institute for Infectious Diseases and the Carnegie Institute in 1902, a host of medical research institutes sprang into life. Soon American scientists began to improve upon the discoveries of their European contemporaries and to make original contributions of their own. Private support for medical science took two main forms, both of which were fully represented by the Rockefeller Foundation. The first and most obvious was the creation of permanent research laboratories. The achievements of the Rockefeller Institute are beyond the scope of this study, but the names of medical scientists such as Simon Flexner, Hideyo Noguchi, and Rene J. Dubos add luster to the Institute's reputation. Meanwhile, in the other Institutes—Phipps, Hooper, Cushing, Sprague, *et al.*—other outstanding scientists were steadily broadening scientific horizons.

As their number increased, it was soon recognized that by attracting able men into full-time research, the Institutes were competing with medical schools and universities, the net effect of which was to weaken the scientific training centers precisely at the time when the need for well-trained individuals was increasing. This realization led the Rockefeller, and other Foundations, into a large-scale program designed to improve medical schools. The process, as indicated earlier, was facilitated by the Flexner report which singled out those institutions best deserving of support. In providing funds, the Foundations generally aided those schools with a research orientation. In the ensuing years, literally millions of dollars were donated to the cause of medical education. Between 1902 and 1934, nine foundations alone gave approximately $154 million for this purpose.[34] By the latter date, medical education had been revolutionized and medical schools had become significant research centers in their own right.

While private philanthropy deserves chief credit for the rise of scientific medicine during the early twentieth century, governmental support for research was slowly expanding. The Department of Agriculture continued to receive the lion's share of research funds, but the Armed Forces, the newly reorganized United States Public Health Service, and other agencies continued to press for laboratory appropriations. World War I provided an impetus to governmental action, although the "Return to Normalcy" of the Harding-Coolidge Era soon put a damper on federal efforts in this direction. The Great Depression, an event which profoundly altered American thinking with respect to governmental responsibility, brought an administration which recognized the value of scientific investigation. With President Roosevelt and Congress receptive, appropriations were increased for all governmental agencies engaged in scientific work, and effective programs for federal-state cooperation were set up.

It was in these years, too, that the federal government made a firm commitment to medical research. As early as 1887, the Marine Hospital Service had established a one-room diagnostic laboratory in New York. In 1901, $35,000 was appropriated to construct the Hygienic Laboratory in Washington, D.C. Subsequently, additional acts gradually increased the scope of medical research until 1930, when the Hygienic Laboratory was reorganized and renamed the National Institutes of Health. In 1937 Congress created, as a special division of this body, the National Cancer Institute, thereby demonstrating that the National Institutes of Health was to become a national research center. Within the next thirteen years, the number of institutes increased to seven and the number of staff from 1,000 to 2,600.[35]

---

[34] The American Foundation, *Medical Research: A Midcentury Survey* (Boston and Toronto, 1955), I, 511.

[35] *Ibid.*, I, 641–42.

Although its precise impact upon scientific development is hard to assess, World War II radically altered the American scene. In all likelihood, the accelerating pace of scientific discoveries and the rapid rise in the American standard of living would have guaranteed a continued interest in medical research, even without the wartime stimulus. This stimulus was not all to the good—at least in its effect on basic research. Vast amounts of money were poured into science, but the emphasis was upon research in the applied fields. Yet it would be hard to estimate the benefits accruing from the stepped-up program which placed penicillin, one of the most significant breakthroughs in medical history, on a mass-production basis. Nor can we measure the indirect benefits to medicine derived from the intensified research in nuclear physics. Whether or not the wartime emphasis upon applied research proved detrimental to basic research, certainly in the popular mind, Allied victories were equated with scientific triumphs. Backed by strong public pressure, the last twenty years have seen an unprecedented interest in scientific exploration.

Significantly, the entrance of the government into the medical research field on a large scale in the late 1930's and the 1940's does not seem to have affected spending by private foundations. On the contrary, not only did the number of foundations increase following World War II, but more of them tended to pour their funds into medical areas.

Prior to the twentieth century, the American contributions to medicine were relatively minor, and the historian can systematically record individual triumphs. The twentieth century, however, is another matter; as it progressed, the vast material wealth and technical knowledge of the United States, combined with an unrivaled system of university, foundation, and industrial research centers, enabled America to assume leadership in a world of science that was expanding at an unprecedented rate. This statement should not be construed as a reflection upon the major contributions from all sections of the world, for scientific medicine, like science in general, possesses a universality. For example, American science and technology was responsible for the rapid utilization of penicillin, but the pioneering work was done by English scientists.

The enormous accumulation of scientific knowledge has virtually eliminated the boundaries between biology, chemistry, and physics, and significant discoveries in any area bring new insights to scientists working far afield. Since medicine utilizes information from widely diverse sources, the term medical science is itself debatable. Whatever the case, advances in medicine are dependent upon developments along the entire front of science. In the twentieth century, it has become impossible to discuss medical progress apart from general scientific developments. Just as the line between basic and applied science is tenuous, so the line between medically oriented science and general science has become almost unrecognizable.

In summarizing medical developments since the emergence of modern medicine in the 1880's, it can be said that the great epidemic diseases of earlier days have largely been overcome. Bacteriology first identified the major communicable disorders and then provided the means for curing and preventing them. Improved laboratory techniques, better instrumentation, and major achievements in biochemistry and physiology provided the answers to the more significant deficiency illnesses. By the 1930's, medicine turned to new fields. With life expectancy steadily rising, problems of old age and degenerative disorders assumed greater significance. The nature of these ailments precludes the dramatic breakthroughs which so often characterized earlier medical triumphs, but slowly and steadily, information is accumulating.

In the 1950's, medical and public health leaders became increasingly preoccupied with mental health. Mental illness is nothing new, nor is it necessarily to be attributed to our complex urban society. Rather, this renewed interest in it stems from the successes of physical medicine, the sophisticated state of medical knowledge, and higher living standards. The challenges provided by the degenerative diseases and mental ailments are as great as any of those which have confronted society in the past. Fortunately many new avenues of attack have opened up in the past half century. Biochemistry, physiology, neurology, metabolic studies, genetics, and other specialized fields, all aided by more refined techniques and instruments, are opening up new vistas in man's search for physical, mental, and emotional well-being.

Science and American Social Thought

Charles E. Rosenberg*

Even the beginning history student learns something of the relationship between science and American social thought. The impact of
Newton on Puritan divines and that of Darwin on Victorian America
have become routine subjects for the college classroom. Intellectual
historians and historians of philosophy have considered in some detail the influence of science on the leaders of American thought. One
thinks immediately of Cotton Mather and Thomas Jefferson, of
Lester Ward and Henry Adams, of Thorstein Veblen and William
James. The following pages will not consider such imposing figures
directly, nor will they deal with social thought of a formal or academic
nature. They are not meant to deny the pertinence of systematic
thought; they are meant to suggest the significance of a number of
other relationships, less familiar, less self-conscious perhaps, but no
less important because less frequently studied.[1]

Before outlining these relationships, however, let me insert several
notes by way of clarification. *Science* in the following pages will be
assumed to mean a number of different things: an accumulating body
of knowledge and the techniques for acquiring it, a community with
peculiar ideas and values, and, in addition, the images and emotions
which scientific knowledge and the figure of the scientist have con-

* CHARLES E. ROSENBERG, born in New York City in 1936, is at present
Assistant Professor of History at the University of Pennsylvania. He holds
degrees from the University of Wisconsin (B.A., 1956) and Columbia University (M.A., 1957, Ph.D., 1961). He is the author of *The Cholera Years: The
United States in 1832, 1849, and 1866* (Chicago, 1962) and has contributed to
the *American Quarterly; Bulletin of the History of Medicine; Agricultural History; Comparative Studies in Society and History;* and the *Journal of the History
of Medicine,* among other publications.

[1] Merle Curti's *Growth of American Thought* (3rd edition) is comprehensive
and includes useful bibliographies. Stow Persons' *American Minds* (New York,
1958) devotes more than the usual amount of attention to science and its effects
on American thinkers.

jured up in American minds. This American mind, encountered with such frequency, is, of course, a conventional fiction; obviously at any moment in time many persons and groups do not adhere to even society's most pervasive and unquestioned ideas and emotions. Most of the descriptive generalizations which follow, if unqualified, refer to the moderately educated, moderately articulate and modestly prosperous, church-going Americans whom we associate with the middle-class concensus. A final caution: this discussion is neither exhaustive nor chronological. It consists of examples chosen in the hope of their illustrating concretely some of the relationships which have existed—and which exist today—between science and American social thought.

One can, I think, distinguish at least four kinds of such interaction. First, science lent American social thought a vocabulary and a supply of images. It served as a source of metaphor and, like figures borrowed from other areas, the similes of science variously suggested, explained, justified, even helped dictate social categories and values. But the role of science in social thought has been emotional as well as expository. This is the second relationship which I hope to describe; it is, essentially, the changing position of science in the hierarchy of American values. As we shall see, one of the most important developments in the relationship between science and American social thought has been the increasing emotional relevance of science, its growing role as an absolute able to justify and motivate individual action.

Both of these relationships are pervasive, limited perhaps by class and region but otherwise widespread. Both are flexible as well, dependent for their particular configuration upon social needs and consequent intellectual and emotional manipulations. A third relationship between science and American society is much less familiar, but perhaps easier to describe in that it is more rigid and clearly structured. This is the role in social thought of the professional scientist's values and attitudes. As is true in any work-defined reference group—and especially the professions—the scientist shares certain values and concepts with his disciplinary peers. These are different from those entertained by society at large, indeed sufficiently different and sufficiently concrete so as to have served as a uniquely creative force in the development of modern industrial society. A fourth and final relationship between science and American social thought can, in a sense, be seen as the converse of the third. That is, not the effect of the scientific community's values in bringing an element of diversity and change to society, but that of society's attitudes and demands on the scientist's work and thought.

The first of these relationships is in a sense the most pervasive. Most aspects of social thought deal with universal human problems, problems which must be answered by each generation in its own way; the need, for example, of society to arrive at an explanation of why some persons are wealthy, others poor, some healthy and vigorous, others sickly and weak. Throughout the nineteenth century the world of science presented a multitude of words and concepts with which such traditional concerns could be discussed. Late nineteenth-century science, for example, provided publicists and scholars of the day with the concepts of the Darwinian synthesis; they employed these ideas to explain social structure and social function. Social Darwinism[2] is only the most familiar among a number of such instances. At the same time, for example, metaphors originating in physics and electro-physiology were made to explain variation in human capacities. Neither folk wisdom nor the physician's clinical acumen doubted that human beings differed greatly in intelligence. They differed as well in their resistance to disease, in their keenness of perception and response to stimuli. For centuries, physicians had spoken of the concepts of vital force and of irritability in an effort to explain such innate differences.

By mid-nineteenth century, scientists had come to accept the electrical nature of the nervous impulse. In 1852, Helmholtz, the German physiologist and physicist, accomplished his successful measurement of the rate of nervous conductivity. Aside from the philosophical implications of this discovery, it seemed to make almost inescapable the conclusions that nervous force might easily be the same as vital force and that this elusive vital force, if not electricity itself, must be some form of energy closely allied to it. In addition, the second law of thermodynamics* seemed to emphasize man's necessarily limited quantity of vital energy and the innumerable possibilities for energy loss from within the closed system that was the human organism.

---

2 The best general survey of Social Darwinism in this country is still that by Richard Hofstadter, *Social Darwinism in American Thought* (Boston, 1955). See also Stow Persons, ed., *Evolutionary Thought in America* (New Haven, 1950). There is some question as to how pervasive social Darwinism as a well-articulated doctrine actually was. See Irvin G. Wyllie, "Social Darwinism and the Businessman," *Proc. Am. Phil. Soc.*, CIII (1959), 629–35.

* The second law of thermodynamics states that in a free and continuous heat exchange, heat is always transferred from the hotter to the colder body.

The nervous system, as visualized by Americans before the acceptance of the neuron theory,† was a closed and continuous channel. A fixed quantity of nervous force, a hereditary endowment assumed to be electrical in nature, filled and coursed through this channel. (Popularizers soon grew fond of comparing the human brain and nervous system to the headquarters and wires of a great telegraph system. "The brain is the central office, and in it there are nine hundred million cells generating nerve fluid. . . ."[3]) Using this schematic model, physicians and social thinkers were able to explain the most varied aspects of human behavior. Thus the artistically gifted maniac was the result of a particularly abnormal imbalance of nervous energies. "The force which is turned away from some channel that is blocked up by disease rushes through the channels of sanity that remain unobstructed with heightened velocity." Hypnotism or trance was the consequence of nervous force being concentrated in "one direction." Insanity might also be explained in these terms. No two persons would be born with the same amount of nervous force; no two persons would be subjected to the same external social pressures. Those individuals whose endowment of nervous force was inadequate to the pressures and crises of daily life would succumb to neurosis or psychosis.

Such crude designs provoked little criticism in this self-consciously materialistic generation; electricity was not metaphysics and nervous force seemed far removed from vital force. We may smile today, perhaps, at the simplistic quality of these explanations, but it must be recalled that men as diverse as Sigmund Freud and Henry Adams were captivated by analogies in which energy relationships served to explain individual and collective behavior in a fashion not really different in form from these ingenuous schemes.[4]

---

† This doctrine holds that the nervous system is composed of neurons or nerve cells. The neurons are structural units which are in contact with other units but not in continuity. The nervous pathways are conceived as chains of such units.

[3] W. J. Hunter, *Manhood Wrecked and Rescued. How Strength, or Vigor is Lost, and How it May be Restored Through Self-Treatment* (Passaic, N.J., c. 1900), p. 129. It was assumed in most of these analogies that man's endowment of nervous energy was not an absolute quantity provided at birth but rather the body's potential for the production of this nervous energy during life.

[4] The preceding quotations have been taken from Charles E. Rosenberg, "The Place of George M. Beard in Nineteenth-Century Psychiatry," *Bull. Hist. Med.,* XXXVI (1962), 250. These formulations, it should be noted, preserved the traditional assumption that both heredity and environmental stress played a role in the etiology of nervous disease. There is, so far as I am aware, no

This same mechanistic formulation helped not simply to explain mental illness and other extreme personal behavior; it served as well to express traditional social and moral sanctions in terms relevant to postbellum America. The electrical nature of the nerve impulse, the conservation of energy, and the second law of thermodynamics served as sources of didactic metaphors, metaphors clothed in the authority of science and yet dramatizing such long-standing concerns as the American desire to shore up middle-class morale and to provide a rationale for moderation in every aspect of behavior. These and other metaphors drawn from the sciences helped similarly to express the ambivalence of many Americans toward progress, toward urbanization, toward the treacherous fluidity of American life.

Moderation was, to nineteenth-century Americans, almost synonymous with morality. And excess was not only immoral, but, they believed, physiologically foolhardy as well. Man's limited complement of nervous energy, if considered in the light of the normal human need to indulge in a great variety of activities, meant that one should not indulge immoderately in any particular activity. Those which stimulated the emotions were particularly dangerous, for it seemed clear that nervous energy must necessarily be expended during the expression of strong emotions. The baleful effects of an excessive devotion to business might be the same as those of an obsessive love affair. All sensual pleasure was—in excess, of course—perilous. As Alexander Bain put it: "Every throb of pleasure costs something to the physical system; and two throbs cost twice as much as one."[5] Yet nervous energies must be discharged, for without physical or emotional release, these energies would accumulate and ultimately create pathological conditions. Sexual abstinence, for example, if not compensated for by a life of vigorous physical activity could lead to neurosis or, indeed, to any one of a score of ailments. Thus the fre-

---

study available of the metaphorical use of energy relationships in American social thought. For Freud, see S. Bernfeld, "Freud's Earliest Theories and the School of Helmholtz," *Psychoanalyst Q.*, XIII (1944), 341–62; for Henry Adams, see William Jordy, *Henry Adams. Scientific Historian* (New Haven, 1952). For an account of research relating to the discovery of electrical nature of the nervous impulse, see E. G. T. Liddell, *The Discovery of Reflexes* (Oxford, 1960), chap. ii, "Animal Electricity," pp. 31–47.

[5] "The Correlation of Nervous and Mental Forces," in Balfour Stewart, *The Conservation of Energy* (New York, 1875), p. 228. Bain, a professor at Aberdeen, was widely read in this country. Particularly significant in the attempt to popularize discoveries relating to the conservation of energy was the editorial work of E. L. Youmans. See his *Correlation and Conservation of Forces: A Series of Expositions, by Prof. Grove, Prof. Helmholtz, Dr. Mayer, Dr. Faraday, Prof. Liebig and Dr. Carpenter* (New York, 1869).

quency of hysteria in the more delicate and protected of middle-class maidens. Morality denied to "young ladies" energy-discharging sexual activities, while fashion dictated their refraining from the active work or outdoor play which might also have reduced to a safe level the body's normal production of nervous energy.

Indeed, physicians argued, many aspects of American life made massive and unnatural demands on the nervous system. Constant choice and opportunity in business and religion, a lack of standards in personal and social life—all created tension and excitement. Competition began in the schools. The smallest of children were forced to specialize and to overwork in the quest for narrow academic distinction, their physical well-being forgotten. Even if the American survived his education with a minimum of psychic or physical damage, he had then to face an adulthood filled with insecurity. He lived his life at a pace too frenetic for relaxation or rest. American ways seemed especially alarming when compared with those of Europe. On the Continent, for example, religion was a source of security and passive reassurance; in the United States Protestantism made constant drafts upon moral and emotional reserves. In politics and business, too, any American, regardless of his social origin, might be subjected to the stress created by his own unbounded aspirations— and the consequent alternation of hope, of elation, of despair. "The result of this extreme activity, is exhaustion and weakness. Physical bankruptcy is the result of drawing incessantly upon the reserve capital of nerve force."[6]

More than a few Americans have felt misgivings in contemplating the dangerous and unsettling freedom of American life. Russian peasants chose neither their religion nor their rulers and suffered from none of the symptoms of nervous exhaustion, from wan faces and hollow cheeks, dyspepsia and sterility. "Insanity," as one editorialist put it, "is the skeleton at the feast of the highest civilization, . . . In proportion as nations have become free has mental disease multiplied."[7] Physicians and social thinkers since the day of Thomas

---

[6] R. V. Pierce, *The People's Common Sense Medical Adviser in Plain English: Or Medicine Simplified* (Buffalo, N.Y., 1895), p. 619. For a clear exposition of the assumption that American life held dangers to mental health, see the many references in Norman Dain, *Concepts of Insanity in the United States, 1789–1865* (New Brunswick, N.J., 1964). See also George Rosen, "Social stress and mental disease from the eighteenth century to the present: Some origins of social psychiatry," *Milbank Memorial Fund Q.*, XXXVII (1959), 5–32 and Mark D. Altschule, *Roots of Modern Psychiatry* (New York and London, 1957), 119–39.

[7] *Independent* (New York), XXII (June 30, 1870), 4.

Jefferson and Benjamin Rush have criticized the peculiar tensions of American life. The speculative pathologies which explain precisely how these tensions injured the body have changed in form since the days of Rush, but the ambivalent attitudes which they express toward American life have not.

Yet neither Benjamin Rush nor his successors later in the century —S. Weir Mitchell, Isaac Ray, and G. M. Beard among others,— were willing, warn as they might of the psychic perils of American life, to exchange its liberties for the placid tyranny of the Russian or Turkish empires (or, most Americans felt, their individualistic Protestantism for the formalistic reassurances of Catholicism). Throughout the nineteenth century, indeed, American warnings of the dangers of modern life to mental stability were not a negative but, in sum, a positive, even nationalistic, doctrine. Progress and liberty were unquestionably desirable, and the ailments which they induced in American m:nds were in a sense additional bits of evidence for the superiority of American ways of life. Technological change might be the cause of mental unease, but almost all Americans were relatively sanguine in their attitude toward the future of such material change. Many Americans believed that the very processes of technological change that appeared to threaten mental health would ultimately provide remedies. Such ills that might develop in the interval were those of a transitional period in history and a small price paid for social progress "We must not go backward, but forward," Irving Fisher wrote in 1908. "The cure for eye strain is not in ignoring the invention of reading, but in introducing the invention of glasses. The cure for tuberculosis is not in the destruction of houses, but in devices for ventilation."[8] Throughout the nineteenth century, American minds were marked by unresolved and ordinarily unstated contradictions— between an ingenuously arrogant nationalism and a chronic national insecurity, between optimism and pessimism, between primitivism and progress. With a peculiar appropriateness, science provided a vocabulary and a source of imagery in which these contradictions could be expressed with some subtlety—indeed with an unself-con-

---

[8] Irving Fisher, *Bulletin 30 of the Committee of One Hundred on National Health. Being a Report on National Vitality its Wastes and Conservation* (Washington. D.C., 1909). p. 96. cf. Rosenberg, "George Beard," *Bull. Hist. Med.*, CCLVII; J. Leonard Corning, *Brain Exhaustion, with Some Preliminary Considerations on Cerebral Dynamics* (New York, 1884), p. 135. For influential statements in regard to the influence of American life on mental health, see Isaac Ray, *Mental Hygiene* (Boston, 1863), especially pp. 219–23 and Benjamin Rush, *Medical Inquiries and Observations upon the Diseases of the Mind* (Philadelphia, 1812), pp. 65–69 and *passim*.

scious sensitivity which might well have been unattainable by the same men in more formal modes of speculation.

A function central to the social thought of any place or time is the formulation and justification of an ideal social type. Until the present century, American formal rhetoric consistently pictured as ideal the responsible, middling, yeoman farmer. The virtues attributed to this thinking agriculturist were physical as well as moral. A rural upbringing seemed to guarantee a far healthier life than a youth spent in the debilitating air of the city. It seemed equally clear that a middling life was more wholesome physically—as well as far more likely to be wholesome morally—than that of either the very poor or the extremely rich. The lower classes, improperly fed, addicted to drink and indulging in other vices, living in improperly ventilated apartments, had little chance to live out a natural life span. The rich, whether they had inherited wealth or risen to it, were alike prey to nervous disease. The idle scion of wealthy parents was likely to suffer from the mental corrosion of inactivity if not from dissipation; the self-made man was necessarily exposed to the tensions and stress which accompanied his financial ambitions. The ideal citizen was rural, moderately prosperous, of good, though not brilliant mental endowment. Genius, authorities on heredity agreed, was often accompanied by insanity, or idiocy, or ill-health; it could hardly be held up as an ideal. Therefore, concluded a prominent eugenicist, expressing a long-felt American conviction, "it would seem wise not to breed for geniuses but for a solid middle class."[9]

And, he might have added, to raise them in contact with nature. Even the least credulous of eighteenth- and nineteenth-century physicians found it difficult to question the well-attested immunity of primitive peoples from most of the diseases which plagued civilized man. It seemed absurd to even suggest that a Congo Negro could suffer from neurasthenia, or a South Sea Islander from epilepsy. Heart disease, cancer, and even liver ailments, some authorities held, were never to be found in non-Western peoples. Childbirth in the American Indian, travelers reported, was, if not completely painless, a relatively casual procedure. Even pauperism, it seemed natural to assume,[10]

---

[9] Charles B. Davenport to D. Starr Jordan, January 27, 1922. "Davenport Papers," Carnegie Institution of Washington, Department of Genetics, Cold Spring Harbor, N.Y. The literature relating to the connection between genius and other forms of mental abnormality is immense. An excellent guide is Wilhelm Lange-Eichbaum, *Genie, Irrsinn und Ruhm* (München, 1961).

[10] Samuel Royce, *Deterioration and the Elevation of Man through Race Education* (Boston, 1880), I, 49.

. . . does not exist in the natural state of man. Under the sweet influences of the skies, he is in the woods as quick and nimble as the bird or deer he pursues. Only in the atmosphere, thick with moral and physical poison of crowded cities, he degenerates into a pauper, robbed of all that elasticity and high potency by which man masters every resistance. . . .

Of course, those Americans who eulogized the health and virtue of primitive peoples would hardly have favored a return to such unsophisticated ways of life. Though it may have had its questionable aspects, Western civilization offered advantages superior to the health gained by that rude life of the savage. The crudeness of nervous organization which protected these simple peoples from illness, prevented them as well from creating a complex society. The highest of human activities—morality, religion, art, and literature—were all consequences of the more finely developed nervous organization of Western man. "There can be no question," physicians assumed, "as to whether the nervous systems of highly cultivated and refined individuals among civilized peoples are more complex and refined in structure and delicate in susceptibility and action, at least in their higher parts, than the nervous system of savages."[11] It seemed clear enough that so delicate an apparatus could easily go awry. The sensitivity and complexity of this superior nervous organization, its greater area for the reception of sensation, its greater capacity for imagination, all helped explain the susceptibility of civilized man to nervous ailments.

There is a logic here, arbitrary and makeshift as these "scientific" analogies may seem. It is to be found, not in their particular scientific content, but in their social function. We must look, not to the internal coherence of the scientific ideas appropriated, but at their external logic—that is, their social purpose. By way of illustration, let me refer to another example, this drawn from the field of legal medicine.

In many of the prominent "insanity" trials held in the years between 1880 and 1900, medical witnesses for the prosecution and defense endorsed contradictory medical interpretations so as to bolster their legal position. Psychiatrists for the prosecution argued that the

---

11 J. S. Jewell, "Influence of our present civilization in the production of nervous and mental disease," *J. Nervous & Mental Disease*, VIII (1881), 4. With the acceptance of Darwinism, it should be noted, these hypothetical mental attributes of civilized man were provided with evolutionary credentials. The traditionally higher faculties, the aesthetic and moral, were, as a matter of course identified with those highest in the scale of evolution. Being the "highest," they were naturally man's last acquisition in his upward path. Primitive peoples were, quite literally, it was believed, more primitive, less complex in their cerebral development.

prisoner understood the nature and consequences of his act, appeared to reason coherently and, hence, following the generally accepted rule of law, was guilty. Psychiatrists for the defense often held, on the other hand, that one might seem rational, even intelligent, and still not be responsible for one's actions. The cause of the individual's irresponsibility, they were convinced, lay frequently in heredity, in a congenital predisposition toward lack of moral perceptivity and control. Indeed, they argued, such men could be identified by physical stigmata which seemed characteristic of criminals.[12] Certainly such offenders could be recognized at autopsy, for the brain of a moral defective or habitual criminal was demonstrably different from that of a sane and law-abiding person.

Many people in the mid-twentieth century may well sympathize with these physicians and lawyers whom they see as fighting to save the mentally ill from capital punishment, applaud their citation of German authorities, their invocation of science, and opposition to the vengeful moralism of the prosecution's expert witnesses. Yet a closer examination of the content of their ideas reveals that the ideas of the prosecution, *not* the defense, experts are the ones, in form, at least, that are in some ways closer to modern views. The current tendency is to explain personality in dynamic terms and to reject the ideas that insanity is inevitably hereditary, that it manifests itself in gross pathological lesions, or that it is necessarily localized in one portion of the brain. Defenders of traditional morality at the end of the nineteenth century refused also to accept such materialistic arguments. The human personality was a whole, they argued, and one part of it, such as the moral sense, could not be diseased while another, the reasoning faculty, for example, remained healthy. They viewed the

---

[12] This doctrine is more commonly associated with the name and influence of Lombroso and his "criminal anthropology," which sought to establish physical characteristics peculiar to the criminal type. Basic to this doctrine and preceding it in time was the theory of degeneration, a concept broadly influential throughout Western Europe in the second half of the nineteenth century. It held mental weakness and abnormality to be protean, hereditary, and progressive. Alcoholism might, in the next generation, appear as insanity, in the next, as idiocy. The basic study of degeneration is still that of G.-P.-H. Genil-Perrin, *Histoire des origines et de l'évolution de l'idée de dégénérescence en médecine mentale* (Paris, 1913). A valuable introduction to the influence of Lombrosianism in the United States, that by Arthur E. Fink, *Causes of Crime. Biological Theories in the United States. 1880–1915* (Philadelphia, 1938), chaps. v–viii. For a valuable contemporary survey which provides a good summary of an American's position, see Eugene S. Talbot, *Degeneracy. Its Causes, Signs and Results* (London and New York, 1899). David Brion Davis' study of *Homicide in American Fiction. 1798–1860* (Ithaca, 1958), provides useful introductory material on earlier views of criminality.

criminal act as the consequence not of a diseased or deformed brain but as a result of traits originating in the habitual actions of earliest childhood.[13]

In a sense, of course, this analysis is irrelevant; defense witnesses seem liberal today not because their ideas are correct in detail but because their values are acceptable, because it is more important that they quote German sources as transcendent authority—even if the authorities are wrong—rather than the Bible or the rules of criminal jurisprudence. The heart of the matter lies in one's attitude toward the criminal offender. Then, as now, forensic "liberals" assume a deterministic stance, conservatives a less deterministic one. That the scientific ideas with which the determinism is justified have changed in this century seems less important than that they serve the same social function. There is, then, a logic here, but a logic imposed by social necessity. It could not, in this case, be imposed by the content of the scientific arguments themselves; the factors determining the development of criminal behavior were—and in many ways still are—simply a subject of unverifiable speculation. The more tenuous an area of scientific knowledge, the smaller its verifiable content, the more easily its data may be bent to social purposes.

This is illustrated clearly by the manner, for example, in which ostensibly scientific formulations have found quite different social roles in different national contexts. A case in point is the differing reception accorded phrenology in the United States and in Europe. (The central notion of phrenology is that particular localized portions of the brain control the several aspects of human behavior. Phrenology was immensely popular in mid-nineteenth-century America.) American historians have seen phrenology as a widely popular, an optimistic and anti-Calvinistic doctrine.[14] It promised understanding and

---

[13] This pattern was a common one, though, of course, only in the trials of prominent persons were a number of physicians recruited by both sides. In the most famous "insanity" trial of the period, that of Charles J. Guiteau for the murder of President Garfield, the twenty-odd witnesses for the prosecution and defense divided in this fashion. Compare, for example, the testimony of E. C. Spitzka and Francis Kiernan for the defense with that of John P. Gray and Fordyce Barker for the prosecution. *Report of the Proceedings in the Case of the United States vs. Charles J. Guiteau* (Washington, D.C., 1882).

[14] A modern study of phrenology in the United States is that by John D. Davis, *Phrenology. Fad and Science. A 19th-Century American Crusade* (New Haven, 1955). For Gall and the development of phrenology, see Owsei Temkin, "Gall and the Phrenological Movement," *Bull. Hist. of Med.*, XXI (1947), 275–331 and Erwin H. Ackerknecht and Henry Vallois, *Franz Joseph Gall, Inventor of Phrenology and his Collection*, University of Wisconsin Medical School, Wisconsin Studies in Medical History, No. 1 (Madison, 1956).

control of man's personality. In Europe, however, phrenology did not partake of these qualities; it assumed a far more deterministic cast. It seemed optimistic in this country simply because Americans would have it so. There is actually more reason logically to interpret phrenology, with its emphasis upon an anatomical basis for behavioral characteristics, as a pessimistic, deterministic doctrine. Yet Americans, eager as they were to find justifications for a hopeful view of human potential, could not ignore so plausible a scheme, one which promised a neat and attractively mechanistic explanation of human behavior. Americans could not ignore the doctrine, but they could —and did—quite easily ignore its more deterministic implications.

At this point a word of caution is due. The social historian, though he has no consuming interest in the history of scientific ideas as such, must still—if he is to investigate the role of these concepts in social thought—comprehend something of science as it was understood by men in the past. Without such knowledge he will inevitably be influenced by the assumptions of modern science. To the extent that this is the case, he will in some measure fail to assess the thought of the period he has elected to study.

This danger is illustrated clearly in the case of nineteenth-century attitudes toward heredity, especially in the use of heredity to explain disease and antisocial behavior. It is natural for us to associate a hereditarian emphasis with social conservatism and a comparatively pessimistic view of the potential for social reform. Yet this was not at all the case until roughly 1900 and the beginning of modern genetics. At no time in the nineteenth century did either physicians or laymen doubt that environmental changes (especially changes originating in long-standing habit or acute pathological conditions) could be transmitted from parents to their children.

Thus, for example, the significance of Richard Dugdale's study of the Jukes family conducted in the mid-1870's is quite different from that usually attributed to it. Dugdale, a self-consciously scientific reformer on many social fronts, was particularly interested in prison reform. As a member of the executive committee of New York's Prison Association, Dugdale conducted a study of county jails in the state and was struck by the frequency with which he encountered a certain family name. Dugdale expanded his study, gathering what data he could concerning the background of this family—christened Jukes for the sake of anonymity. He concluded that the congenital inadequacy of this family—its immorality, criminality, idiocy, and insanity—had cost the state of New York over a million and a quarter dollars. But to Dugdale and most of his contemporaries, these alarming results did not provide a brief for eugenic marriage laws or compulsory sterilization. They made, on the contrary, an urgent plea for environmental reform. That the Jukes's antisocial traits could be inherited dramatized the need for immediate reform of the conditions in which they lived; otherwise, drinking, narcotics addiction, poor moral and hygienic surroundings would not simply menace one generation but would contaminate as well all succeeding generations. Environment, as Dugdale himself put it, "is the ultimate controlling factor in determining careers, placing heredity itself as an organized result of invariable environment." "If these conclusions are correct," he reasoned, in terms of social policy, "then the whole question of the control of crime and pauperism becomes possible, within wide limits, if the necessary training can be made to reach over two or three generations."[15]

By the 1880's and early 1890's, however, this attitude had begun to change. Dugdale's optimistic use of hereditarian arguments to bolster his melioristic position had been transformed into a defensive and hostile emphasis on the deterministic aspects of heredity. But a few short decades after Dugdale's work, many students of heredity were calling for the sterilization of the unfit—and no longer with enthusiasm for environmental reform. And it must be recalled that such environmental reform was still logically implied; almost without exception physicians and biologists in the 1890's still assumed that at least some pathological conditions exerted a deleterious influence on heredity. It was not until well into the first decade of the twentieth century that Weismannism was generally accepted. Thus between 1850, let us say, and 1900, the consensus of science in regard to heredity had not changed; yet social thinkers had clearly moved in this period toward an emphasis upon the deterministic quality of heredity. They had selected those scientific plausibilities which fitted most conveniently into their social needs and presuppositions. Clearly, the nature of this selection and the changed social needs it implies demands explanation. It is equally clear that it is the task of the social historian to explain such change; it is a change, however, which would not be recognized without some consideration of the scientific context

---

15 *The Jukes. A Study in Crime, Pauperism, Disease, and Heredity*, 4th ed. with an intro. by Franklin H. Giddings (New York and London, 1910), p. 66. Despite the abundance of historical treatment accorded the evolution problem, there is, so far as I am aware, no comprehensive study of heredity in nineteenth-century thought.

from which had been drawn the figures who dramatized this social debate.

The social use of scientific concepts is more than arbitrary. Ultimately, the content of the scientific building blocks employed in social thought do have a limiting effect on their employment—though not until the particular ideas utilized acquire a generally agreed-upon definition. Thus, the gradual rejection of the assumption that acquired characteristics could be inherited made inevitable a connection between thoroughgoing hereditarianism and social conservatism.[16] Though it took several decades, the acceptance of the new genetics created a situation in which hereditarianism became the stronghold of social conservatives; the reformists in temperament tended—as the logic of their emotional position dictated—to dissociate behavioral characteristics entirely from hereditary determination. They had no choice, for they too felt hereditary characteristics to be immutable. Yet their motivation was primarily humanitarian, and thus humanitarianism demanded the performance of those melioristic acts which social conservatives derided as useless in the face of implacable heredity.

Science as an Absolute

Attempts to use science to explain and to order social and individual behavior have been significant, not for the manner in which Americans employed science as an idiom, but for the motivation which led them to turn to this new source of authority. In the nineteenth century, science for the first time took a significant place in the value system of many educated Americans. As it did so, the idea of science not only served more frequently as a mode for the communication of social thought but served as well to motivate and sanction social action.

It is not that faith in science was a new development in nineteenth-century America; nor is it true that science was until relatively recent

---

[16] For a well-balanced, recent account of the eugenics movement, see Mark H. Haller, *Eugenics. Hereditarian Attitudes in American Thought* (New Brunswick, N.J., 1963). An illuminating contrast is that made by a comparative reading of Dugdale's *Jukes*, and H. H. Goddard's *The Kallikak Family. A Study in the Heredity of Feeble-Mindedness* (New York, 1912). Nicholas Pastore's *The Nature-Nuture Controversy* (New York, 1949) represents an attempt to correlate social views with attitudes toward heredity in a group of American scientists. For a study emphasizing the importance of Weismannism in the early development of the social sciences in this country, see George W. Stocking, Jr., "Lamarckianism in American Social Science: 1890–1915," *J. Hist. Ideas*, XXIII (1962), 239–56.

times a somewhat distrusted competitor of religion. As all modern studies of seventeenth- and eighteenth-century American intellectual life have shown, science played a very real and in some ways prominent place in the intellectual life of colonial America.[17] Science and Medicine, like Greek verbs and systematic theology, were accepted parts of a learned man's intellectual equipment. Certainly, the study of God's works need imply no scepticism toward their author. Quite the contrary. "Nature," in the conventional rhetoric of formal oratory, "is one volume of God's Bible; and the more *thorough* your acquaintance with God's book of nature, written in *character*, the more clear and consonant will appear its harmonious correspondence with God's book of revelation, written in *letter*." Without an excessive amount of distortion, it can, I think, be said that this was the position of educated Americans from the seventeenth century until the beginning of the twentieth. It was, on the other hand, not until the nineteenth century that science offered to Americans generally a set of values and rationales rivaling, and even exceeding in some minds, those of religion in emotional relevance. Though science, or the idea of science, unquestionably played a liberating role in the social philosophy of the revolutionary generation in America and throughout the nineteenth century for some Americans, it was only gradually in the course of the century that science as an emotionally meaningful value came to be accepted outside of a relatively small intellectual elite. Even in the age of Jefferson, and among the more educated classes, it seems questionable how genuinely "popular" science may have been.[18]

---

[17] It is obvious, of course, that there were very real and in some cases bitter conflicts between "science" and "religion" in American history. It is my feeling, however, that this conflict has been much overemphasized. Even the most zealous in their religious faith, even those most hostile in educated circles to particular aspects of materialism, ordinarily made it clear that they did not intend to attack science as such. An excellent place for the prospective inquirer to begin the study of the history of the relationship between science and religion in America is James Ward Smith and A. Leland Jamison, eds., *Religion in American Life*, Princeton Studies in American Civilization, No. 5; Vol. IV, *A Critical Bibliography of Religion in America* by Nelson R. Burr with editors (Princeton, N.J., 1961). See the section "Theology and Modern Science," pp. 1043–1109. (N.B. This volume is bound as two books with continuous pagination to 1219 pages and separate Index.)

[18] John C. Greene, "Science and the Public in the Age of Jefferson," *Isis*, XXXIX (1958), 13–25. For a study of the place of science in the world of Jefferson and his immediate circle, see Daniel J. Boorstin, *The Lost World of Thomas Jefferson* (Boston, 1960). The breadth of Jefferson's own interests can be sampled in Edwin T. Martin, *Thomas Jefferson: Scientist* (New York, 1952). Brooke Hindle's *The Pursuit of Science in Revolutionary America* (Chapel Hill, 1956) provides many glimpses of attitudes toward science in this period—and implicit contrasts with the attitudes of American scientists a century later.

The advance of secularism in the nineteenth century should be seen, not as a struggle between conflicting ideologies, but as a constantly shifting equilibrium between secular and religious imperatives. It is, in many ways, the similarity rather than the difference between scientific and religious values which made it so natural for many Americans to move fluidly from one intellectual and emotional realm to another. Science, like religion, offered an ideal of selflessness, of truth, of the possibility of spiritual dedication—emotions which in their elevating purity could inspire and motivate. Moral and scientific progress did not seem contradictory but, to the ordinary American, inevitably parallel and complementary. "The three great civilizing influences cô the age," Josiah Strong, spokesman of militant Protestantism, was able casually to state, "are Christianity, the press, and steam, which respectively bring together men's hearts, minds and bodies into more intimate and multiplied relationships."[19]

There was never a pervasive and genuinely divisive discontinuity between scientific and religious imperatives in the minds of educated Americans; the remarkable thing about Darwinism, for example, is not the conflict it inspired but the lack of conflict. The comparatively rapid acceptance of Darwinism by the scientific community mean its acceptance within a relatively short time by most articulate Americans. Educated, servant-employing, churchgoing Americans could not help but ultimately accept knowledge endorsed by men of science, its philosophical implications notwithstanding. How could it be otherwise? The structure of accepted and acceptable knowledge is very much a part of social structure, indeed of social order itself. To reject an idea endorsed by men of learning was to reject, at least partially, order and stability in society. "Whatever is scientifically defended and maintained," admonished Noah Porter, orthodox president of Yale in 1872, "must be scientifically refuted and overthrown." The profoundest scientific inquiry would, he never doubted, serve inevitably to "strengthen and brighten the evidence for Christian faith." Insofar as social discord has revolved about Darwinism in America, it has been largely a class and regional conflict.[20]

---

[19] Josiah Strong, *Our Country. Its Possible Future and its Present Crisis*, rev. ed. (New York, c. 1891), p. 121. See also in this connection, Arthur A. Ekirch, Jr., *The Idea of Progress in America, 1815–60* (New York, 1951), especially chap. iv, "The Advancing Faith in Science."

[20] Introduction, *Half-Hours with Modern Scientists. Lectures and Essays by Prof. Huxley, Barker, Sterling, Cope and Tyndall. First Series* (New Haven, 1872), x–xi. It would seem apparent that one of the reasons for the time lag between the publication of the *Origin* and *Descent* and the most egregious aspects

Students of American social and intellectual history will in many cases find it more profitable not to think in terms of a necessary conflict between religion and science but to describe and understand the intricate symbiosis which they maintained. He will not want for subjects to investigate.

Just as naturalists and physical scientists assumed that their researchers illuminated the glory of God in his works, so, for example, did the physician assume that there could be no conflict between his findings and those of morality. In a period of changing values, this simultaneous appeal to both reference areas was supplementary, not contradictory. The human body was unquestionably a thing both material and divine, and offenses either physical or moral were punished with disease. Drinking, overeating, sexual excess all carried with them inevitable retribution—not because the Lord deigned to intercede in mortal affairs but because He had created man's body so that infringement of God's moral law meant at the same time infringing the laws of physiology. When the lecher failed to heed the Seventh Commandment, he at the same time ignored those commandments of physiology which promised syphilis or insanity as the price of his dissipations. Moralism thus drew upon the prestige of science, while medicine flourished in the assurance that its findings inevitably supported the dictates of morality.[21]

Nowhere was this more striking than in the arguments for temperance reform. As early as the 1820's and 1830's, temperance advocates used medical and statistical data to support their cause. Benjamin Rush had, a generation earlier, phrased a plea for temperance in scientific terms, but his was an appeal to the humanitarianism of the educated. In the 1820's, however, the nation's growing evangelicalism broadened and democratized the temperance cause. Yet these pious reformers saw no inconsistency in employing temporal arguments in their efforts to hasten the millennium. They believed, indeed, that addiction to alcohol was a consequence of both moral and physio-

---

of the evolution controversy lay in the decades necessary for these new ideas to become better-known outside of opinion-forming urban centers. Though many educated Americans did have their reservations, it is clear that by the late 1870's and early 1880's, they—and their children, certainly—felt little active hostility toward Darwin and his doctrines. This statement is based primarily but not exclusively on a reading of the obituaries and editorials written at Darwin's death in some forty religious publications (1882). See also Norman Furniss, *The Fundamentalist Controversy. 1918–1931* (New Haven, 1954).

21 For a more detailed study of the peaceful co-existence between moral admonition and medical theory, see Charles E. Rosenberg, *The Cholera Years: The United States in 1832, 1849, and 1866* (Chicago, 1962).

logical factors. Alcohol was a material substance with particular physiological properties. The decision to drink, however, was a moral failing, a failure of will. Once habituated, nevertheless, it was almost impossible for the drunkard to return to morality and sobriety without the supernatural strength imparted by conversion and God's saving grace. The ravages of alcohol, the argument continued, deadened man's higher moral centers, making it impossible for him to respond to conscience—even, some implied, to accept the grace of God. (The most zealous refused even to accept alcohol as part of God's natural order. It never occurred in nature, they argued, but was a product of man's depraved ingenuity—not a natural substance but one formed through degradation and decay. The appetite for spirits, it followed, was not part of man's normal physical makeup but itself a symptom of disease, an unnatural craving induced by the effects of the alcohol already consumed.)[22]

Though such appeals by religious reformers to the prestige and data of science were common well before the Civil War, the habit of mind they foreshadowed did not become pervasive until well after mid-century. In the decades after Appomattox, science tended to play an increasingly important role in the minds of generations still inspired by the zeal of an earlier, more specifically religious, earnestness, but unable any longer to accept solutions in traditional religious terms. The absolute of science became increasingly autonomous, increasingly able to motivate and justify social behavior—without acting in concert with specifically religious ideas.

As early as the 1840's and 1850's, for example, sanitation and hygiene had come to be accepted as a necessary auxiliary to reform, either temporal or eternal. The soul, religious reformers assumed, could not be saved while the body it inhabited remained in filth. By the 1870's and 1880's however, the ultimate goal of religious conversion had, in the spectrum of American reform, been relegated to a subordinate role. Sanitation and tenement reform were becoming goods sufficient in themselves. Filth was no longer in essence an external symptom of spiritual decay; it had become a sin in itself,

---

[22] Marcus Cross, *The Mirror of Intemperance, and History of the Temperance Reform* (Philadelphia, 1850), p. 18; American Temperance Society, *Permanent Temperance Documents* (Boston, 1835), p. 1. The latter publication provides a convenient compendium of temperance arguments. The "scientific" history of the temperance movement has yet to be written. For references to twentieth-century materials, see Bartlett C. Jones, "Prohibition and Eugenics 1920–1933," and "A Prohibition Problem: Liquor as Medicine 1920–1933," *J. History Med.*, XVIII (1963), 158–72, 353–69.

irredeemable without cleanliness. Yet the zeal which inspired many reformers to improve tenement conditions and abolish sweatshops clearly reflected the emotional heritage of an earlier generation. Though, perhaps, phrased in the measured terms of empirical analysis, proposals for reform in late nineteenth-century America were often suffused by a vision of transcendent moral benefits. Eugenical sterilization, for example, in the mind of one enthusiast was not simply a means of reducing criminality and mental retardation. It would rid man of all "the ills which flesh is heir to." They would "vanish with the mists of its night of suffering and sorrow, dissatisfaction and jealous rage, before the glorious dawn of its millennial day of comfort, hope, peace, and promise." "Social Science," an undergraduate orator announced in the mid-1880's "is the Healer, the life-thrilled Messianic Healer of the human race. It is the herold on the misty mountaintop, proclaiming, through all this burdened earth, that THE KINGDOM OF MAN IS AT HAND."[23] And, it will be recalled, that this is the generation of college students which provided so much of the leadership for that political movement we call progressive.

The faith of many progressives in science was a real one. But it was more than an allegiance to a program of specific measures scientifically determined. It was a faith in science and the scientist as a kind of *deus ex machina*, as a means of righting the worst of an industrial society's inequities without calling into question the essential structure of this society. Expertise, efficiency, disinterested inquiry were the means by which social injustice might be approached—not as an indictment of American society as a whole, but as a series of specific solvable problems. Thus conceived, reform could proceed by limited, manageable steps. The remedies for social dysfunction proposed by science had, moreover, qualities which assured for them the approval of a good proportion of educated Americans. Those reform measures which could be presented as the product of disinterested inquiry benefited not only from the uncritical faith of Americans in the procedures of science but as well from their belief that such proposals were untinged with narrow and sordid partisanship, unwarped by the ideology of the political extremist.

---

[23] The first quotation is from Henry M. Boies, *Prisoners and Paupers: A Study of the Abnormal Increase of Criminals, and the Burden of Pauperism in the United States* (New York, 1893), p. 291; the second is from Florence T. Griswold, "The Social Problem," *The Badger* (Madison, Wis.), IV (June 13, 1885), 201–3. Student newspapers and magazines, like the University of Wisconsin *Badger* just cited, provide invaluable and little-used sources for social and intellectual history.

These are optimistic and inspiriting attitudes. Believing in science and its essential neutrality as they did, it was natural that some reformers at least should find in this faith emotional assurance of their unselfish and necessarily righteous course.[24] The schematic similarity between science in progressive America and religious faith in the reformist currents of an earlier day seems clear enough. It must be noted, however, that the appeal of science as an absolute was limited largely to the educated, to the middle-class elite group which played so prominent a role in many areas of American politics in this period. Science did not appeal with the same cogency to the urban lower class or, with some exceptions, to the uneducated generally. Scientific absolutes, with their self-consciously moral quality, appealed as little to an Irish longshoreman in 1910 as the pietistic dogmas which justified reform in ante-Bellum America would have appealed to his grandfather.

Scientists' Values and Attitudes

The use of science as an idiom of social thought and its place as a transcendent motivating value are both pervasive. This is not true of our third relationship between science and American society, that between social values generally and those of the scientific community. This subrealm of society at large, created by a shared vocation, accepts a mosaic of values and attitudes in some ways distinct from those of other social groups. In this distinctiveness they have added an element of diversity to the sum of group and individual attitudes and values which make up American social thought. The intellectual and emotional guidelines of the scientific disciplines have, moreover, played an indispensable role in the creation of modern America.[25]

One can, I think, mark the beginning of modern academic science in the United States at that moment when American investigators

---

[24] For a case study of science in the progressive political environment, see Samuel P. Hayes, *Conservation and the Gospel of Efficiency. The Progressive Conservation Movement, 1890–1920* (Cambridge, Mass., 1959). Hay's emphasis is somewhat different from that which I have suggested.

[25] Many of these values are peculiar, not to science as a broad enterprise, but to particular disciplines. It is for this reason that scientific development is often best approached in terms, not of particular men and institutions, but of individual disciplines; it is the discipline which defines the scientist's problems and provides the tools and techniques with which he approaches his research tasks. Few histories of particular scientific disciplines in America have been written with these considerations in mind. Useful exceptions are Daniel H. Calhoun, *The American Civil Engineer: Origins and Conflicts* (Cambridge, Mass., 1960), and Frank M. Albrecht, "The New Psychology in America. 1880–1895" (unpublished dissertation, The Johns Hopkins University, 1960).

began to care more for the approval and esteem of their disciplinary colleagues than they did for the general standards of success in the society which surrounded them. All students of American intellectual history are aware that the decades between 1850 and 1880 saw Americans in a number of the sciences beginning to accept these values. All students realize, as well, that this process was connected with the experience of scores of Americans at European universities (and with other, less affluent or fortunate, Americans, the image at least of these universities). It was not simply scientific data and laboratory techniques which were transferred, but those values and attitudes which make the life of science seem important and define the way it should be lived.[26] Once he had accepted the values of the world of academic science, the American scholar could measure achievement only in these terms. And success, in this world, meant acceptance as a creative scholar by one's disciplinary peers. Concretely, this demanded the publication of books and articles and the research support which could alone make this publication possible. And the formulation of one's aspiration in terms of research, in terms of adding to the fund of man's knowledge is an emotionally fulfilling goal. It did not seem sordid, as the businessman's mundane quest, but selfless, indeed spiritual, inasmuch as the scientist's role involved rejection of the compromising standards by which success was ordinarily judged in American society. As an absolute good, the cause of abstract research justified, even encouraged, any steps which could be seen as attempts to further scientific investigation—a cause transcending mere personal ambition.

In studying the history of the agricultural experiment station movement in this country, for example, it has become surprisingly clear that the creation of these institutions was peculiarly a product of the training and ideas of a handful of American chemists educated in Germany in the mid-1850's. These men might travel from Göttingen

---

[26] A recent exception is Thomas N. Bonner's *American Doctors and German Universities: A Chapter in International Intellectual Relations 1870–1914* (Lincoln, Nebr., 1963). There are, of course, many treatments of particular aspects of the American experience in Europe in biographies and the journal literature. Cf. Daniel B. Shumway, "The American Students of the University of Göttingen," *German-American Annals*, VIII (1910), 171–252; George Rosen, "Carl Ludwig and his American Students," *Bull. Hist. Med.*, IV (1936), 609–50. The biographies of many scientists trained in Europe contain excellent accounts of their student days. A good example of the genre is G. Stanley Hall's *Life and Confessions of a Psychologist* (New York and London, 1923). An excellent general survey, though written from a somewhat different point of view, is Walter P. Metzger's *Academic Freedom in the Age of the University* (New York, 1961), chap. iii, "The German Influence," pp. 93–138.

to Leipzig, to Heidelberg, but wherever they were, they formed an American colony, a tightly knit group in which ideas, friendships, and values were tenaciously preserved. Two of these students, companions at Göttingen, were Evan Pugh and Samuel William Johnson. Upon his return to the United States, Pugh guided the development of Pennsylvania's agricultural college, in the years before his premature death, into a model for other such institutions. Johnson returned to New Haven, an eventual professorship at Yale's Sheffield Scientific School, and unquestioned leadership in the establishment of America's first agricultural experiment stations. Both pioneered in the creation of a demand for advanced research and teaching in the United States. Their German teachers, as Pugh put it, gave us "a contempt for that superficial smattering of everything without even an idea of what thoroughness is in anything which is too characteristic of our American system of education." A scholar's true vocation was not to disseminate knowledge, but to add to it. Once exposed to the laboratories of Liebig and Wöhler, these young men could no longer applaud as laudable the vague groupings of American science. Popular or democratic science was a contradiction in terms:[27]

> When it becomes so popular as to be understood by a promiscuous audience, who have never been trained in the classroom by the study of its abstractions, it loses that scientific *essence* from which it derives its value, and is therefore no longer science, but simply . . . so much worthless "*clap-trap*."

The letters of these young chemists and their friends wrote after returning to the United States were filled with wistful nostalgia for their "*alte Heimat*" in Göttingen, sprinkled with amusingly gratuitous German phrases and puns and a pervading frustration at the limitations placed by American conditions upon their desire for achievement as scientists. They wanted time for research and funds to support it; they needed students to help in their work; they sought leisure in which to write the books and articles which could alone win the respect of their disciplinary peers. It is hardly surprising to learn that

---

[27] The first quotation is from Evan Pugh to S. W. Johnson, Nov. 18, 1861, "Pugh Papers," Pennsylvania State University; the second is from Pugh, *Address to the Cumberland County Agricultural Society* (Carlisle, Pa., 1860), p. 24. Representative letters of the Göttingen circle have also been published in: Elizabeth A. Osborne, *From the Letter-Files of S. W. Johnson* (New Haven, 1913) and C. A. Browne, "European laboratory experiences of an early American agricultural chemist—Dr. Evan Pugh (1828–1864), *J. Chem. Educ.*, VII (1930), 499–517.

these enterprising young Americans began as soon as they returned home to write memorials, to cultivate politicians, and to seize every possible opportunity in which to spread the gospel of research. Nor is it surprising that they began to instill in their students a reverence for original investigation and a contempt for American conditions. For to accept these conditions was to deny the values which ruled the world of international science. "I can never adjust myself to my surroundings here," an unhappy Göttingen graduate wrote from the rural Kentucky academy where he taught, "to do so would be to proclaim my stay in Europe a failure."[28]

Such desires acted as a catalyst not only in the creation of facilities for agricultural research but in the reshaping of American higher education generally. Innovation in scientific education must not be thought of simply in terms of farsighted reformers struggling to introduce electives and graduate programs; it must be seen as well in terms of young scholars attempting to create an environment in which they could find achievement within their own discipline. These working scientists provided the motivation and specific knowledge necessary to crystallize in institutional form the amorphous enthusiasm of Americans for science and the progress it seemed to imply. College administrators soon found that they could hire and keep such young men only if they accepted at least some of the young men's goals. Without research facilities, for example, and with a heavy teaching schedule, no academic position could attract the most eligible candidates. In 1889, for example, President James K. Patterson of the University of Kentucky wrote to T. H. Morgan, a young Kentuckian studying at the The Johns Hopkins University, offering him a position as professor of natural history. Though refusal would involve financial hardship, Morgan could not accept the position. "Today," he wrote in explanation, "a man is known in his own field by his original work —& this takes both time & energy—& now to give up one's strength to the classroom would leave little or no opportunity for original work."[29]

---

[28] W. B. Smith to Stephen M. Babcock, Nov. 23, 1879, "Babcock Papers," State Historical Society of Wisconsin.

[29] Morgan to James K. Patterson, June 13, 1889, "Patterson Papers," University of Kentucky Educational Archives. It is hardly surprising that many American scholars were beginning to argue that professional standing, rather than moral or other personal criteria, should be the deciding factor in the hiring of faculty; cf. F. W. Clarke, "The appointment of college officers," *Popular Sc. Month.*, XXI (1882), 173–74.

That Morgan was to become a Nobel laureate merely dramatizes the personal decision made by many Americans of his generation. As these scholars achieved status within their chosen field, and as it became increasingly difficult to ignore such criteria in employment, these young men became candidates for the leading chairs in American universities. Once appointed, they utilized these strategic positions to help create an academic environment suitable for professional achievement. And this environment included, of course, graduate training programs, freedom of research and teaching, all those idealized standards behind which professors have gathered and which have played so great a role in the creation of modern higher education.

And of society as well, for the establishment of academic science in this country was a necessary step in the economic and technological development of modern America. American enterprise and the North American continent's natural resources had, by mid-nineteenth century, created a complex and, in some ways technologically sophisticated economy. As the history of the electricity industry, for example, was to show, however, progress beyond this steam and iron technology could occur only with the help of academic science.[30] This was a lesson which German technological success had taught not only to scientists but to many educated and articulate Americans. The only way, however, in which the scientific disciplines could establish themselves in this country was through the antecedent creation of a dynamic group of would-be scholars, enthusiastic in their motivation, secure in their righteousness, and decided in their knowledge.

Society's Values and Attitudes

The relationship between society and the scientific community it supports is, however, no unilateral one. Just as the creation of new reference groups in the scientific disciplines meant the creation of a novel strain in American social thought, so American thought and values have and still do effect the scientist in his intellectual and institutional life. This is the final relationship between American science and social thought which I will discuss. The lines of force created by the needs and attitudes of society at large have had throughout American history a significant influence upon American

---

[30] This is clear, for example, in career of that dramatically transitional figure Thomas Edison; as early as the 1870's, he was calling upon the aid of academically trained associates. Matthew Josephson, *Edison* (New York, 1959); Harold C. Passer, *The Electrical Manufacturers, 1875–1900* (Cambridge, Mass., 1953).

scientific development, first preparing a ground in which science could ultimately flourish, then dictating patterns of research support and —at times—influencing the scientist as he attempted to evaluate and explain his research findings.

Though abstract science and the institutions which foster it did not flourish in ante-Bellum America, a social climate favorable to its ultimate growth was created. Science was, on the whole, unchallenged by religion, encouraged by a vigorous faith in the efficacy of scientific means, and reinforced by a romantic interest in the things of nature. Americans could view science as an admirable, even socially prestigious, avocation—if not as a practical vocation. Science clubs and botanical and mineralogical trips sponsored by academies and secondary schools all helped to provide young men and even young ladies with a sedate interest in science and left in the minds of a few an inspiration sufficient to encourage the devotion of later years to its pursuit.

Despite these early displays of enthusiasm that Americans willingly accorded to the theoretical virtues of science, they didn't until relatively recently, encourage its academic practitioners. Though perhaps overemphasized, there is at least some truth in the commonly accepted view of a materialistic, success-driven American, willing to tolerate a roseate view of science in the abstract or a zealous enthusiasm for science in the guise of technology, but hostile to anything which seemed merely idle speculation. Only gradually and in circumscribed areas did Americans show themselves willing to support abstract investigation. The first areas to be supported, of course, were those which promised immediate and practical compensation. State geological surveys, for example, were created throughout the Union and, in some cases, generously maintained a generation before the Civil War.[31] (As might have been expected, there was often bitter misunderstanding between the legislators who had paid, they believed, for practical results and the scientists in whose charge the surveys had necessarily to be placed. Their system of values was not always

---

[31] Cf. Walter B. Hendrickson, "Nineteenth-Century State Geological Surveys: Early Government Support of Science," *Isis*, LII (1961), 357–71. Even during wartime, a social context in which modern nations must and have supported science and technology, the place of science and the scientist is determined by preexisting popular assumptions. The persistent faith of Americans, for example, in the ingenuity of the isolated inventor was somewhat justified in the Civil War, but clearly misplaced during World War I. Nathan Reingold, "Science in the Civil War. The Permanent Commission of the Navy Department," *Isis*, XXXXIX (1958), 307–18.

identical with that of state representatives.) But the desire for economic gain was not, of course, the only factor influencing the pattern of research support in nineteenth-century America.

Why, turning to another example of the influence of social attitudes upon scientific development, did American agricultural science receive such early and generous support from government? One reason, of course, was the vulnerable position of agriculture in an increasingly competitive world market. Even more important was the political power of rural areas and the status of the farmer in the nation's formal ideology. Like science itself, agriculture assumed a neutral and benevolent cast in our traditional mythology. It was peculiarly virtuous and deserving of support; legislation in support of the yeoman's interests was not class legislation, for his interests were not class but national interests. It is clear, as well, that at least some congressmen could assuage their constitutional qualms in voting scientific support for agriculture with the conviction, possibly even sincere, that the infusion of science and systematized knowledge into his workaday concerns would improve the farmer's low social status. (In reality, if not in theory.) Agriculture might, it seemed, become a learned profession. It is these oddly assorted ideas which America's first generation of European-trained academic entrepreneurs were able to turn to account in their campaign for government support of scientific research. (First, through state governments; then, through the national Bureau of Agriculture; finally, in 1887 and 1906, by direct federal grants in the Hatch and Adams Acts.[32]) Thus, the future of the biological sciences in America was materially affected by the peculiar place of agriculture in America's social mythology; a not inconsiderable portion of the pioneer generation among American geneticists, bacteriologists, and biochemists, received their research training in laboratories supported with funds appropriated in the hope of finding solutions for the economic problems of American agriculture.

Social ideas and values may have an even more intimate role in the internal life of science. These ideas and values have not only helped dictate the problems which the scientist should work at but have, in some cases, affected as well the answers which he has formulated. The more closely related to social problems, the more likely is a scientific field to be influenced by society's ever present demands.

---

[32] For a case study of the passage of the Adams Act and the role of academic leaders in its passage, see Charles E. Rosenberg, "The Adams Act: Politics and the Cause of Scientific Research," *Agricultural History*, XXXVIII (1964), 3–12.

(And those sciences, the behavioral and biological, which still seem difficult of reduction to mathematical terms and controlled experimental situations, are those closest to human needs and interests.) Human genetics, for example, was slow in becoming established, not simply because of the difficulty of working with the human organism, but because of the imperative demands made by society for the answer to social problems. The gauche solutions so readily provided by eugenicists early in this century discredited the field among academic biologists and may well have retarded less spectacular work in this area.[33]

But this is not true of genetics alone. At about the same time that some of the earlier and more enthusiastic of the Mendelians were establishing the new science of eugenics, eminent nutritionists had come to argue that energy requirements were the key factor in determining a correct human die. Prior to the 1890's, it had been generally believed that a ration sufficient for man or experimental animals could be caculated in terms of a balance between fats, carbohydrates, and proteins (plus appropriate inorganic salts). At the end of the nineteenth century, however, scientists began to add a new and centrally important factor to the traditional equation—energy as measured by the calorie.

The vogue of the calorie resulted from a number of different factors, one of them being a concern for the poor and their physical well-being. Metabolic studies seemed to show that the worker should spend his food allowance on starches and carbohydrates, since these provided the cheapest sources of calories. Meat and fresh vegetables were—calorie for calorie, scientist's believed—far more expensive, and their place in the diet might well be curtailed. Thus, the diet of the poor could be improved without adding at all to their monetary income. (Studies in the first decade of this century seemed, moreover, to show that protein requirements were greatly overestimated; a diet low in protein seemed indeed to be far healthier than one high in proteins.) Here was a concept equally attractive to legislators, to philanthropists, to newspapermen, and to ambitious and public-spirited scientists. This research seemed rigidly scientific and yet eminently practical and humanitarian. It is hardly surprising that metabolic studies, with their immediate human implications, found comparatively generous support in a generation still sparing in its

---

[33] Cf. Haller, *Eugenics*; L. C. Dunn, "Cross Currents in the History of Human Genetics," *Am. J. Human Genetics*, **XIV** (1962), 1–13.

support of abstract physiological research; nor is it surprising that scientists were perhaps overenthusiastic in their acceptance of the calorimeter and its results.[34] That many of the leaders in this research were slow in accepting newer problems and methods in nutrition research was equally to be expected.

This discussion has become complex and perhaps tangled in a series of somewhat arbitrary illustrations. Perhaps, indeed, these illustrations have obscured the general outline of this discussion: that there is a rich and complex relationship between science and American social thought. It is a relationship of great significance and one which has, moreover, had comparatively little attention paid it by American historians. The bare statement that such a relationship exists is no longer a meaningful one; it is the task of historians to explore specific instances and define the texture of specific relationships. There is, I think, an aesthetic of complexity in history. Any way in which seemingly disparate developments can be brought together, any way in which the juxtaposition of unfamiliar materials can shed light on the interdependence of human life and thought is, in itself, inherently laudable. Certainly, the interaction between science and social thought is one such relationship.

[34] A useful introduction to this calorimeter work, especially valuable because written by a contemporary and leader in the field, is: Graham Lusk, *The Elements of the Science of Nutrition* (Philadelphia and London, 1909), especially pp. 17–45. The basic source for the history of American work in this field is the papers of W. O. Atwater, scientific and administrative leader in these metabolic studies. They have been microfilmed by the Cornell University Collection of Regional History. For the broad context of nutrition research, see E. V. McCollum, *A History of Nutrition. The Sequence of Ideas in Nutrition Investigations* (Boston, 1957), and Richard O. Cummings, *The American and his Food. A History of Food Habits in the United States* (Chicago, 1941), pp. 111–137.

Science and Higher Education

Charles Weiner*

The development of the relationship between science and higher education in the United States is an essential part of the history of education and of American social and intellectual history in general. An understanding of this relationship illuminates the changing role of science, since the college and the university have been the main arenas of scientific change. From colonial days on, science has been an integral part of higher education in the United States, although its relative position has varied with changes in the content and social organization of science as well as with changes in education. Thus, as educators changed their views on the cultural role of science, they had to revise its educational role; as science became more specialized and more professional, scientists demanded a new kind of relationship to higher education. Industry, recognizing the increasing need for technical and scientific personnel, and government, relying more on scientists in decision making and in the operations of its agencies, both sought help from institutions of higher education and subsequently assumed more responsibility for the fostering of science in education.

An important tension in higher education stems from the nature of science itself. On the one hand, science is a dogma—a body of knowledge contained in treatises and textbooks and taught in science classrooms. On the other hand, science is an activity directed at altering and increasing that very body of knowledge. Thus, those teachers of science who are also engaged in science research have been faced

* CHARLES WEINER, Director of the Center for History and Philosophy of Physics at the American Institute of Physics, heads the Institute's Project on the History of Recent Physics in the United States. He also teaches a graduate course in the history of science at the Polytechnic Institute of Brooklyn. Dr. Weiner received an M.A. and Ph.D. in the history of science and a B.S. in metallurgy from the Case Institute of Technology. He has written on historical and scientific subjects and is presently completing a new edition of Joseph Henry's *Scientific Writings* to be published by the Smithsonian Institution.

with the problem of achieving a balance between the demands of teaching and the demands of research. This problem has been of great importance in the past century, because institutions of higher education have become responsible for the advancement, as well as the diffusion, of science.

From the viewpoint of both the history of education and the history of science, the expression "science and higher education" is not entirely satisfactory, since each of its component terms involves the other. But it is more appropriate than "academic science," which means an institutional base for scientific research and not the reciprocal relationships between science and higher education in general. This essay will examine the place of science in higher education and the processes by which its place has been changed.

COLLEGES AND ACADEMIES

In the colleges of eighteenth-century America, science was one of the basic components of a curriculum aimed at building character and teaching mental and moral discipline to a select group of young men who were likely to be the leaders of the future. Science, seen as the study of nature, bolstered religion in the religion-oriented colleges by showing the order, magnificence, and beauty of the natural world.[1]

All nine of the colonial colleges—Harvard, Yale, New Jersey (Princeton), King's (Columbia), William and Mary, Rhode Island (Brown), Dartmouth, Philadelphia (Pennsylvania), and Queen's (Rutgers)—included natural philosophy in their basic course of study, and professorships in this field had been established at six of the colleges by 1766.[2] Natural philosophy usually covered the general properties of matter, mechanics, pneumatics, hydrostatics, optics, electricity, magnetism, and astronomy. Along with ethics, metaphysics, and mathematics, it supplemented the studies in Latin, Greek, Hebrew, logic, and rhetoric which were the foundation of the curriculum. This was the basic course of study of the English universities on which the colonial colleges were modeled.[3]

---

[1] See Brook Hindle, *The Pursuit of Science in Revolutionary America* (Chapel Hill, 1956), pp. 84–86.

[2] Frederick Rudolph, *The American College and University* (New York, 1962), p. 30. This book provides an excellent comprehensive survey of the history of higher education in America and places major developments in science education in an overall historical context.

[3] For a comparison of the curriculum at various colleges see Theodore Hornberger, *Scientific Thought in the American Colleges 1638–1800* (Austin, Texas, 1945). A basic study is Louis Franklin Snow, *The College Curriculum in the United States* (New York, 1907).

Scientific apparatus was available in the colleges for the use of students and professors, and the graduating senior's ability to conjugate Latin verbs was frequently accompanied by a familiarity with scientific instruments.[4] Latin verbs and telescopes were tools that could be used to acquire knowledge, and practice in manipulating them helped to discipline the intellect. Instruction in the content and methods of science was considered by eighteenth-century educators to play a necessary role in preparing young men for the professions, primarily the ministry and the law.

The cultural value of science as an ally to religion guaranteed it a place in the curriculum and provided an academic base for activities that reflected the scientific interests of some of the professors of science. For example, John Winthrop at Harvard, Ezra Stiles at Yale, and William Small at William and Mary, among others, made use of available college facilities and support for experiments and expeditions that contributed to work in astronomy, geophysics, and electricity.[5] The scientific pursuits of these professors reflected growing interest in Newtonian science.

Science, which had entered through the back door, was a flexible component of the curriculum in the last half of the eighteenth century and was increasingly emphasized during this period of social and intellectual upheaval. The study of science both justified and was justified by the view that nature was orderly and rational, and thus capable of being understood. Once understood, nature could be controlled and used for the benefit of man. By the end of the century, the emphasis was on the utility of science and a major argument for increasing the teaching of science was that it could provide the knowledge and skills needed by those who were destined to be charged with managing the temporal affairs of the world. The social, intellectual, political, economic, and geographic environment of post-Revolutionary America all bolstered the desire to understand and utilize nature for the benefit of man.[6]

---

[4] See I. Bernard Cohen, *Some Early Tools of American Science* (Cambridge, Mass., 1950), for the importance of scientific instruments at colonial colleges. Cohen's study did much to revise the view that colonial colleges paid little or no attention to science.

[5] Samuel Eliot Morison, *Three Centuries of Harvard 1636–1936* (Cambridge, Mass., 1936), pp. 80–93; Louis W. McKeehan, *Yale Science: The First Hundred Years, 1701–1801* (New York, 1947); G. W. Ewing, "Early Teaching of Science at the College of William and Mary in Virginia," *Journal of Chemical Education,* XV (1938); Donald Fleming, *Science and Technology in Providence, 1760–1914* (Providence, R.I., 1952).

[6] Rudolph, pp. 40–43.

The movement for democracy and the needs and opportunities in an unexplored and undeveloped nation placed burdens on higher education after the Revolution. Within twenty years, nineteen colleges which are still in existence today were founded, and many of these new institutions, as well as the older ones, introduced "useful" subjects into the curriculum.[7] French, economics, history, geography, surveying, navigation, chemistry, natural history—these were the studies proposed by men who were attempting to cope with a new political and physical environment. In some cases, proposals for these curriculum changes remained just that, and in other cases, were introduced (with varying degrees of success).[8] However, despite the increasing intrusion of practical science into the course of study, the old curriculum remained intact at most institutions. The most successful improvements in science education in the young Republic appear to have been due more to the efforts of a science teacher with a genuine interest in his subject than to specific curriculum changes or to a generally more enthusiastic attitude towards science.[9]

In the first half of the nineteenth century, territorial expansion, population growth, industrialization, and urbanization proceeded at an extremely rapid pace in an environment of democratic optimism accompanying the "rise of the common man." Technology played an increasingly important role in national life during this period because of the technical problems involved in exploration, transportation, communication, manufacturing, and public health.

In the three decades after the War of 1812, public interest in technology was excited by the widespread applications of steam power, the rapid growth of canal and rail networks, the success of the electromagnetic telegraph, and the introduction of laborsaving machinery. National pride and democratic optimism also played an important role in building popular interest in, and enthusiasm for, the new technology.[10] The bountiful resources of the American continent promised abundance for all, and technology was viewed as the means of pro-

---

[7] *Ibid.*, pp. 35–36.

[8] Very few of Jefferson's proposals for curriculum changes at William and Mary were introduced. At Columbia, Union, and the University of North Carolina "practical" subjects were introduced.

[9] Benjamin Silliman, for example, joined the Yale faculty in 1802 as professor of chemistry and natural history and his lectures created considerable interest in science, attracting students to study chemistry at Yale.

[10] An excellent study of contemporary attitudes is Hugo A. Meier, "Technology and Democracy, 1800–1860," *Mississippi Valley Historical Review*, XLIII, (March 1957), pp. 618–40.

viding access to this abundance.[11] This spirit was reflected in the remarks of leading public figures, which elevated technology to a national virtue.[12] The common man's interest in science and technology, as well as his desire for self-improvement, was evident in the tremendous popularity of public lectures on chemistry, steam engines, geology, and astronomy. The new societies "for the diffusion of useful knowledge," the growing number of lyceums (3,000 in 1835) and libraries dealt to a large extent with science and its applications, and an eager public freely partook of their offerings. This method of popular science education was cheap, quick, and available in contrast to the traditional academic approach to science.[13]

What effects did these developments have in the field of higher education? Three main factors are involved in the answer to this question: the desire for practical knowledge on the part of the common man; the need for people specially trained in science and technology; and the development of a national scientific community.

The sharp increase in the number of colleges during this period did not substantially affect the amount and level of science in the curriculum. Since they were often founded to satisfy the popular desire to extend college opportunities or as the result of interdenominational rivalry, many of the schools had poorly trained faculties and log cabin facilities. In most of them the prescribed classical curriculum predominated.

Recognition of the lag resulting from the lack of adjustment to changing practical demands and social needs throughout the era stimulated some colleges to offer new courses in chemistry, geology, and engineering subjects. Civil engineering courses, for example, began to appear in college catalogs after the completion of the Erie Canal in 1825.[14] Such occasional courses served as important precedents for later large-scale curriculum revisions.

---

[11] David Potter, *People of Plenty: Economic Abundance and the American Character* (Chicago, 1954).

[12] Levi Woodbury, who served as Secretary of the Treasury and was a promoter of applied science, expressed his views on the subject in his *Annual Address before the National Institute* (Washington, D.C., 1845). Thomas Ewbank's plea for a form of technocracy is expressed in his *Report of the Commissioner of the Patents for 1852* (Washington, D.C., 1853) and in his *The World a Workshop* (New York, 1855). See also Harvard professor Jacob Bigelow, *Elements of Technology* (Boston, 1829); and Zachariah Allen, *The Science of Mechanics* (Providence, 1829).

[13] For a full discussion of the popularization of knowledge see Merle Curti, *The Growth of American Thought*, 3rd ed. (New York, 1964), pp. 335–57.

[14] See Daniel H. Calhoun, *The American Civil Engineer* (Cambridge, Mass., 1960), p. 46.

Perhaps more important were the content revisions in the established science courses. The extent of such revision often depended on the degree of sectarian control of the school as well as the scientific competence of the professor. Although the classical curriculum remained intact, "internal" revisions of subject matter did much to improve science teaching by updating and raising the level of the standard natural philosophy course.[15]

Academies and mechanics institutes and a few special schools filled the gap between the need for technical skills and the slow response of the colleges. The number of academies increased rapidly to 6,000 by 1850.[16] These low-cost institutions often supplemented the classical curriculum with modern languages and basic science and engineering courses. The Franklin Institute, founded in Philadelphia in 1825, was the best of the many mechanics institutes that had been formed to give mechanics and apprentices a greater understanding of applied science. The preceding year, the Rensselaer School had been established in Troy, New York, offering a one-year course of specialized training in applied science. This school introduced the laboratory method of scientific instruction in chemistry and physics, and students were directly involved in experiments and in field work. An engineering curriculum was set up in the 1830's, and the first engineering degree was granted in 1835. Yet the enrollment at the Rensselaer School averaged only seventy students a year in the 1840's.[17] More important during this period, as a source of trained technical personnel, was the United States Military Academy at West Point, where up-to-date science and mathematics constituted a major part of the curriculum which was designed to train military engineers.[18] The graduates of West Point were in great demand for the various civilian canal-building projects of the 1830's.

During the 1840's, the colleges themselves began to feel greater pressure to bring their courses of study into line with the spirit of the times. President Wayland of Brown and President Everett of Harvard called for elective courses and closer connection of college science

---

[15] Joseph Henry's revision of the natural philosophy course at Princeton will be discussed later in this essay.

[16] Curti, p. 351.

[17] Palmer C. Ricketts, *History of the Rensselaer Polytechnic Institute 1824–1934*, 3rd ed. (New York, 1934), p. 91; Ethel M. McAllister, *Amos Eaton: Scientist and Educator* (Philadelphia, 1941).

[18] Sidney Forman, *West Point: A History of the United States Military Academy* (New York, 1950), pp. 23–60.

courses to the needs of the nation.[19] They found support among the science professors, whose number had increased along with the number of colleges. Almost all of the men who were involved in research were professors of science in the nation's colleges. They were publishing the results of their research in a number of scientific journals established after 1815, as well as writing popular scientific texts and giving public lectures. Many of them, as individuals or through scientific societies, also served as advisors to government and industry. American scientists were becoming more specialized and professional and felt the need for recognition of their new status within the colleges.[20]

The growing national appreciation of the importance of applied science was given effective expression in the late 1840's, when both Harvard and Yale took the first steps towards establishing scientific schools as separate divisions of the university. Abbot Lawrence gave $50,000 for the establishment of an undergraduate school at Harvard that would emphasize engineering. But under the leadership of the eminent zoologist Louis Agassiz, the Lawrence Scientific School emphasized biological sciences instead of engineering.[21] At the same time, Yale set up a school of science that at first emphasized applied chemistry, adding civil engineering later, and becoming the Sheffield Scientific School in 1860 through a $100,000 gift from Joseph Sheffield.[22] These special schools had only a three-year course of study and were not integrated into the rest of the university for many years.

Despite their separate and unequal status, the scientific schools at Harvard and Yale marked the beginning of a trend that culminated in full acceptance of the college's role in the training of scientists and engineers. In the 1850's, several agricultural and technical schools were established, and some of the older colleges awarded bachelor of science degrees and engineering degrees. In the 1860's, vocational and technological training gained an assured position in college curricula with the passage of the Morrill Federal Land-Grant Act and

---

[19] Francis Wayland, *Thoughts on the Present Collegiate System in the United States* (Boston, 1842); for Everett see Richard J. Storr, *The Beginnings of Graduate Education in America* (Chicago, 1953), pp. 46–48.

[20] For an excellent study of scientific thought in America during the period, including biographical and bibliographical sketches of 55 leading scientists, see George Harrison Daniels, Jr., "Baconian Science in America, 1815–1845," Ph.D. dissertation, State University of Iowa, 1963.

[21] Morison, p. 279; Edward Lurie, *Louis Agassiz: A Life in Science* (Chicago, 1960), pp. 135–40.

[22] Rudolph, p. 232; Russell H. Chittenden, *History of the Sheffield Scientific School of Yale University 1846–1922* (New Haven, 1928).

the founding of Massachusetts Institute of Technology and Cornell University. Within the decade, twenty-five institutions added scientific departments.[23] During this period, scientists created new institutional forms to fill the needs of the growing professionalism in science. They established new scientific journals and shaped the form and direction of the Smithsonian Institution from its founding in 1846, organized the American Association for the Advancement of Science in 1848, and in 1863, the National Academy of Sciences. Thus, the development of facilities for scientific education encouraged the increased professionalization of science, which included the establishment of qualification and performance standards and a recognition of the need for specialized training for those engaged in scientific work.

The many developments in science and science education in the United States from the early 1820's to the early 1870's can be better understood by focusing on the role of the science teacher during this period. An examination of the education and career of Joseph Henry, an outstanding scientist and teacher, clarifies the role of the academies in providing scientific training, the conditions under which science was taught in the colleges, and the relationship between teaching and research. As a teacher of science at the Albany Academy and the College of New Jersey (Princeton) from 1826 to 1847, he earned an international reputation for his investigations and discoveries in physics. In later years, he was one of the leaders in the drive for professionalism in science. He organized, headed, and guided the policies of the Smithsonian Institution from its inception in 1846 to his death in 1878, and played a leading role in the American Association for the Advancement of Science and the National Academy of Sciences. In these capacities, and as president of the American Association for the Advancement of Education in 1853, he was concerned with science education on a national scale. Because of Henry's unusual talents, his experiences obviously do not illustrate those of the usual professor of science. However, his career does show some of the major problems in the relationship between science and higher education in the nineteenth century.[24]

Henry managed to acquire a good scientific background at a time when there were no prescribed ways and few opportunities to prepare

[23] Rudolph, pp. 232–33, 247–57.

[24] Sections of the following account of Henry's education and teaching career are included in my article, "Joseph Henry and the Relations Between Teaching and Research," *American Journal of Physics* (in press). For a full biography, see Thomas Coulson, *Joseph Henry: His Life and Work* (Princeton, N.J., 1950).

for a scientific career. He received a rudimentary education in a country school near Albany, New York, and in 1819, when he was twenty-one years old, he resumed his schooling by attending classes at the Albany Academy. Although the Albany Academy was a relatively new school (classes began in 1815), it had high scholastic standards and a curriculum which reflected the scientific interests of its trustees and faculty. Stephen Van Rensselaer, the wealthiest landowner in the state and a well-known patron of science, headed a board of trustees composed of Albany's leading citizens.[25] Dr. T. Romeyn Beck, a leading authority in medical science, was principal of the Academy.[26] Three courses of study were offered during Henry's student days there: English and mathematics, mercantile, and general. The general course was the most comprehensive and included rigorous studies in Latin and Greek as well as chemistry, natural philosophy, and a mathematical program consisting of Euclid's geometry, algebra, trigonometry, mensuration, surveying, navigation, conic sections, and fluxions (calculus).[27] Graduates of the Academy were qualified to transfer to the junior year of college. Describing the curriculum of the 1820's in later years, Henry stated that the Academy "paralleled the course of study at Yale College and was more exacting in its requirements than were many of the smaller colleges."[28]

Even after his student days, Henry continued his association with the Academy, the center of Albany's scientific activities. He learned to handle apparatus by assisting in Dr. Beck's public lectures on chemistry. Henry also became the librarian of the Albany Institute, the local scientific society which met at the Academy. This scientific society was headed by Stephen Van Rensselaer, the leading figure and major financial supporter of the academy-centered scientific circle who has been described as "the first great patron of science in America."[29] Van Rensselaer financed a series of geological surveys made

[25] Arthur J. Weise, *History of the City of Albany* (Albany, 1884), p. 452.

[26] Beck's *Elements of Medical Jurisprudence* (Albany, 1823) soon became a standard work in the field, going through many editions and translations. He was president of the New York Medical Society, 1829–1831, and was a leader in state educational activities.

[27] *Statutes of Albany Academy* (Albany, 1816).

[28] Quoted in *Celebration of the Centennial Anniversary of the Founding of the Albany Academy—May 24, 1913* (Albany, 1914), pp. 18–19.

[29] H. S. van Klooster, "The First Great Patron of Science in America," *New York History*, XXI (1940), 270–83. Van Rensselaer was a regent of the University of the State of New York from 1819 to 1839 and a congressman from 1823 to 1829. In addition to his Albany scientific activities he founded the American Society for the Diffusion of Useful Knowledge, formed in 1836 to promote publication of popular scientific textbooks.

by the well-known botanist, chemist, and geologist, Amos Eaton, and was a leading promoter of science education and of the diffusion of scientific knowledge to the common man. In 1824 he established at Troy one of the first technical schools in the nation. Headed by Eaton, the object of the Rensselaer School was to qualify teachers "for instructing the sons and daughters of farmers and mechanics . . . in the applications of experimental chemistry, philosophy, and natural history to agriculture, the domestic economy, the arts and manufactures."[30] Thus, Henry's formal training was supplemented by informal training through public lectures, books, activities of scientific societies, and contact with scientific educators.

He was about to begin a career in civil engineering in 1826 when he was selected to fill the chair of mathematics and natural philosophy at the Albany Academy. The attraction of a career as a teacher of science, and the implication that his continued association with the Academy and its scientific library and apparatus would give him an opportunity to pursue the experimental work he enjoyed, must have contributed to Henry's decision to accept the post. An academic position was one of the few niches in the occupational structure that provided an opportunity to engage in scientific research.

On May 2, four days after his appointment, Henry left Albany to take part in a unique six-week experiment in science education that helped prepare him for his new teaching duties in the fall. Amos Eaton had hired a boat to transport a party of twenty students and teachers along the canal to Lake Erie for a summer tour of study and field work. The purpose of this floating school of science was to extend the scope of the Rensselaer School and to publicize its teaching method of student participation and demonstration. As the boat made its way along the canal, the group frequently debarked to make a geological survey of the adjacent region, collect specimens, and visit points of interest. The students gained experience by delivering lec-

---

30 S. Van Rensselaer to Rev. Samuel Blatchford, November 5, 1824, quoted in Ethel McAllister, *Amos Eaton: Scientist and Educator* (Philadelphia, 1941), p. 368. The Rensselaer School (now Rensselaer Polytechnic Institute) had close ties with other science-oriented schools in the region. T. R. Beck, principal of the Albany Academy, was vice president of the School from 1824 through 1826 and trustee from 1824 through 1828. Its president from 1829–45 was Reverend Eliphalet Nott who was also president of Union College in nearby Schenectady (*Ibid.*, pp. 395–96). Nott made important inventions in steamboat technology and was responsible for many innovations in science education at Union, the largest college in New York State in the 1820's. See C. Van Santvoord's *Memoirs of Eliphalet Nott* (New York, 1876), pp. 265–67, for an account of Nott's interest in science.

tures on botany, chemistry, and geology to the townspeople who could be gathered to hear them.[31]

Henry's training at the Albany Academy, his "postgraduate" work as a member of Albany's scientific circle, and his participation in new approaches to science education prepared him well for his role as a teacher of science. He was at least as well equipped as most American science professors of the period, most of whom were college educated. The academies were significant in the training and careers of many of these men, because it was there that they were first introduced to science and, after subsequent training, were later employed as science teachers.

As a teacher at the Albany Academy from 1826 to 1832, Henry consistently upgraded the science curriculum, introducing new texts and new courses in mathematics, civil engineering, and electromagnetism, which reflected his own scientific interests as well as the needs of the time. Despite an extremely heavy teaching load and additional responsibilities in Albany's scientific circle, he was able through his position at the Academy to pursue his investigations in basic science. His career as a teacher was soon joined with a career as a scientific researcher, and he successfully combined the two for twenty years. Within a year after he assumed his teaching duties at the Academy, Henry had begun a series of investigations of electromagnetism, including his pioneering work in electromagnetic induction, which added immensely to the knowledge of the subject.

Conditions at the Academy were far from ideal, however. Despite the trustees' generosity with funds for apparatus, Henry's extremely heavy teaching load was not diminished, and he had very little time for research. Space was at a premium in the growing Academy, and he often had to suspend his investigations for want of an adequate work area.

In 1832 Henry was offered the chair of natural philosophy at the College of New Jersey at Princeton.[32] At Princeton he corrected the

---

[31] In addition to Henry and Eaton, the teachers included Dr. Lewis C. Beck, physician, chemist, and science educator. Diaries of two of the participants give details of the trip. Asa Fitch's diary is the basis for Samuel Rezneck's "A Traveling School of Science on the Erie Canal in 1826," *New York History*, XL (1959), 255–69. George W. Clinton's diary was published in *Publications of the Buffalo Historical Society*, XIV (1910), 275–305.

[32] This account of Henry's career at Princeton is based on a study of his unpublished letters, laboratory journals, and his lecture notes and syllabus, as well as the diaries and notebooks of some of his students. Most of these materials are in the Princeton University Library and in the Smithsonian Institution

imbalance between his teaching and research, but he still complained that lack of time to do research and to prepare the results of research for publication were serious handicaps. Yet his research opportunities at Princeton were far better than at the Albany Academy. Within a few years after he arrived on the campus, he began to publish the results of his new investigations, producing more than thirty-five original research publications from 1835 to 1847. This was by no means a paltry contribution to physics, especially since many of the papers were of such importance that they were soon republished in European science journals.

Princeton in the 1840's was, in the words of a former student at the college, "entirely in the hands of the strictest of the 'Old School' Presbyterian theologians. Piety and mathematics rated extravagantly high in the course."[33] Yet, unlike many of the colleges of the day in which chemistry, physics, and astronomy were combined in the required natural philosophy course, these subjects were taught separately to all students by specialists that included Henry, astronomer Stephen Alexander, and botanist and chemist John Torrey.[34] In addition to his regular two-semester courses in physics for seniors, Henry occasionally offered short lecture courses in geology, civil engineering, and architecture, available to the students on a special fee basis. He was an innovator of new educational methods, and an extremely effective teacher who had a warm personal relationship with the students. He invented economical lecture demonstration devices that dramatically illustrated the newest discoveries in physics, and he told other academic scientists throughout the nation how to make and use these instruments.

Henry met his class daily for lectures, recitations, and demonstrations. The students were required to copy the course syllabus and to take notes during the lectures and demonstrations. Every week, Henry examined the notebook of each of the more than sixty students in the class. He did not take any shortcuts in his teaching, despite the fact that they would have given him more time for research. His lectures—reconstructed from his manuscript notes and the notebooks of some of his students—demonstrate that his students were treated

Archives, and my study of them was made possible by permission of these institutions and with financial support from the Case Institute of Technology Research Fund and the National Science Foundation.

[33] Charles Godfrey Leland, *Memoirs* (New York, 1893), p. 84.

[34] Thomas Wertenbaker, *Princeton, 1746–1896* (Princeton, N.J., 1946), pp. 219–24.

to a well-organized, high-level presentation of up-to-date physics. They reflect his awareness of the state of contemporary work and were enriched with his own research.

Henry's combination of teaching and research at Albany and Princeton is an excellent illustration of his attempt to connect the discovery, teaching, and application of science. His experiences also demonstrate how the science curriculum could be revised and improved by a good teacher working within the existing framework. Although his teaching duties, and the seriousness of his approach to them, left him little time for research, he still made first rate contributions to fundamental science. His problems were similar to those of other science professors of the period. Pressures to write textbooks, to give popular lectures, and to advise enthusiastic amateurs were felt by most of the eminent American scientists, and these activities further reduced the time that college professors had available for research.[35]

Our knowledge of the teaching and research accomplishments of American scientists in the nineteenth century is severely limited because of a historiographic tradition that emphasizes the complaints of contemporary scientists that "nothing of significance happened in American science." This view is now being challenged and subjected to closer scrutiny through detailed studies of the careers of individual scientists and their institutions.[36]

UNIVERSITIES AND GRADUATE SCHOOLS

In the second half of the nineteenth century, the increasing complexity of science and specialization of scientists encouraged a self-conscious professionalism with its accompanying institutional apparatus of associations, journals, and standards. These trends, combined with the continued national emphasis on the "democratic utilitarian" role of higher education, led to new attempts to define the place of science in higher education.

The desire to improve science teaching and opportunities for research in the colleges led some of the leading scientists to attempt to

[35] See A. Hunter Dupree, *Asa Gray* (Cambridge, Mass., 1959), pp. 130–31, 212–15.

[36] For a critique of the older historiographic tradition and for suggestions of more productive approaches to the study of the history of science in America, see Edward Lurie, "An Interpretation of Science in the Nineteenth Century: A Study in History and Historiography," *Journal of World History*, VIII (1965), 681–706.

establish a new university at Albany, in the early1850's, where learned men would be brought together to teach advanced science and to do research. In such a university, the study of science would be elevated from the inferior position it occupied in the traditional college where inadequate attention was given to scientific courses within the established curriculum. The new scientific schools at Yale and Harvard would not suffice as models, because they were isolated from their older parent institutions and were slow to develop. The scientists' solution was to consolidate scientific talent in one great national university where the nation's leading scientists would benefit from close association with each other and where the teaching of science would be on a more advanced level than possible elsewhere in the country. This plan for a University of Albany was actively promoted by Harvard scientists Benjamin Peirce, Louis Agassiz, Benjamin A. Gould, Jr., and Josiah D. Whitney, as well as Coast Survey superintendent Alexander D. Bache, chemist Wolcott Gibbs, and Albany geologist James Hall. The project won the support of a large group of scientists and laymen, but was abandoned after it failed to obtain the financial support that had been requested from the New York State legislature. Like many similar attempts to found institutions for graduate training before the Civil War, the proposed scientific university at Albany never became a reality.[37]

Invidious comparisons of the European approaches to science education were offered by American scientists to bolster their criticism of the situation in the United States. In the first half of the nineteenth century, the Ecole Polytechnique had served as a model to some American scientists, who felt that its combined role as a research institution and an educational institution for technical training could be the basis for an American system of scientific and technological education that would serve the needs of democracy, utility, and the advancement of scientific knowledge. In the second half of the century, the German universities, with their emphasis on scholarly research, served as a model to many American educators desirous of developing new institutions in the United States. Many American scientists and educators had gone to Europe for an education and had returned imbued with enthusiasm for the teaching laboratory, the graduate seminar, and the research professor. At the same time, English scientists were also citing German examples to emphasize the need for new forms of scientific education and new sources of support for science

---

[37] Richard J. Storr, *The Beginnings of Graduate Education in America* (Chicago, 1953), pp. 67–74; Lurie, *Louis Agassiz*, pp. 181–82.

in England. However, the ideal of the German university was only one of the many elements that encouraged the development of a more firmly structured place for science in higher education.[38]

The Smithsonian Institution was the first national institution in the United States devoted to "the increase and diffusion of knowledge among men." In 1846 Joseph Henry was selected as the first secretary of the Smithsonian and the following year, he left Princeton to devote the rest of his life to the task of organizing and directing it. The problems of relating scientific research to scientific education still remained to be solved in 1872 when Henry wrote to the British scientist John Tyndall:

> It is only after nearly twenty-five years of struggle and entire devotion to [the Smithsonian Institution] that I have begun to make the country appreciate the difference between the discovery of new truths, and the teaching of old ones; to make apparent the three relations of knowledge, namely, (1) The discovery of new truths; (2) The teaching of scientific principles; and (3) The application of scientific principles to useful purposes in the arts. The 2nd and 3rd of these relations have almost exclusively been recognized and provision made for their advancement. There are however, many wealthy individuals in this country who may be induced to found establishments for investigations either in connection with our older educational institutions or on [a] separate basis.[39]

Six months later, Henry expanded these views in a public address:

> In this country, science is almost exclusively prosecuted by those engaged in the laborious and exhaustive employment of imparting instruction. . . . Those who from a love of truth would pursue it for its own sake are so overworked with the drudgery of elementary teaching, and so poorly supplied with the implements of investigation, that it is not surprising that science has made comparatively *little* advance among us, but that, under existing conditions, it should have made *so much*.[40]

These statements, though somewhat exaggerated, reflect Henry's own experiences and those of many of his colleagues, and suggest that

---

[38] Ricketts, pp. 95–96; Storr, pp. 4–6; Rudolph, pp. 333–34; Everett Mendelsohn, "The Emergence of Science as a Profession in Nineteenth Century Europe," in K. Hill, ed., *The Management of Scientists* (1964), pp. 3–48; "Examination of Prof. Henry by the English Scientific Commission—June 1870," *Smithsonian Miscellaneous Collections*, XVIII, 793–97.

[39] Joseph Henry to John Tyndall, October 22, 1872, Rhees Collection, Henry E. Huntington Library, San Marino, Calif.

[40] Joseph Henry, "On the Importance of the Cultivation of Science," *Popular Science Monthly*, II (April 1873), 646.

although *scientists* had found a "home" in the nation's colleges, *science* itself had not. It is true that in the early 1870's the principles and applications of science were being taught to a wider audience and at a higher level than ever before—and that science courses were increasingly becoming a part of a general liberal education as well as the basis for training in technical fields. But Henry and his colleagues believed that educational institutions should have the responsibility for the *advancement* of science as well as its diffusion. They called for improvements in institutions of higher learning, so that they could provide a properly furnished academic home for science, housing scientists who combined teaching and original research.

Henry and other American scientists felt that the imbalance between teaching and research could be corrected by freely endowed colleges or universities whose faculties consisted of men hired on the basis of their research accomplishments. These professors would be given ample time and facilities for original investigations while limiting their teaching to advanced courses in their specialities. This was a program to be discussed, amended, and implemented by Henry's younger contemporaries, who hammered out new approaches in the state universities and in the science-oriented professional schools.

Important changes were taking place in American science education in the 1870's. The number of engineering schools quadrupled between 1870 and 1872, laboratory work was required in more and more institutions, and science was introduced in a larger number of colleges than ever before. Harvard's new president, chemist Charles W. Eliot, stimulated renewed emphasis on the cultural value of science. Eliot believed that science, with its antidogmatic open-mindedness, could counteract the materialistic tendencies of a business society. The uplifting value of science was also stressed by President James McCosh of Princeton, who was concerned with the need to reconcile science with religion.[41] At the same time, the role of the university in advancing knowledge through original research was being tested in the new Johns Hopkins University, which opened in 1876 under the leadership of Daniel Coit Gilman, a graduate of Yale's scientific school. The practical, cultural, and professional approaches to science education were well represented in the 1870's.

Yet, not until the 1890's did the schools of applied science start to attract large numbers of students, the academic home for scientific research become firmly established, and science begin to exert

---

[41] Daniel J. Kevles, "The Study of Physics in America, 1865–1916," Ph.D. dissertation, Princeton University, 1964, pp. 52–72.

an active rather than a passive cultural role. For in the last decade of the century, industry and government recognized their need for technical expertise, the scientific community became more desirous of professional achievement within their own specialized fields, and the widely spread confidence in science as a social good reached new heights.

The changes that had taken place and the outlook for the future of science in higher education were revealed by the events and discussions of the period. For, like many other aspects of American culture, science and higher education were subject to public discussion in the closing years of the nineteenth century, when Americans assessed the value and implications of the things and ideas they had acquired in the preceding generation. The approach of the new century seemed to be an incentive to reflect on the past and speculate about the future.

Technological innovations in the last half of the century had effected vast social changes in the nation and were continuing at a rapidly accelerating rate. Modern machinery, electrical appliances, the telephone and telegraph, and mass transportation had transformed the lives of millions. The perpetual technological revolution reached new high stages in the 1890's, and this was emphasized by the exhibits at the World's Columbian Exposition in Chicago in 1893, the military victory over Spain in 1898, and the unprecedented national prosperity in the final years of the century. At the same time, the automobile was becoming a practical reality, and aerial transportation was beginning to emerge from its fledgling stage—and they both carried the potential of even greater social change. By the late 1890's, Americans were more than conscious of change—they expected it. The word "new" was rapidly being applied to a host of social institutions and intellectual disciplines, and the idea of the approaching "new" century touched off a wave of expectancy and optimism.

The optimistic outlook was based to a large extent on the belief that science was the mainspring of inevitable progress. This was the "lesson" of the nineteenth century and its achievements. To a large group of intellectual leaders, including scientists, the key to progress was the increased application of the tools, knowledge, and methods of science to all spheres of human activity. To the general public, science was the harbinger of technology, the wonder worker, the creator of electrical marvels, and it promised more of the same.

The scientific community shared the overall general optimism of the times, and many articulate scientists rejoiced in the triumphs of the nineteenth century, writing articles in scientific, literary, and mass-circulation magazines promoting science as the beneficient force that would elevate man materially and morally. They were eager to apply science to all spheres of life and thought that scientists had a special role as leaders, educators, popularizers, and as "ministers of nature." At the same time, they were concerned with the attitudes of a public that was overcredulous toward anything "scientific." As a newly professional group, they were concerned with their relations with the government, their role as expert advisors, the training of new recruits to the profession, career opportunities and limitations, and greater support for research.

The spirit of the times was concisely expressed in the title of a book that was read and discussed by American scientists: *The Wonderful Century*, by British biologist Alfred Russell Wallace. The book described the nineteenth century as a period of unprecedented gains in knowledge and its application to human welfare.[42] A professor of zoology at Johns Hopkins University reviewed the book and commented: "It is not invention and discovery and the extension of man's dominion over nature, but the establishment of the conviction that we know no limit to this movement, that is the chief distinction of our century."[43]

To many scientists, the progress of science meant that science *was* progress. They pointed to the immensity of knowledge yet to be gained and placed their confidence in the methods of science as the path to wisdom. Typical of these views was this statement by a leading government scientist: "For the material advancement of mankind the nineteenth century has done more than all the preceding ages combined, and science has been the chief instrument of progress."[44] He forecast even greater triumphs for the coming century through the use of better facilities and organization of research and observed that "the greatest laws are yet undiscovered; the invitation of the unknown was never more distinct than now."[45]

The culmination of many of these end-of-the-century tributes to science was the argument that education in the methods and content of science would make it possible for its utilitarian and cultural values

[42] Alfred Russell Wallace, *The Wonderful Century* (New York, 1899).

[43] W. K. Brooks, "Review of *The Wonderful Century*," *Science*, April 7, 1899, p. 511.

[44] F. W. Clarke, "A Hundred Years of Chemistry," *Popular Science Monthly*, LVI (April 1900), p. 68.

[45] *Ibid.*, p. 69.

to be more fully realized in the twentieth century. Greater support of research would enlarge the boundaries of scientific knowledge, which could be diffused and applied through more widespread incorporation of science in the elementary, secondary, and college curricula and in the mass media, because "the times call for very special efforts to spread the knowledge and culture which are the product of the age, so that the intellectual life of the whole mass of society may be quickened."[46] Scientists emphasized the cultural value of science education more than its practical value, because they felt that in the last half of the nineteenth century, science had been introduced into education as, in the words of Charles E. Bessey, "merely a minister to man's material interests." Bessey went on to say, "What wonder, too, that some men, dazzled and bewildered by the splendid achievements of science in many fields of human industry, became materialistic and set up science as their educational goddess."[47] The science that had been substituted for the language and literature of the old curriculum often included only the more practical parts of the subject, and this could be remedied, according to several critics, by teaching science for its cultural and not for its money value. The underlying thesis in many of these arguments was that the acceptance of science courses as part of general education would expand the basis of support for academic research and graduate training.

To many American scientists the need to improve science education had a special urgency that was based on professional self-interest. Not only would science education create an appreciation of the need to support scientific research but it would also protect the public from being deceived by charlatans and well-intentioned amateurs who threatened to infringe on the domain of the professional scientist. Sensationalism ran rampant in the press in the late 1890's, and the reporting of science news was no exception. The scientific community's alarm at the effect this had on the public was expressed by Professor Robert Simpson Woodward, a mathematical physicist and dean of the science faculty at Columbia University, who presided over the American Association for the Advancement of Science meeting in 1900:

> An almost inevitable result of the rapid developments of the last three decades especially is that much that goes by the name of science

[46] "The Scientific Advance," *Popular Science Monthly*, LII (December 1897), p. 265.

[47] Charles E. Bessey, "Science and Culture," *Science*, July 31, 1896, p. 122.

is quite unscientific. The elementary teaching and the popular exposition of science have fallen, unluckily, into the keeping largely of those who cannot rise above the level of a purely literary view of phenomena. Many of the bare facts of science are so far stranger than fiction that the general public has become somewhat overcredulous, and untrained minds fall an easy prey to the tricks of the magazine romancer or to the schemes of the perpetual motion promoter. Along with the growth of real science there has gone on also a growth of pseudo-science. It is so much easier to accept sensational than to interpret sound scientific literature, so much easier to acquire the form than it is to possess the substance of thought that the deluded enthusiast and the designing charlatan are not infrequently mistaken by the expectant public for true men of science. There is, therefore, plenty of work before us; and while our principal business is the direct advancement of science, an important, though less agreeable duty, at times is the elimination of error and the exposure of fraud.[48]

Science education was actively promoted as a solution to this already apparent gap between the gains in scientific knowledge and the public's understanding of it. More widespread inclusion of basic science courses in the standard curriculum was viewed as a practical measure that would protect the average citizen from being victimized by pseudo science and impossible inventions.[49]

How did these turn-of-the-century arguments for science education reflect the developments in institutions of higher education where science was taught? By the 1890's, applied science was firmly established as a course of study, and about 22,000 science and engineering students were enrolled in technological institutes and science departments of colleges.[50] Of the institutions devoted to science and technology, Massachusetts Institute of Technology was the largest. It offered thirteen distinct four-year courses, in civil engineering, mechanical engineering, mining engineering and metallurgy, sanitary engineering, architecture, naval architecture, chemical engineering, electrical engineering, chemistry, biology, physics, general studies, and

[48] R. S. Woodward, "Presidential Address," *Popular Science Monthly*, LVII (August 1900), p. 444.

[49] T. C. Mendenhall, "Presidential Address Before the Society for Promotion of Engineering Education," *Science*, August 18, 1899, p. 196; Edward Orton, "Proper Objects of the American Association for the Advancement of Science," *Popular Science Monthly*, LV (August 1899), p. 468; P. E. M. Berthelot, "Science as an Instrument of Education," *Popular Science Monthly*, LI (June 1897), p. 255 (translated from *Science et Morale*); Albert B. Crowe. "Science Study and National Character," *Popular Science Monthly*, LVII (May 1900), pp. 90–98.

[50] James G. McGivern, *First Hundred Years of Engineering Education in the United States (1807–1907)* (Spokane, 1960), pp. 132–33.

geology. By 1899, about 1,200 students were enrolled and the number who had graduated since the doors were opened in 1865 had reached nearly 2,000. At least ten other independently organized and endowed schools of technology were flourishing in 1899, and the number of their graduates was about 4,500. Only one of these institutions had been in existence before the Civil War.[51]

Yale, Harvard, Columbia, Dartmouth, Pennsylvania, and Princeton were among the older private colleges which had closely affiliated schools of science and technology. Institutions that were wholly or partly supported by state or national appropriations also included scientific schools or departments, and in 1899, there were flourishing scientific divisions at such universities as Cornell, Michigan, Purdue, Wisconsin, California, Illinois, Ohio State, and Minnesota.

In all of these institutions, the emphasis was on applied science and technology. The course of study led, in most cases, to a bachelor of science degree if the student successfully completed a four-year course that involved laboratory work. The majority of the students majored in one of the fields of engineering and could anticipate expanding opportunities for technically trained young men in industry.

At the same time that applied science was being more widely taught at the undergraduate level as the basis of engineering curricula, basic science was finding a home in the graduate schools. By the end of the nineteenth century, the value of research as an educational factor was being demonstrated at Johns Hopkins, Clark, Chicago, Columbia, and several other universities. These institutions were producing professional research scientists and required that their advanced graduate students engage in original research. Facilities and opportunities for research were provided for professors and students not only because this was the way to train professional scientists but because of a conviction that it was the university's role to advance knowledge as well as to diffuse it. The leaders of these graduate schools expected their professors to be researchers as well as teachers, and the scientists heartily agreed.[52]

An academic home for scientific research had long been sought in the United States, and important steps toward this goal had been taken

---

[51] T. C. Mendenhall, "Scientific, Technical and Engineering Education," Monograph No. 11, in Nicholas Murray Butler, ed., *Monographs on Education in the United States* (1900), pp. 554–92.

[52] D. C. Gilman, "The Future of American Colleges and Universities," *Atlantic Monthly*, LXXVIII (August 1896), pp. 175–79 and *Science*, 1896, pp. 141–42.

by individual science professors at various colleges before 1876, when Johns Hopkins University dedicated itself to advanced graduate studies and the advancement of knowledge through research. These early efforts to support research in the university finally gained significant public acceptance in the 1890's, when the American scientific community emerged as a professional, institutionalized group against a background of favorable social, cultural, and economic trends.

The institution which best reflected and contributed to the new-found status of scientific research was the University of Chicago, which emphasized research and backed it up with a healthy Rockefeller endowment. The University announced its serious interest in science by raiding the faculties of other fledgling graduate schools to create an "instant" center for scientific research and education at the expense of such institutions as the newly founded Clark University. Chicago's emphasis on research stimulated competition for research men, and Johns Hopkins, Cornell, and Clark immediately sought to improve their facilities and opportunities for faculty research.[53]

Albert A. Michelson, who had already achieved an international reputation for his research in physics and who was to become America's first Nobel Prize winner, was one of those who was induced, in 1892, by promises of more time and equipment for research to make the westward trek from Clark. Within two years after his arrival at Chicago, the Ryerson Physical Laboratory opened its doors with Michelson as head professor. The proceedings of the dedication celebration are especially interesting because they provide evidence of how the cultural, utilitarian, and professional aspects of science education were combined in a single institution. Martin Ryerson, wealthy Chicagoan and president of the board of trustees of the University, explained that the instruction and investigations that would be conducted in the modern, well-equipped building that he was giving to the University would "be of little value unless they keep in view and tend to enlarge the higher ideals of life."[54] He urged that science "be encouraged to go beyond the immediately utilitarian field and be numbered with those subjects which are cultivated for their intellectual and moral value."[55] President William Rainey Harper promised that the building would be used for such purposes and stressed the labora-

[53] Rudolph, pp. 349–52.

[54] [Martin] Ryerson, "Presentation of the Formal Gift of Ryerson Physical Laboratory," *Quarterly Calendar of the University of Chicago,* III (August 1894), p. 31.

[55] *Ibid.,* pp. 31–32.

tory facilities that had been provided for research and instruction.[56] Twenty-three physicists from other institutions convened in the Ryerson Laboratory on the day of its dedication for "discussion of methods of teaching physics" and to hear a paper by Professor Michelson on his research on the use of light waves for accurate measurement.[57] In the issue of the University's *Quarterly Calendar* that carried the dedication proceedings, President Harper proudly reported that in the two years since the University had started instruction the 150 faculty members accomplished a "large amount of work in addition to the regular classroom duties."[58] He was referring to the more than 515 articles and reviews that had been published in 101 periodicals by members of the faculty since their connection with the University.

TWENTIETH-CENTURY PROBLEMS

Nonteaching research; specialized science departments; laboratory facilities for undergraduates, graduates, and faculty; support of science education for its cultural value as well as its utilitarian value; and the consciousness of professional status and responsibilities—all of these were embodied in the new universities. They were the culmination of the developments of the nineteenth century and set the pattern for the place of science in higher education for the twentieth century. The problems of the twentieth century have developed within this framework and have been especially intertwined with the development of the professional community of American scientists that came into existence by the end of the century.

An indication of these future developments was given by Henry A. Rowland, who, as a physics professor at Johns Hopkins University, was renowned for his research accomplishments. He was the acknowledged spokesman for American physicists who had established their first research journal at Cornell in 1893 and had organized into a professional society in a meeting at Columbia University in 1899. All of the thirty-eight charter members of the American Physical Society were from the academic world. In his presidential address at the second meeting of the Society in 1899, Rowland deprecated the gains that had been made and bemoaned the lack of great laboratories of research. He complained that there were only a "few miserable

---

[56] *Ibid.*, pp. 32–33.

[57] *Ibid.*, pp. 34–37.

[58] *Ibid.*, p. 17.

structures here and there, occupied by a few starving professors, who are nobly striving to do their best with the feeble means at their disposal. . . ."[59] He had hopes for the future, however, and asked the professional physicists: "But the twentieth century is near, may we not hope for better things before its end? May we not hope to influence the public in this direction?"[60]

Physicists, astronomers, chemists, biologists, mathematicians, engineers—by the end of the nineteenth century all were organized into professional groups based on the specialized subfields of their disciplines. How did this professionalization of science affect the place of science in higher education in the twentieth century? The specific answers to this question are related to the general characteristics of professional behavior and to the social process of professionalization that had been underway in the nineteenth century.

The professionalization of science, said Alfred North Whitehead, was one of the major achievements of the nineteenth century:

> The full self-conscious realization of the power of professionalism in knowledge in all its departments, and of the way to produce the professionals, and the importance of knowledge to the advance of technology, and of the methods by which abstract knowledge can be connected with technology, and of the boundless possibilities of technological advance,—the realization of all these things was first completely attained in the nineteenth century. . . .[61]

At the beginning of the twentieth century, the academic base for professional science was consolidated. The doctorate had become important as a symbol of professional competence in the 1890's, and it was soon required for teaching positions. Specialized science departments in the colleges and universities were established, reflecting research specialization and the need to produce trained specialists in response to increasing demands from government and industry. Departmentalization was also effective in organizing the faculty, obtaining research support, and in public relations. Professional achievement was linked to research output, measured in terms of papers approved by professional peers for publication in specialized journals of the profession.[62] The process of establishing and furnishing the academic

---

[59] Henry A. Rowland, "The Highest Aim of a Physicist," in Nathan Reingold, ed., *Science in Nineteenth Century America*, p. 328.

[60] *Ibid.*

[61] Alfred North Whitehead, *Science and the Modern World* (New York, 1960), p. 92.

[62] Rudolph, pp. 395–404; also see Richard Hofstadter and Walter P. Metzger, *The Development of Academic Freedom in the United States* (New York, 1955).

home for science proceeded at an uneven rate, varying with economic and political conditions, and with the availability of local leadership and sources of support. But it was clear by the first decade of the twentieth century that the place of science in higher education was firmly entrenched.

Scientists in the universities still had difficulty in obtaining adequate funds for research, but this situation gradually improved, especially after World War I, when government, foundations, and industry increased their support of research. As science became more professionalized, specialized, and expensive, it needed greater public understanding and support. However, the public understanding of science did not keep pace with new scientific developments such as those in genetics, X rays, radioactivity, and relativity, because many American scientific leaders who had achieved institutional security no longer accepted the responsibility of explaining their work to the public as part of their task.[63]

In the consolidation and extension of the place of science in the colleges and universities, the emphasis was on research and not on science education. In physics, for example, there was a tendency in the professional society to discourage discussions of the teaching of physics for fear of diluting the newly won acceptance of research in the universities. In 1930 the lack of professional attention to the methods, techniques, and content of physics teaching in the colleges led a group of physicists to organize the American Association of Physics Teachers, which grew rapidly and soon founded a journal "devoted to the instructional and cultural aspects of physical science."[64] This renewed professional interest in the teaching of physics came at a time when several American universities were winning recognition as first-rate centers of physics research and the United States was emerging as a leading contributor in both quantity and quality to contemporary work in experimental and theoretical physics.[65] Academic research had become secure enough by the early 1930's to minimize any fears that professional concern with improving teaching might lead to the return of the situation that had irked Joseph Henry in the 1870's, when he complained that scientific research was being stifled because scientists were overburdened with elementary teaching.

---

[63] Kevles, pp. 263–67.

[64] David L. Webster, "Reminiscences of the Early Years of the Association," *American Journal of Physics*, XXV (1957), pp. 131–34.

[65] John H. Van Vleck, "American Physics Comes of Age," *Physics Today*, XVII (June 1964), pp. 21–26.

Since the 1940's, when the campus became a center for government-sponsored wartime research, federal government support of
academic science, including both science education and research, has
steadily increased. About 65 percent of the research funds received
by institutions of higher education now come from the federal government. The cost of academic science was $3.1 billion in 1961 and
is expected by 1975 to exceed the $7 billion mark. About half of the
1961 total was spent for instruction, fellowships, and improving science education, and the remainder was spent on research, physical
plant, and science information.[66] The high cost of academic science
and the need for outside support has had serious effects on the entire
university structure in the United States. In the early 1960's, a bar-
rage of criticism was leveled by educators, researchers, and students
in the sciences and humanities at the givers and receivers of research
grants for not paying enough attention to the effects of the large in-
flux of research money on the total aims of the university. The modern
American university is expected to preserve, synthesize, and interpret
existing knowledge; to acquire and diffuse new knowledge; and to
provide training in the application of existing knowledge to practical
needs. Contemporary critics contend that the emphasis on research
and the availability of funds for specific areas of research interfere
with the multipurposes of the university by channeling scholarly and
research activity into those areas most likely to be supported and by
neglecting the teaching role of the professor.[67]

The teaching of science did receive considerable attention in the
mid-twentieth century, however, when a series of science curriculum
reform projects were initiated. The rapid advances in knowledge in
the fields of physics, biology, chemistry, and mathematics and in
science-based technology demands a new approach to the teaching
of science if potential recruits to the profession are not to be hope-
lessly handicapped in their attempt to acquire the knowledge and
skills needed for scientific pursuits. The dramatic demonstration of
the Soviet Union's scientific and technological achievements with the
launching of the first Sputnik in 1957 spurred the curriculum reform
projects for college and high school science studies. These projects

[66] William V. Consolazio, "The Fiscal Dilemma of Academic Science,"
Bulletin of the Atomic Scientists (February 1965), p. 15.

[67] For a review of the present relation of science to the overall aims of
the university, see Paul Weiss, "Science in the University," *Daedalus*, XCIII
(1964), pp. 1184–1218; a continuing discussion of the contemporary relations
between teaching, research, and grants can be found in the articles and letters
published in recent issues of *Science*.

appear to be developing into a permanent part of educational activities in the field of science. With some notable exceptions, the continuing movement to reform the science curriculum has been aimed at attracting and training new recruits to the scientific professions, and the success of this effort has not yet been adequately demonstrated. Relatively little attention has been given to improving science education as part of the liberal learning imparted to the nonscientist.

The major, and as yet unfulfilled, task of twentieth-century science educators is the infusion of science into the liberal arts curriculum. As science becomes increasingly relevant to American society, it becomes less relevant in the higher education of the nonscientific citizen. In the age of the highly specialized scientific expert, educational resources tend to be devoted to the production of professional scientists, and only a backward glance is given to increasing the scientific literacy of those not directly involved in scientific pursuits. The "cultural role" of science in higher education is frequently restricted to a one-year elective course in either biology, physics, or chemistry that has little relation to the content or methods of contemporary science. Part of the "two cultures" dilemma that has provided grist for the academic orator's mill ever since C. P. Snow emphasized its significance, the scientific education of the nonscientist has been the subject of much recent debate and a few experimental pedagogical programs. One of the earliest and most effective spokesman for the need to revise and amplify the role of science in general education is former Harvard president James B. Conant. He has emphasized our need to understand science as a human enterprise and to teach the nonscientist its methods, its limitations, and the processes by which it undergoes change. It is likely that a major chapter in the history of science and higher education in the second half of the twentieth century will be related to these attempts to revitalize the cultural role of science in the colleges and universities.

Science and Private Agencies

Howard S. Miller*

In 1869 the astronomer Benjamin Apthorp Gould delivered his farewell address as retiring president of the American Association for the Advancement of Science. He might have recounted his recent attempts to plot stellar coordinates from photographic plates, or he might have told of his forthcoming journey to the Argentine to direct a new observatory at Cordoba. But instead, Gould chose a more engrossing theme. "With your permission," he said, "I will speak of the position of the scientific investigator in the community; of the duties incumbent upon him, and of what he may rightfully expect in return." Gould went on to repeat the familiar protest that American culture stifled the full development of native scientific talent. "There must be in every community men specially endowed with scientific tastes and impulses," he affirmed. "Now the social problem here evidently is, so to order the influences and attune the public sentiment in the community as to allow the ablest minds to labor in those fields for which they are best adapted."[1]

During the course of the next century, mounting industrial, agricultural, and military applications all but solved what Gould had termed the social problem of science. By the 1960's, few Americans seriously questioned the value of basic scientific research. Science had become

---

* HOWARD S. MILLER is currently an Assistant Professor of History at the University of Southern California, Los Angeles. Born in 1936 in Pontiac, Illinois, he obtained his A.B. at Bradley University (1958), and his M.S. (1960), and Ph.D. (1964), at the University of Wisconsin. He has previously published *The University of Wisconsin Summer Session, 1885–1960* (Madison, 1960); *The Legal Foundations of American Philanthropy, 1776–1844* (Madison, 1961); and has contributed articles to *Notable American Women, A Biographical Dictionary*.

[1] *Proceedings of the American Association for the Advancement of Science,* XVIII (Cambridge, Mass., 1870), 2, 7. The most complete biographical notice of Gould, with a bibliography of his extensive writings, is George Comstock, "Benjamin Apthorp Gould, 1824–1896," *National Academy of Sciences Biographical Memoirs,* XVII (Washington, D.C., 1924), 153–80.

the foundation of economic progress and a strategic instrument of national security. The scientist, whether astronaut or television hero, was now a popular idol. In 1961–1962 alone, total research and development expenditures in the United States reached $14.7 billion, of which roughly 10 percent was earmarked for basic scientific investigation.[2]

Succored on every hand by foundation grants and research and development contracts, twentieth-century scientists and laymen alike often failed to appreciate that such largess was a recent phenomenon in the United States. They forgot that the very term, scientist, though coined by an English philosopher in 1840, was uncommon in the American vocabulary until the turn of the century.[3] Until the man of science assumed a vital and recognized role in American life, there simply was no need for a shorthand term to describe his vocation. With a few notable exceptions, in the nineteenth century even the nation's numerous scientific societies failed to contribute substantial, tangible support for scientific discovery. The venerable American Philosophical Society was typical in its "long and distinguished career of honorable penury."[4] Furthermore, scientific societies often failed to adjust their operations to dynamic changes in the very nature of scientific enterprise. As a result, much of the tone and tempo of science long depended on the informal mechanisms of private philanthropy rather than upon the systematic support of private agencies. The research establishments of modern America evolved only when the progress of scientific discovery had outdistanced traditional scientific agencies and exhausted the resources of piecemeal, private patronage. Such agencies owed their financial base and organizational structure to general trends in late nineteenth-century economic life. Their strategy in meeting the social problems of science, however, derived from the aspirations of American scientists during the Middle Period.

---

[2] National Science Foundation, *Annual Report*, 1963 (Washington, D.C., 1963), 132–35.

[3] "We need very much a name to describe a cultivator of science in general. I should incline to call him a *Scientist*. Thus we might say, that as an Artist is a Musician, Painter, or Poet, a Scientist is a Mathematician, Physicist, or Naturalist." William Whewell, *The Philosophy of the Inductive Sciences, Founded Upon their History*, 2 vols. (London, 1840), I, cxiii.

[4] Frederick P. Keppel, "The Responsibility of Endowments in the Promotion of Knowledge," *Proceedings of the American Philosophical Society*, LXXVII (Philadelphia, 1937), 591–603. The A.P.S. received its *first* funds for research grants in the 1930's through the bequest of Richard A. F. Penrose. Helen R. Fairbanks and Charles P. Berkey, *Life and Letters of R.A.F. Penrose, Jr.* (New York, 1952), pp. 717–53.

FROM AVOCATION TO PROFESSION

Throughout the colonial period and during the early years of the republic, the pursuit of science had been highly episodic, a series of occasionally brilliant but essentially disconnected efforts. It was true that many an old-time college or academy, though officially concerned only with mental discipline and Christian nurture, was the scene of creditable research, but such examples only pointed up the absence of a solid institutional foundation for continuous scientific enterprise.[5] Most Americans who called themselves men of science were clergymen, physicians, educators, public servants, and country squires for whom science was a diverting pastime, part of their cultural heritage as gentlemen. Unique for his energy, but typical for his breadth, was Dr. Samuel Latham Mitchell of New York. This errant savant was simultaneously a physician, editor, paleontologist, essayist, chemist, geologist, icthyologist, and politician who "supported the Republican party because Jefferson was its leader and supported Jefferson because he was a philosopher."[6]

For such men a well-stocked cabinet was the visible sign of a scientific calling. The cabinet, like the scientific Lyceum lecture of the 1830's, symbolized the catholicity of early American science.

> The cabinet still broods with varnished wings
> Above its nest of rare and curious things—
> The ostrich egg, the fish-hook, and the shell,
> The sculptured chamois from the land of Tell,
> The Pine-Tree shilling with its quaint device, . . .

---

[5] For a perceptive treatment of early nineteenth-century science, see George H. Daniels' dissertation, "Baconian Science in America, 1815–1845" (State Univ. of Iowa, 1963). I. Bernard Cohen has pointed out that Harvard undergraduates took more required science courses in the 1840's than in the 1940's. I. Bernard Cohen, "Harvard and the Scientific Spirit," *Harvard Alumni Bulletin*, XL (1948), 393–98.

[6] Henry Adams, *History of the United States during the Administration of Thomas Jefferson*, 9 vols. (New York 1891), I, 111; Courtney R. Hall, *A Scientist in the Early Republic: Samuel Latham Mitchell, 1764–1831* (New York, 1934), pp. 5, 64, 127. Other revealing studies of universal savants include Edwin T. Martin, *Thomas Jefferson, Scientist* (New York, 1952); Edmund S. Morgan, *The Gentle Puritan: A Life of Ezra Stiles* (New Haven, 1962); and Brooke Hindle, *David Rittenhouse* (Princeton, N.J., 1964). Samuel Miller's classic *Brief Retrospect of the Eighteenth Century*, 2 vols. (New York, 1803) should not be overlooked. The most comprehensive modern survey is Brooke Hindle, *The Pursuit of Science in Revolutionary America, 1735–1789* (Chapel Hill, N.C., 1956), while the most suggestive work for the entire period to 1820 is Whitfield J. Bell, Jr., *Early American Science: Needs and Opportunities for Study* (Williamsburg, Va., 1955).

> The Spider with its feelers long and limp,
> Bottled and labeled like a pickled shrimp,
> And sprawling lizards with their fleshless legs,
> Put up in jars like cucumbers in kegs.[7]

In 1828 Noah Webster had commented knowingly on the science of his day. He noted that during the last century language had lagged behind the profound advances in scientific knowledge. "*Pure* science, as in Mathematics," he declared in the *American Dictionary of the English Language*, "is built on self-evident truths; but the term science is also applied to other subjects founded on generally acknowledged truths, as *metaphysics*; or on experiment and observation, as *chimistry* [*sic*] and *natural philosophy*; or even to an assemblage of the general principles of an art, as the science of *agriculture*, the science of *navigation*." In common parlance science was as it had been in Samuel Johnson's day, a general term for knowledge, "the comprehension or understanding of truth or facts by the mind."[8]

The governing characteristic of early American science was its eclectic quality, not its apparent division into theoretical and applied varieties. Three years after Webster's *Dictionary* appeared, Alexis de Tocqueville arrived to investigate the effects of democracy in America. His classic explanation of why Americans seemed indifferent to basic science was in part valid, but it was also misleading. The Frenchman correctly surmised that hardly anyone devoted himself "to the essentially theoretical and abstract portion of human knowledge." But his implied explanation, that the democrat dissipated his energies on the "immediate and useful practical results of the sciences," overrated the American technological accomplishment.[9] In truth, practical science had fared little better than abstract speculation in the new nation. The industrial and transportation revolutions owed more to experience and luck than to the conscious, systematic applica-

[7] Poem, *circa* 1830, as quoted in Carl Bode, *The American Lyceum, Town Meeting of the Mind* (New York, 1956), p. 53. Quoted with the permission of Carl Bode.

[8] Noah Webster, "Science," *An American Dictionary of the English Language*, 2 vols. (New York, 1828); Samuel Johnson, "Science," *A Dictionary of the English Language*, 2 vols. (London, 1755).

[9] Alexis de Tocqueville, *Democracy in America*, trans. Henry Reeve, 2 vols. (New York: Alfred A. Knopf, Inc., 1945), II, 42–49. An updated and influential version of Tocqueville's thesis is Richard Shryock, "American Indifference to Basic Research in the Nineteenth Century," *Archives Internationales d'Histoire des Sciences*, No. 5 (October 1948), 50–65. John D. Bernal draws opposite conclusions from Shryock's evidence in his Marxist analysis of *Science and Industry in the Nineteenth Century* (London, 1953).

tion of scientific principles. At a time when Yankee ingenuity was world famous, Yankee engineering was nondescript. The distance from modern industrial science was clearly evident in the 1820's, when Jacob Bigelow, a physician, botanist, and Harvard's first Rumford Professor on the Application of Science to the Useful Arts, groped for a term to characterize his novel discipline. After considerable reflection, Bigelow settled uneasily upon "technology," an archaic word which he assured his readers was "sufficiently expressive," and which was currently experiencing a revival "in the literature of practical men."[10]

As farsighted practical men looked toward modern technology, a new generation of scientific men was moving to revolutionize the conduct and meaning of science itself. Smarting from invidious comparisons with European scientific achievements, yet simultaneously inspired by the European example, the young men of science deprecated the work of their predecessors. United by technical competence and driven by a strident, professional attitude toward their calling, they insisted that there was more to science than Lyceum lectures and a cabinet of curiosities. "We are over-run in this country with charlatanism," complained Joseph Henry, the nation's foremost physicist. "Our newspapers are filled with puffs of Quackery and every man who can burn phosphorous in oxygen and exhibit a few experiments to a class of young ladies is called a man of science."[11]

FROM CABINETS TO LABORATORIES

Long before the allure of a continental Ph.D. drew large numbers of American intellectuals to Europe, scientific men had established lasting personal and institutional ties with the Old World. They went abroad for information, for apparatus, but especially for inspiration. The usually taciturn Joseph Henry found England a "fairy land." After visiting the laboratory of Sir David Brewster in Edinburgh, Henry confided to his diary that "the information given me by Sir David was precisely the kind for which I came to this country. The

---

[10] Jacob Bigelow, *Elements of Technology, Taken Chiefly from a Course of Lectures Delivered at Cambridge, on the Application of the Sciences to the Useful Arts,* 2nd ed. (Boston, 1831), pp. iv–v, 1–2. An interesting study might be made of those Americans who *doubted* the need for science in technology. See the review of Bigelow's volume in *The Christian Examiner and General Review,* 2nd ser., II (November 1829), 187–202. A somewhat different picture emerges from Dirk J. Struik, *Yankee Science in the Making* (Boston, 1948).

[11] Joseph Henry to [   ], February 27, 1846, Joseph Henry Papers, Smithsonian Institution, Washington, D.C.

methods of original experimentation . . . cannot be learned from books." Charmed by the manner and the sophistication of their European peers, impressed by the support which they received in their work, Joseph Henry's generation vowed to "put down quackery" at home. "I am now more than ever of your opinion," wrote Henry to his friend Alexander Dallas Bache on his return, "that the real working men in the way of science in this country should make common cause and endeavor by every proper means unitedly to raise our scientific character, to make science more respected at home, to increase the facilities of scientific investigators and the inducements to scientific labours."[12]

The divergence between the old and the new was obvious as soon as "real working men in the way of science" opened their campaign. The objective was not a great cabinet but rather a research agency, a kind of American version of the Parisian *Institut* and the Royal Institution of London. Through such an agency and others like it, scientific men hoped to secure financial support for their researches and an avenue for the publication of its results. The model was clearly European. The first promise of fulfillment came unexpectedly from the Old World as well. In 1826 James Smithson, an eccentric English gentleman-chemist, had died leaving the residue of his estate in trust to the United States "to found at Washington, under the name of the Smithsonian Institution, an Establishment for the increase & diffusion of knowledge among men."[13] No one knew precisely what Smithson had envisioned, nor why he had selected the United States as trustee. His ambiguous twenty-two-word directive left an open field for interpretation, however, and guaranteed that whatever the Englishman's intentions might have been, the end result would be a product of American needs and aspirations.

In its broadest outlines, the history of the Smithsonian Institution is familiar enough.[14] Yet some aspects of its early development war-

---

[12] Joseph Henry to Asa Gray, November 1, 1838, Historic Letter File, Gray Herbarium, Harvard University; Joseph Henry to Alexander Dallas Bache, August 9, 1838, Joseph Henry Papers, Smithsonian Institution; Joseph Henry, mss. "Diary," entries for April 3, April 22, [August   ], 1837, Joseph Henry Papers, Smithsonian Institution.

[13] Will of James Smithson, October 23, 1826, printed in William J. Rhees, ed., *The Smithsonian Institution, Documents Relative to its Origin and History, 1835–1899*, 2 vols. (Washington, D.C., 1901), I, 5–6.

[14] The extensive literature on the Smithsonian is of very uneven quality. The best scholarly treatments are Madge E. Pickard, "Government and Science In the United States: Historical Backgrounds," *Journal of the History of Medicine and Allied Sciences*, I (July 1946), 446–81, and A. Hunter Dupree, *Science in the Federal Government* (Cambridge, Mass., 1957), pp. 66–90.

ranted special notice, for they illuminated general trends of critical significance in shaping the character of private scientific agencies in the United States. After eight years of sporadic debate, in August 1846, Congress passed a compromise act of incorporation that was hardly more definitive than James Smithson's will. Purposely vague in passages that called for precision, the organic act reflected congressional willingness to leave the precise formulation of policy up to the regents and Secretary Joseph Henry, the chief administrative officer. During his three decades as secretary, Henry gave character and direction to the Smithsonian, making it a rallying point for the rising scientific generation. Under his deft management, the Institution combined the flexibility of a private trust with the resources of a public agency.

Not all Americans, however, shared Henry's vision. When President Van Buren had suggested that Congress seek the advice of "persons versed in science, and familiar with the subject of popular education," he had singled out only two of the many special-interest groups who regarded the half-million-dollar bequest as an exclusive and providential treasure.[15] Proposals for national universities, agricultural experiment stations, and an odd assortment of less reasonable projects, found their champions and vied for congressional favor. The old scientific community lobbied for a museum, a great national cabinet of curiosities and scientific lore to be administered by the National Institute for the Promotion of Science. In 1840 the Institute had risen from the ruins of its predecessor, the Columbian Institute, as the hopeful nucleus of scientific life in the nation's capital. A peculiar mixture of savants and statesmen, amateur science and political opportunism, the National Institute busily gathered a stock of artifacts and secured the endorsement of such old-style scientific men as Peter S. Duponceau, the aged president of the American Philosophical Society.[16] The high tide of the National Institute came in April 1844, when Joel Poinsett, Francis Markoe, Jr., and other organizers staged the first national congress of scientific men in American history. Meet-

---

15 Rhees, *Smithsonian Documents*, I, 102, 109–10, 145–46. Rhees carefully edited and published the legislative documents related to the Smithsonian during its formative years. For convenience sake all citations are to this source.

16 Richard Rathbun, "The Columbian Institute for the Promotion of Arts and Sciences," *United States National Museum Bulletin*, No. 101 (Washington, D.C., 1917), *passim*; George Brown Goode, "The Genesis of the United States National Museum," *Annual Report of the United States National Museum*, 1897, Pt. 2 (Washington, D.C., 1901), 85–191. The extensive mss. records of both the Columbian and National Institutes are available in the archives of the Smithsonian Institution.

ing in Washington, they hoped to impress Congress with a show of institutional strength.[17]

Although several hundred savants participated, the congress was doomed to fall short of its objective. The April gathering was the dramatic ending of an era in the history of science in the United States. The National Institute could no more cope with the power politics of scientific organization than could most of its members any longer keep abreast of the latest technical discoveries. Moreover, the rising scientific generation, convinced that a "promiscuous assembly of those who call themselves men of science in this country would only end in our disgrace," worked within the organization to "direct . . . the host of pseudo-savants . . . into a proper course."[18] As their spokesman, Alexander Dallas Bache lectured the delegates pointedly on the new conditions being wrought by scientific specialization. The universal savant was obsolescent. The inevitable differentiation of scientists from amateurs demanded a new orientation of both. In the future, argued Bache, laymen would play a diminishing role in the process of actual discovery. Instead, their special responsibility would be the material support of professional research scientists. "Is it the diffusion of science, or the encouragement of research that American science requires?" he demanded. "Is it sympathy and kindly communion of which we have the most need . . .? Or opportunities, means and appliances for research? Do we need talkers or workers?"[19]

The divisive effects of specialization were also becoming evident in the relations between men of science and men of letters. In April 1844, Senator Benjamin Tappan of Ohio introduced a Smithsonian bill which substituted an agricultural experiment station for a national museum.[20] The Senator's emphasis upon scientific agriculture prompted the opposition of Rufus Choate of Massachusetts. "On the basis of a somewhat narrow utilitarianism," he complained, Tappan

---

[17] *Third Bulletin of the Proceedings of the National Institute for the Promotion of Science, Washington, D.C., February, 1842, to February, 1845; Also, Proceedings of the Meeting of April, 1844* (Washington, D.C., 1845), pp. 429–34, 437–39; Washington *National Intelligencer*, April 2–3, 1844; Charles Francis Adams, ed., *Memoirs of John Quincy Adams*, 12 vols. (Philadelphia, 1874–1877), XII, 5.

[18] Joseph Henry to Alexander Dallas Bache, August 9, 1838, April 16, 1844, Joseph Henry Papers, Smithsonian Institution.

[19] Alexander Dallas Bache, "On the Condition of Science in Europe and the United States." A holograph copy of the unpublished discourse is located in the Joseph Henry Papers, Smithsonian Institution.

[20] Rhees, *Smithsonian Documents*, I, 266–68.

would limit the increase and diffusion of knowledge to applied science. "This is knowledge, to be sure," Choate remarked condesendingly, "but it is not all knowledge, nor half of it, nor the best of it." Ethics and intellectual philosophy were at least as vital as soil chemistry and a knowledge of noxious weeds. Speaking for men of letters everywhere, Choate called for a "grand and noble public library," an agency best suited to the nation's "actual literary and scientific wants."[21]

Choate's library plan, and the counterproposal that the Smithsonian limit itself to the sciences, revealed a widening split within the American intellectual community. Men of science and men of letters could, and often did, unite to defend the life of the mind from outside attack, but by the 1840's, the rush of discovery had undermined the common ground on which such men had formerly discussed scientific topics. Already, educated Americans were separating into what Sir Charles Snow would characterize in modern times as the "Two Cultures."[22] Outside the scientific community itself, few men as yet fully recognized the implications of such a division. Senator William Rives had sensed the drift of events in 1845, but he had rejected the necessity for "any distinction between the moral and the physical sciences."[23] One could not, echoed George P. Marsh, an ardent bibliophile and the leader of the library faction in the House, limit science "to the numerical and qualitative values of material things." True science depended upon meditation, on the search for "that higher knowledge which served to humanize, to refine, to elevate, to make men more deeply wise."[24]

The contest between books and laboratories was temporarily resolved by compromise. In its final form, the Smithsonian bill provided for scientific investigations, a museum, and a library. Nevertheless, Secretary Henry and Alexander Dallas Bache, the most influential of the Smithsonian Regents, determined from the outset to minimize the library and museum functions while still remaining technically within the letter of the organic act. "In this Democratic Country we must do what we can, when we cannot do what we would," Henry later observed, neatly summarizing his administrative career. "We must recollect that great changes are seldom or never produced

---

[21] Rhees, *Smithsonian Documents*, I, 280–87.

[22] Rhees, *Smithsonian Documents*, I, 346; Charles P. Snow, *The Two Cultures and the Scientific Revolution* (Cambridge, Mass., 1961), pp. 3–14.

[23] Rhees, *Smithsonian Documents*, I, 299–301.

[24] Rhees, *Smithsonian Documents*, I, 375.

percaltum and that we frequently waste our strength in endeavouring to suddenly overcome an obstacle which will gradually give way under a gentle constant pressure."[25]

In the mid-1850's, George P. Marsh, Rufus Choate, and other men of letters suddenly awoke to the cumulative effects of gentle, constant pressure. The "promotion of abstract science," as Henry put it in his *Annual Report* for 1853, had eclipsed all other Smithsonian activities.[26] In 1854 Choate, who had continued to serve the Smithsonian as a Regent at Large even after his retirement from Congress, quit his post in noisy protest. His public letter of resignation charged Joseph Henry with misfeasance, and gained the support of influential journalists like Horace Greeley, whose New York *Tribune* accused the Secretary of converting the Smithsonian into "a lying-in hospital for a little knot of scientific valetudinarians."[27] Yet, though the charges were serious and in large measure justified, in 1855 the Senate Judiciary Committee sustained Henry's policies.

In the House, once again Smithsonian affairs polarized around the "Two Cultures." Rufus Choate deputized his protegé Charles W. Upham, a Unitarian clergyman turned Whig politician, to represent men of letters. "I entreat you to do two things," he wrote. "1. Vindicate the sense of the law. 2. Vindicate art, taste, learning, genius, mind, history, enthnology, morals—against sciologists, chemists, & catchers of extinct skunks."[28] Upham carried out his instructions with eloquent precision in pinpointing the issue between scientific and literary men. "The word science," he complained, "is getting to be quite generally used to denote what are called the physical sciences, excluding political, moral, and intellectual science—excluding history, the arts, and all general literature." Surely James Smithson, a cultured English gentleman, would have rejected such a narrow and technical definition.[29]

---

[25] Joseph Henry to Louis Agassiz, August 13, 1864, as quoted in Nathan Reingold, *Science in Nineteenth Century America: A Documentary History* (New York, 1964), pp. 212–16; Joseph Henry to Alexander Dallas Bache, September 6, 1846, December 5, 1846, Joseph Henry to E. Sabine, November 6, 1849, Joseph Henry Papers, Smithsonian Institution; Joseph Henry to Asa Gray, May 23, 1848, December 23, 1848, Historic Letter File, Gray Herbarium.

[26] *Annual Report of the Smithsonian Institution*, 1853 (Washington, D.C., 1854), p. 10.

[27] Rhees, *Smithsonian Documents*, I, 511–12, 540–43; New York *Tribune*, January 19, 1855.

[28] Rufus Choate to Charles W. Upham, February 19, 1855, Joseph Henry Papers, Smithsonian Institution; Samuel G. Brown, *The Works of Rufus Choate with a Memoir of his Life*, 2 vols. (Boston, 1862), II, 92–108.

[29] Rhees, *Smithsonian Documents*, I, 562.

Upham was probably correct in his assessment of Smithson's scientific tastes. What he did not realize was that James Smithson was irrelevant. In a rapidly changing situation, American men of letters and old-style men of science had clung doggedly to the traditional understanding that science was synonymous with all departments of human knowledge. Their efforts to make the Smithsonian a cabinet of curiosities or a bastion of the liberal arts were outflanked by a few determined devotees of specialized, technical knowledge. Thanks to Joseph Henry's persistence, by mid-century the Smithsonian had gone far toward placing "in bold relief the laborers in the field of original research."[30] These young men of science would play a determining role in the subsequent history of American science. As amateur scientists and men of letters kept alive the learned-society tradition inherited from the eighteenth century, the younger generation would be instrumental in establishing most of the private scientific research agencies in the United States.

OBSERVATORIES AND TELESCOPES—POPULAR SUPPORT OF ASTRONOMY

Early American astronomy shared many of the general characteristics of early American science. Save for the work of a few outstanding practitioners like David Rittenhouse of Philadelphia, astronomy was principally the avocation of clergymen, physicians, and other natural philosophers. What passed for an observatory was more often than not a spyglass set up in an open field or perched on a rooftop. In the 1830's, not even Harvard College possessed instruments suitable for significant original work. The new nation had produced many observers but few astronomers, considerable stargazing but little systematic research.[31]

---

[30] Joseph Henry, "Programme of Organization of the Smithsonian Institution," *Annual Report of the Smithsonian Institution, 1847* (Washington, D.C., 1848), 3–18. On the position of the sciences in the 1850's, see Theophilus Parsons, "The Tendencies of Modern Science," *North American Review,* LXXII (January 1851), 94; James Dwight Dana, "Address on Retiring From the Duties of President," *Proceedings of the American Association for the Advancement of Science,* IX (Cambridge, Mass., 1856), 3; Benjamin Silliman, Jr., "American Contributions to Chemistry," *American Chemist,* V (August-September 1874), 93–94.

[31] William Cranch Bond, *History and Description of the Astronomical Observatory of Harvard College,* Annals of the Astronomical Observatory of Harvard College, I (Cambridge, Mass., 1856), v–vi, lxxxv–lxxxvi. Brooke Hindle, *The Pursuit of Science in Revolutionary America, 1735–1789* (Chapel Hill, N.C., 1956), pp. 146–76, 333–38, and Willis I. Milham, *Early American Observatories* (Williamstown, Mass., 1938), *passim.* are convenient summaries of as-

In the absence of governmental subsidies, the common means of sustaining science abroad, nineteenth-century American astronomers had to rely upon private individuals and agencies. Mapping the siderial universe to prove Newton's laws was an exacting task, and one requiring sizable capital investment. When projected millions of miles into space, a miniscule flaw in a telescope could easily render a series of observations worthless. Only costly and intricate instruments could discriminate seconds of arc or seconds of time, instruments doubly expensive because until mid-century they had to be imported from Europe. Few would-be astronomers could afford a transit instrument and a clock, the barest essentials for serious work. Fewer still commanded the resources necessary to outfit a complete observatory. Moreover, as Benjamin Peirce of Harvard pointed out in the 1840's, the nature of his discipline demanded that an astronomer be a full-time, professional man of science. "He cannot live two lives; if he works while others sleep, he must sleep while others work. While he sustains science, we must sustain him."[32]

The rapid rise of American astronomy dated from the late 1830's. A series of brilliant comets and meteoric showers focused public attention skyward. Religious sentiment, patriotic concern for the world reputation of American culture, and, to a lesser extent, practical needs reinforced general interest in the study of the stars. Less than a quarter century after derision had greeted President John Quincy Adams' plea for a national observatory, the nation boasted more than a dozen "lighthouses of the sky."[33] During the second half of the century, the so-called New Astronomy, astrophysics, required larger and even more intricate apparatus. The spectrograph replaced the transit as the center of attention in many observatories. Astrophysicists of the Gilded Age, like the practitioners of the Old Astronomy of position, turned to private patronage in the massive retooling operation which the New Astronomy required. Like their predecessors, they too found that an infinite diversity of motive and situation governed the support of research. American astronomers proved

---

tronomy in the colonial and early national periods. Hindle's recent biography of *David Rittenhouse* (Princeton, N.J., 1964) shows the colonial astronomer at his best.

[32] Benjamin Peirce, "American Astronomical and Magnetic Observers," *The Cambridge Miscellany of Mathematics, Physics and Astronomy*, I (1842), 25. On the instrumental demands posed by modern astronomical research, see Agnes M. Clerke, *A Popular History of Astronomy* (London, 1908), pp. 1–8, 108–23, a volume that remains the best general history for the period.

[33] For a listing and brief description of these observatories, see Elias Loomis, *The Recent Progress of Astronomy; Especially in the United States* (New York, 1850), pp. 161–202.

themselves remarkably resourceful in meeting the challenge of the contingent and the unforeseen. Astronomy and astrophysics, two of the least immediately utilitarian of the sciences, became the most richly endowed of all, a circumstance that suggested the need to revise blanket condemnations of "anti-intellectualism" in American life.

In 1838 Albert Hopkins, Professor of Mathematics and Natural Philosophy at Williams College, established the first permanent observatory in the United States. It was a modest, transitional institution, equipped for original work but lacking both trained personnel and a conscious institutional commitment to research. As John Bascom, class of 1849, later characterized the Williams faculty, "the instructors . . . were little more than the driven stakes to which we were tethered; they defined the circuit of our range, but did nothing to expand or to enrich it."[34] What the faculty lacked in research it more than made up in piety. Revivals periodically convulsed Williamstown, as Albert Hopkins divided his time between the college and the local pulpit. Moreover, as in most American colleges of the day, it was often difficult to distinguish natural philosophy from natural theology; the wonders of Creation bulked large in the science curriculum. For Albert Hopkins and his colleagues an observatory was as much a place for worship as for research.[35]

Other motives joined with the religious impulse, as new observatories sprang into existence following the pioneering effort at Williamstown. Since Newton's day, astronomy had been the most elegant of sciences, and a nation's contributions were commonly regarded as a sure index of cultural achievement. Sensitive to the jibes of foreign critics, many Americans fostered astronomy as a matter of national pride. Nothing, wrote a fawning Edward Everett in 1838, "would be half so acceptable to the men of Science in Europe" as for the United States to erect an observatory.[36]

Within the next five years, Everett saw major observatories erected in Cincinnati, Ohio, and in Cambridge, Massachusetts. Each institu-

[34] John Bascom, *Things Learned by Living* (New York: G. P. Putnam's Sons, 1913), pp. 47–48; Arthur L. Perry, *Williamstown and Williams College* (Norwood, Mass., 1899), pp. 562–72.

[35] Albert C. Sewall, *Life of Prof. Albert Hopkins* (New York, 1870), pp. 106–61, 165; Bascom, *Things Learned By Living*, p. 109; Frederick Rudolph, *Mark Hopkins and the Log, Williams College, 1836–1872* (New Haven, 1956), pp. 134–43. Historians tend to underestimate the significance of natural theology in the history of science in America.

[36] Edward Everett to John Quincy Adams, November 30, 1838, The Adams Papers, Letters Received, Reel 510, microfilm of the mss. at the Massachusetts Historical Society. See also Loomis, *The Recent Progress of Astronomy*, p. 291.

tion, founded on the fruitful union of individual zeal and public enthusiasm, illustrated the mechanics of informal, private patronage
and suggested the almost hypnotic attraction of the heavens. The
prime mover in Cincinnati was Ormsby MacKnight Mitchel, a foot-
loose West Point graduate of 1829. He had left the Army to study
law, then quit law to accept a chair of mathematics and engineering
at the Cincinnati College.[37] Though his technical training went no
further than the standard West Point fare, Mitchel aspired to become
a professional astronomer. He also resented Tocqueville's charge that
the very nature of democratic institutions was inimical to the advancement of abstract knowledge. Mitchel determined to prove otherwise,
and to launch himself in a new career, by settling "the great question,
as to what a free people will do for pure science." During the winter
of 1841–1842 the promoter awakened local interest through a series
of illustrated astronomical lectures. He convinced Cincinnati citizens
that national and local honor required them to possess a telescope
superior to the finest European instruments.[38]

Mitchel proposed a subscription observatory, and soon walked
the streets selling three hundred $25 shares in the Cincinnati Astro-
nomical Society. Membership brought the privilege of viewing the
heavens through the best obtainable telescope. Not surprisingly, the
local cultural elite responded enthusiastically. What was remarkable
was Mitchel's success among ordinary townspeople. Appealing to the
same indigenous concern for self-improvement that sustained the
lyceum and the mechanics institute, he enrolled more grocers than
physicians, more landlords than lawyers, more carpenters than clergymen.[39] Cincinnati soon possessed the largest telescope in the Western
Hemisphere, a twelve-inch refractor of the best German manufacture.
In November, 1843, old John Quincy Adams, nearly eighty and
racked with fever, made the long journey from Washington to lay the
cornerstone.[40]

Due to a variety of circumstances, Cincinnati never fulfilled its

---

[37] F. A. Mitchel, *Ormsby MacKnight Mitchel, Astronomer and General*
(Boston, 1887), pp. 23–24, 41–48; Edward D. Mansfield, *Personal Memories,
Social, Political, and Literary, with Sketches of Many Noted People, 1803–1843*
(Cincinnati, 1879), pp. 227, 288, 309–10.

[38] Ormsby MacKnight Mitchel, *Siderial Messenger*, I (July 1846), 1–2.

[39] Ormsby MacKnight Mitchel, "Reminiscences," in Mitchel, *Mitchel*, pp.
49–57; Ormsby MacKnight Mitchel, "The Cincinnati Observatory," *The Siderial
Messenger*, I (August 1846), 9–11.

[40] Adams, *Memoirs of John Quincy Adams*, XI, 183, 425–28, 441; John
Quincy Adams, *An Oration Delivered Before the Cincinnati Astronomical Society, on the Occasion of Laying the Corner Stone of an Astronomical Observatory* (Cincinnati, 1843).

promise. Mitchel's own lack of professional training was partly responsible. So was the rise of industry in southern Ohio, for factory smoke soon shrouded the observatory in haze. But equally important was the fact that Mitchel had capitalized on a genuine but transient enthusiasm. Without an endowment fund or the ongoing support of an established agency, the observatory lacked operating revenue. Tedious, exacting research hardly satisfied the idle curiosity of the subscribers, who merely wanted to look at the stars and planets.[41] Still, the Cincinnati Observatory was an important indication, as Mitchel put it, of what a free people would do for pure science. The road to Mount Palomar led from Cincinnati, not from the richer, well-established communities along the Atlantic seaboard. It was no mean accomplishment for a bustling river town.

Harvard astronomers were more fortunate than the Cincinnati promoter. He had fired astronomical interest with lantern slides and oratory. In New England the heavens themselves ignited the spark. On the last day of February 1843, a comet suddenly appeared beside the sun. Its fiery head and tail, among the brightest of the nineteenth century, prompted many observers to recall the Millerites' predictions that the first of March would herald the millenium.[42] While the faithful prepared for the Second Coming, other Bostonians appealed to Harvard men of science for reliable information. Struggling along on a $2,000 subscription raised in 1839, in part equipped with instruments borrowed from the Coast Survey, the old Dana House Observatory was unequal to the task. Benjamin Peirce and William Cranch Bond had frequently complained about their instrumental deficiencies in the past; now the comet offered an excuse for a direct public appeal. On March 22, a crowd of one thousand assembled to hear Peirce lecture on the comet. He seized the occasion to lament Harvard's inability to provide precise information under existing conditions. He then chided his audience for permitting upstart Cincinnati to outdistance cultured Boston in the patronage of science and learning.[43] Within

---

[41] On the plight of the observatory, see Mitchel, "Reminiscences," in Mitchel, *Mitchel*, pp. 153–57, and Ormsby MacKnight Mitchel, *The Planetary and Stellar Worlds: A Popular Exposition of the Great Discoveries and Theories of Modern Astronomy, in a Series of Ten Lectures* (New York, 1858), Preface.

[42] *Boston Daily Advertiser*, March 2, 4, 10, 14, 1843; Benjamin Peirce, "The Great Comet of 1843," *The American Almanac and Repository of Useful Knowledge for the Year 1844* (Boston, 1843), pp. 94–100; Clerke, *Popular History of Astronomy*, pp. 103–5; Ira V. Brown, "The Millerites and the Boston Press," *New England Quarterly*, XVI (December 1943), 592–614.

[43] *Boston Semi-Weekly Courier*, March 13, 27, 1843; *Boston Daily Advertiser*, March 16, 24, 1843; *Boston Evening Transcript*, March 25, 1843; Bond, *History of the Harvard Observatory*, lxxv–lxxvi.

a week the city's patrician merchants were holding meetings and circulating subscription lists. By May Harvard boasted a new observatory site and $20,000 for a fifteen-inch refractor. Soon other donors complemented the new apparatus with permanent endowment funds, insuring that unlike Cincinnati, Harvard College Observatory would assume a prominent position in the annals of astronomical research.[44]

Like the instruments of the Middle Period, the giant telescopes of the Gilded Age owed their existence to energetic scientific men who made the most of fortunate circumstances. In 1871, for example, Joseph Henry visited California for his health. Staying at the Lick House, a leading San Francisco hotel, he chanced to meet its owner, James Lick, an elderly and eccentric millionaire then fretting over the disposition of his estate. Sensing that Lick's governing desire was to perpetuate his name, Henry cited the ready example of James Smithson to prove the renown that proceeded from gifts to science.[45] Their conversation probably influenced Lick's initial contribution to the California Academy of Sciences in 1873, a gift which drew together the millionaire and George Davidson, President of the Academy and a protégé of Alexander Dallas Bache. Davidson, who had long urged the establishment of a mountain-top observatory on the west coast, cultivated the philanthropist and in time convinced him that an observatory would at once satisfy his desires and serve to advance human knowledge.[46] The thirty-six-inch Lick refractor, turned skyward for the first time in June 1888, probed the universe to new depths. James Lick, whose ashes were sealed in the instrument's

---

[44] *Boston Daily Advertiser*, March 27, 29, April 1, 1843; the subscription lists, first published in the *American Journal of Science*, XLVI (April-June 1843), 222–25, are reprinted in Bond, *History of the Harvard Observatory*, lxiii–lxvi. See also Bond, cxlii, 8–9, and Edward S. Holden, *Memorials of William Cranch Bond . . . and George Phillips Bond* (San Francisco, 1897), pp. 29, 64. The subsequent development of the observatory is chronicled in Solon I. Bailey, *The History and Work of the Harvard Observatory, 1839–1927* (New York, 1931).

[45] Joseph Henry to James Lick, December 13, 1873; Joseph Henry to Thomas Huxley, August 3, 1874, both in Joseph Henry Papers, Smithsonian Institution.

[46] George Davidson to Joseph Henry, February 2, 1873; Joseph Henry to James Lick, March 10, 1873; George Davidson to Joseph Henry, April 3, 1873; James Lick to Joseph Henry, October 22, 1873, all in the Joseph Henry Papers, Smithsonian Institution. George Davidson's brief memorandum on his relations with James Lick, as quoted in Milicent Shinn, "The University of California: The Lick Astronomical Department," *Overland Monthly*, 2nd ser., XX (November 1892), 482–83, is supplemented by Oscar Lewis, *George Davidson* (Berkeley, 1954), pp. 58–60, 80. William W. Campbell, *A Brief Account of the Lick Observatory of the University of California, Prepared by the Director of the Observatory*, 3rd ed. (Sacramento, 1902), is a convenient summary.

massive supporting pier, gained lasting recognition in the annals of science.

Ironically, James Lick's astronomical monument only spurred others to outdo him. For years southern Californians had resented the cultural monopoly seemingly enjoyed by the cities around San Francisco Bay. The prestigious Lick Observatory only heightened the imbalance. Just as the observatory neared completion, however, an unprecedented land boom brought sudden wealth and boundless optimism to the Los Angeles area.[47] In June 1887, Edward F. Spence, a civic leader and Trustee of the University of Southern California, launched a regional campaign to secure a forty-inch refractor, a lens which would be, and would remain, the largest in the world. A larger lens would sag under its own weight, distorting images beyond recognition.[48]

The enterprise was well under way when the Los Angeles land bubble burst. The promoters were wiped out, and in 1892 defaulted on their contract with Alvin G. Clark, the Cambridgeport, Massachusetts, optician commissioned to grind the giant lens.[49] Clark was understandably upset. His firm had invested $16,000 in time and material; the crowning achievement of his career lay unfinished in the Cambridgeport shops. Luckily the American Association for the Advancement of Science was then meeting in Rochester, New York. Clark hurried to the convention to urge the nation's astronomers to locate a wealthy patron of science who would finance completion of the instrument.

George Ellery Hale, fortunately, overheard the optician's tale. Troubled by problems involved in his recent appointment as Professor of Astrophysics at the new University of Chicago, he had interrupted an Adirondack fishing trip to attend the convention. A large telescope occupied his thoughts because his Chicago appointment brought no promise of apparatus suitable for his investigations of solar spectra. Alvan Clark's forty-inch refractor would tempt any astronomer, but it was irresistible to a brilliant and ambitious twenty-

[47] Los Angeles *Daily Herald*, June 8, 1887; Carol G. Wilson, *California Yankee: William R. Staats, Business Pioneer* (Claremont, 1946), pp. 56–61; Glenn Dumke, *Boom of the 'Eighties in Southern California* (San Marino, 1944), p. 249.

[48] Los Angeles *Daily Herald*, June 7, 1887, January 19–January 30, 1889; Hiram Reid, *History of Pasadena* (Pasadena, 1895), pp. 325–26. Specific details concerning the Spence donation came to light when his heirs later contested his will. See *Spence* vs. *Widney*, 46 Pacific 463 (October 1896).

[49] *Spence* vs. *Widney*, 46 Pacific 464–67.

four year old just launching his professional career. Whoever directed the great telescope would command a leading position in the scientific world. "It goes without saying that Clark's story gave me food for thought," Hale later recalled. "I returned to the Adirondacks, packed my fishing tackle, and hastened to Chicago."[50]

In Chicago the energetic university president, William Rainey Harper, had been systematically proceeding down his list of local millionaires securing land, buildings, and endowment funds. In February 1892, Chicago's rapacious traction magnate, Charles T. Yerkes, had agreed to contribute a biological laboratory but later, for uncertain reasons, had repudiated his pledge.[51] When Harper heard Hale's report from Rochester, he concluded that the prospect of seeing his name on the world's largest telescope might rekindle Yerkes' interest in the university. Harper and Hale went to the millionaire with the story of the giant lens and suggested that a mere $300,000 was a small price for making Chicago "a Mecca of thousands of science-loving pilgrims, as the Lick Observatory . . . is today. And the donor could have no more enduring monument."[52] Anxious to court public favor as a patron of science and learning, Yerkes agreed. Five years later, the observatory was dedicated at Williams Bay, Wisconsin. "Whatever opinion we may hold of Mr. Yerkes in his relations with the people of Chicago," wrote the reform-minded editor of the Chicago *Times-Herald* in guarded praise, "there can be only one opinion, and that extremely complimentary, of Mr. Yerkes as the founder of the observatory."[53]

---

[50] George Ellery Hale, "The Beginnings of the Yerkes Observatory," unpublished reminiscences prepared for the American Astronomical Society in 1922. Miss Helen Wright of New York City, Hale's official biographer, graciously supplied a copy of the original document in the family papers.

[51] William Rainey Harper to Charles Hutchinson, January 30, 1892; William Rainey Harper to Frederick T. Gates, February 23, 1892; Thomas Goodspeed to Frederick T. Gates, April 1, 1892; Charles T. Yerkes to Herman Kohlsaat, April 1, 1892, all in the University of Chicago Archives. The best summary of Yerkes' Chicago career is Sidney I. Roberts, "Portrait of a Robber Baron: Charles T. Yerkes," *Business History Review*, XXXV (Autumn 1961), 344–71.

[52] Charles T. Yerkes to William Rainey Harper, April 24, 1897; George Ellery Hale to William Rainey Harper, September 23, 1892, both in the University of Chicago Archives. These documents and Hale, "The Beginnings of Yerkes Observatory," p. 2, refute the tale related by Edwin B. Frost, *An Astronomer's Life* (Boston, 1933), pp. 97–98, and repeated with embellishments by Ray Ginger, *Altgeld's America* (New York, 1958), pp. 108–9. According to the latter, Yerkes, facing a loss of credit, *went to Harper* with the offer of an observatory. The university took the bait, Yerkes's public stature (and credit rating) rose, and he thereby multiplied his fortune.

[53] Chicago *Times-Herald*, October 22, 1897.

Yerkes' timely patronage had frustrated the efforts of Edward C. Pickering, director of the Harvard Observatory, in his efforts to secure the great refractor. His unsuccessful contest with Chicago was only one incident in a busy career promoting scientific enterprises. For nearly a quarter century, Pickering labored to bring order and reliability to the traditionally chaotic process of subsidizing research. He worked to pool individual contributions, large and small, in a centralized international agency for astronomical research. There Pickering, with the help of an advisory committee of professional astronomers, would dispense research grants in the fashion of the modern foundation.[54] "Like all schemes of this day," noted *Science* in 1886 when the astronomer announced his plan, "Professor Pickering's is one of consolidation."[55] It was understandable that American science took on certain general characteristics of its surrounding culture. In the 1880's, business leaders were discovering the control that came with concentration. Pickering watched pools and trusts multiply, marveling especially at the organizational genius of John D. Rockefeller and Andrew Carnegie. He saw himself doing for science what they had done for industry.[56]

Except for a single year's trial run in 1890, underwritten by an elderly recluse who specialized in subsidizing astrophysicists, Pickering failed in his master plan for organizing science.[57] A number of influential scientists suspected, probably unfairly, his disinterested posture and accused Pickering of having monopolistic designs for the endowment field. Furthermore, wealthy laymen showed little willingness to see their contributions absorbed into a large, anonymous fund.

[54] Edward C. Pickering, "Large Telescopes," *Boston Advertiser*, March 26, 1878; Edward C. Pickering, "The Endowment of Research," *Proceedings of The American Association for the Advancement of Science*, 1878 (Salem, 1878), 63–72; Edward S. King, "Edward Charles Pickering," *DAB*, XIV 562–63.

[55] *Science*, VIII (September 24, 1886), 267.

[56] Edward C. Pickering, "The Endowment of Astronomical Research," *Science*, XVII (May 8, 1903), 721–22; Edward C. Pickering, "The Endowment of Research," *Science*, XIII (February 8, 1901), 201–2; Edward C. Pickering, "The Aims of an Astronomer," *Popular Astronomy*, XIV (December 1906), 586–91.

[57] Edward C. Pickering, "History of the Bruce Photographic Telescope," mss. notebook in the Harvard Observatory Records, Harvard University Archives. Numerous letters pertaining to the philanthropist, Miss Catherine Wolf Bruce, are located in the Bruce Donation Correspondence File, Harvard Observatory Records, Harvard Archives. The New York *Tribune*, March 15, 23, 1900, contains fragmentary biographical information on Miss Bruce; William W. Payne, "The Late Catherine Wolfe Bruce," *Popular Astronomy*, VIII (May 1900), 237–38 includes an apparently complete listing of her astronomical benefactions.

The gift of a major piece of apparatus made better newspaper copy. Edward Pickering was thus a transitional figure, slightly ahead of his time. A working astronomer-promoter in the tradition of Benjamin Peirce, he also previewed the rise of the professional, full-time foundation executive typified by the one-time astronomer Henry S. Pritchett.

Due to the continuing popularity of the telescope as a philanthropic object, by 1902 the United States could claim 142 astronomical observatories, more than any other country and more than could be utilized to best advantage by the existing scientific community. Simon Newcomb grumbled that "a great telescope is of no use without a man at the end of it."[58] Almost alone among American scientists, astronomers suffered from a surfeit of apparatus. Yet, even they lacked the reliable assistance that only established agencies could supply.

QUEST FOR PERMANENT RESEARCH FUNDS

During the second week in October 1872, as late returns multiplied President Grant's plurality over Horace Greeley and liberal reform, hardly anyone outside the scientific community noticed the arrival of Professor John Tyndall in New York. The famous English physicist had come on a special mission; twenty-five American scientists had invited him to tour the country advertising scientific research. It was a revealing tactic, for since the 1840's, many responsible scientists had held that popular science smacked of sideshow entertainment. Their willingness now to resort to popular lectures, going so far as to import a skilled performer from abroad, indicated the failure of existing scientific agencies to meet the day-to-day needs of the scientific community.[59]

Michael Faraday's successor as superintendent of the Royal Insti-

[58] Simon Newcomb, "Aspects of American Astronomy," *Astrophysical Journal*, VI (November 1897), 304–5. The Smithsonian Institution *List of Observatories*, Smithsonian Miscellaneous Collections, No. 1259 (Washington, D.C., 1902), is a convenient check list.

[59] New York *Times*, October 10, 1872; Joseph Henry to John Tyndall, August 14, 1871, Joseph Henry Papers, Smithsonian Institution; John Tyndall, *Lectures on Light, Delivered in the United States in 1872–73* (New York, 1873), pp. 10–11; Arthur S. Eve and C. H. Creasey, *Life and Work of John Tyndall* (London, 1945), pp. 166–67. Two notable discussions of the dangers inherent in "popular" science are Frank W. Clarke, "Scientific Dabblers," *Popular Science Monthly*, I (September 1872), 594–600, and Thomas C. Mendenhall, "The Relations of Men of Science to the General Public," *Science*, XVI (October 24, 1890), 229–33.

tution of London, Tyndall was already well known in America both as a research scientist and as a dynamic lecturer and writer on scientific subjects. His volume on *Heat as a Mode of Motion* (1863) had been the first popular explanation in English of the mechanical theory of heat. Now Tyndall proposed to lecture on the physical and optical properties of light, a subject well adapted to impressive displays in large lecture halls.[60] His reception in seven eastern cities was a little reminiscent of Louis Agassiz's triumphal tour three decades before. In each case, the first five performances were a come-on for the sixth, which Tyndall concluded with a ringing appeal for the support of science. "Keep your eye upon the originator of knowledge," he pleaded. "Give him the freedom necessary for his researches, not overloading him either with the duties of tuition or of administration, not demanding from him so-called practical results."[61] At the conclusion of his tour, Tyndall offered the net proceeds from his lectures as an endowment to assist American students who sought scientific training abroad. The gift of a European, the $13,000 Tyndall Fund was one of the first postgraduate fellowships available to American men of science. It was somehow appropriate that the first recipient, Michael Pupin, was himself a recent European immigrant.[62]

The Tyndall Fund was the most tangible product of the Englishman's American mission. Though his lectures were well publicized and well attended, he failed to awaken a general interest in scientific research. Partly to blame was his often belligerent materialism, which offended the pious and doubtless detracted from his general effectiveness. Nor were the uneasy months before the Panic of '73 an auspicious time to beg money for any purpose.

Tyndall's rhetoric, however, echoed for a quarter century and helped provide the framework in which American scientists perceived the changing social relations of science. Tyndall had phrased his analysis in Tocqueville's classic terms, drawing a distinction between basic and applied science. If more imagined than real in the 1830's, by the 1870's Tocqueville's scheme was particularly timely. The achieve-

---

[60] Tyndall, *Lectures on Light*, pp. 3–6, 190.

[61] Tyndall, *Lectures on Light*, pp. 151–83.

[62] Joseph Henry to John Tyndall, May 11, 1872, January 6, 1873, Joseph Henry Papers, Smithsonian Institution; John Tyndall to Joseph Henry, February 7, 1873, Smithsonian Letterbook, Smithsonian Institution Archives; *Proceedings at the Farewell Banquet to Professor Tyndall, Given at Delmonico's, New York, Feb. 4, 1873* (New York, 1873), pp. 47–50. Pupin praises Tyndall in his autobiography, *From Immigrant to Inventor* (New York, 1924), pp. 201–6.

ments of applied science, especially telegraphy and steam engineering, seemed about to eclipse science itself. "Such applications," said Tyndall, "are so astounding . . . as to shut out from view those workers who are engaged in the quieter and profounder business of original investigation."[63] Ultimately science would profit, both because technology derived from scientific knowledge and because industrial enterprise produced pools of surplus capital that could be drained into scientific channels. But in the short run (and like other men, scientists generally lived in the short run), the imbalance between applied science and original discovery made added support for the latter imperative. The old, informal mechanics of private patronage no longer served. Scientists began to speak of "enduring and universal" rather than "local and transitory" assistance. Robert H. Thurston, an engineer, put it plainly to the American Association for the Advancement of Science in 1878. "The Endowment of Research has formed no part of a complete scheme for the advancement of science, or, at least, it has never had the attention and the time given to its procurement that it should have had."[64]

Until late in the century, there were very few endowments on which to draw. The multitude of local and national scientific societies had for decades devoted their meager assets to publishing memoirs and bolstering morale by awarding medals and cash premiums for research already accomplished. The private agencies that did aid research before the 1870's owed their resources most often to scientists themselves. Personally involved in the business of research, such men understood the relative value of before-the-fact and after-the-fact support. The first, venturing capital on the unknown, made advancement possible; the second only rewarded success. Benjamin Thompson, Count Rumford, had established the first research endowment in 1796 with a $5,000 gift in trust to the American Academy of Arts and Sciences for a biennial premium and medal for significant researches in light and heat. In 1832 the Academy, frustrated by the precise wording of Rumford's will, secured permission from the

---

[63] Tyndall, *Lectures on Light*, p. 174.

[64] Robert H. Thurston, "The Science of the Advancement of Science," *Proceedings of the American Association for the Advancement of Science*, 1878 (Salem, 1879), 56. Thurston expanded his argument in "The Mission of Science," *Proceedings of the American Association for the Advancement of Science*, 1884 (Salem, 1885), 227–53. See also John W. Draper, "Science in America," *Popular Science Monthly*, X (January 1877), 319.

courts to devote the rapidly accumulating residue of the Rumford Fund to research.[65] During the following decades, light and heat proved sufficiently broad categories to cover the purchase of apparatus for Harvard Observatory, to subsidize photometric and spectrascopic researches by Wolcott Gibbs and Edward C. Pickering, Samuel P. Langley's investigations of radiant energy, and Henry A. Rowland's new determination of the mechanical equivalent of heat. By 1900 the American Academy had awarded more than eighty grants from the Rumford Fund with a cumulative value of $28,765.[66]

Save for the Smithsonian Institution, the Rumford Fund stood alone in its field until 1867. In that year Alexander Dallas Bache died, leaving the National Academy of Sciences (founded in 1863) $50,000 for general purposes and the residue of his estate in trust for "the prosecution of researches in Physical and Natural Science by assisting experimentalists and observers." The $40,000 estate passed to the National Academy in 1871.[67] Bache established an important precedent. In 1878 three of Joseph Henry's friends, Joseph Patterson, Fairman Rogers, and George W. Childs, collected $40,000 as a personal tribute to the physicist. Alive to Henry's sense of propriety, his admirers knew he would never accept a personal gift. Instead they established a lifetime trust fund for Henry's family, which later would revert to the National Academy as a research endowment.[68] By 1903, when the Henry Fund became available, John C. Watson, O. C. Marsh, Wolcott Gibbs, the widows of J. Lawrence Smith and Henry Draper, and Benjamin A. Gould's daughter already had contributed additional sums to the National Academy's resources for research. By 1895, the aggregate principle totaled $94,000, making the National

---

[65] *The American Academy* vs. *Harvard College*, 12 Gray 582; American Academy of Arts and Sciences, *The Rumford Fund of the American Academy of Arts and Sciences* (Boston, 1905), pp. 1–7. On the general topic of scientific societies and research, see Addison Brown, "Endowment for Scientific Research and Publication," *Annual Report of the Smithsonian Institution*, 1892 (Washington, D.C., 1893), 624, 635–36. A discussion of tangible research support is virtually nonexistent in Ralph Bates' standard survey of *Scientific Societies in the United States*, 2nd ed. (New York, 1958).

[66] American Academy of Arts and Sciences, *The Rumford Fund*, pp. 14–19.

[67] Frederick W. True, *A History of the First Half-Century of the National Academy of Science, 1863–1913* (Washington, D.C., 1913), pp. 33–34, 361–63.

[68] Joseph B. Patterson to Joseph Henry, December 20, 1877; Joseph Henry to Joseph B. Patterson, January 10, 1878, copies in the Cyrus H. McCormick Papers, State Historical Society of Wisconsin, Madison, Wisc. The complete list of contributors appeared in the *Proceedings of the National Academy of Science*. Vol. I, Pt. 1 (Washington, D.C., 1915), 135–36.

Academy easily the most important single agency in the United States providing grants for scientific investigation.[69]

The American Association for the Advancement of Science, despite its name and its position as the nation's largest scientific association, offered no tangible encouragement of research from its founding in 1848 until 1873. The Association had traditionally operated from year to year solely on membership dues. In 1873, however, Elizabeth Thompson became its first patron by donating $1,000 for research. A strong, independent-minded New York philanthropist, Mrs. Thompson frequently took the initiative in seeking out philanthropic objects. In this case, she claimed an awareness of the "financial difficulties which beset those noble men of science who labor more for truth than for profit's sake."[70] The gift awakened the Association to the possibility of a permanent research fund. Hitherto an unincorporated society without a legal existence, in 1874 the organization hurriedly secured a formal charter from the Commonwealth of Massachusetts and set aside the proceeds from life memberships for a research endowment.[71]

In 1884 Elizabeth Thompson made a second donation to science. Advised by Dr. Charles Minot of the Harvard Medical School, she established the $25,000 Elizabeth Thompson Science Fund. "It is certainly very remarkable," observed Dr. Minot, "that a person not especially versed in science . . . should be induced . . . not to give for some temporary need, but with exceptional insight, to give for the development of the very sources of progress." Thereafter, yearly notices in *Science* testified to the far-reaching results of her vision.[72]

---

[69] The wills and trust deeds are printed as Appendix VI in True, *History of the National Academy of Sciences*, pp. 361–73. See also *Annual Report of the National Academy of Sciences*, 1895 (54 Cong., 1st sess., Senate Doc. No. 55), 15. The papers of Oliver Wolcott Gibbs, a founder of the National Academy and a long-time manager of its research endowments, reveal the day-to-day operations of the fund. They are preserved in the library of the Franklin Institute, Philadelphia.

[70] *Proceedings of the American Association for the Advancement of Science*, 1873 (Salem, 1874), 422, 439–40; "A Talk with Elizabeth Thompson," New York *Times*, August 25, 1885; *The American Annual Cyclopaedia*, 1899 (New York, 1900), 642.

[71] *Proceedings of the American Association for the Advancement of Science*, 1873 (Salem, 1874), 422–23; *Proceedings*, 1891 (Salem, 1892), 451; *Proceedings*, 1894 (Salem, 1895), 469.

[72] *Proceedings of the American Association for the Advancement of Science*, 1884 (Salem, 1885), p. 707; *Science*, IV (September 19, 1884), 269; "A New Endowment for Research," *Science*, VI (August 21, 1885), 144–45.

During the last quarter of the nineteenth century, a period notable for active private agencies in the field of higher education, strictly scientific agencies still suffered from inefficient organization and haphazard finance. Between 1875 and 1902, the already substantial endowment of American higher education *increased* by $153 million. By the latter date the *total* endowment in the United States specifically earmarked for scientific investigation was less than $3 million, nearly four fifths of which was localized at Harvard and the Smithsonian Institution. Even at the turn of the century, American scientists were still largely dependent, as George Davidson put it, on their ability to "wrestle with the generous and the wealthy."[73]

PRIVATE FOUNDATIONS, THE NEW PATRONS OF SCIENCE

Andrew Carnegie recalled in his *Autobiography* that, after he had published his timely essays on the gospel of wealth (1900), "it was inevitable that I should live up to its teachings."[74] Within a year the self-made steelmaster, motivated by business considerations as well as by his sense of stewardship, had sold out to J. P. Morgan and retired to teach the gospel of wealth by example. Carnegie's early benefactions covered a wide range of social and educational needs, but none was more rewarding than the $10 million Carnegie Institution of Washington. Through the Institution, chartered in January 1902, Carnegie hoped to relieve what he termed America's "National Poverty in Science" and win for his adopted country a commanding position "in the domain of discovery."[75]

---

[73] *Annual Report of the United States Commissioner of Education*, 1875 (Washington, D.C., 1876), p. lxxxii; *Report*, 1902, 2 vols. (Washington, D.C., 1903), II, 1351, 1354. The estimate of scientific research endowments is based on a detailed survey conducted in 1902 for the Carnegie Institution of Washington and published as Appendix B to the *Confidential Report of the Executive Committee to the Board of Trustees, November 11, 1902* (Washington, D.C., 1902). See also George Davidson, *The Endowment of Research* (n.p., n.d. [Presidential Address, California Academy of Sciences, 1892]), p. 6.

[74] Andrew Carnegie, *Autobiography* (Boston: Houghton Mifflin Co., 1920), p. 255.

[75] Andrew Carnegie to Simon Newcomb, January 3, 1902, Simon Newcomb Papers, Library of Congress, Washington, D.C.; Carnegie Institution of Washington, *Yearbook*, No. 1 (Washington, D.C., 1903), p. xiv. Edward C. Kirkland's introduction to the John Harvard Library edition of *The Gospel of Wealth and Other Timely Essays* (Cambridge, Mass., 1962), pp. vii-xx, is the best brief analysis of Carnegie's social ideas. Burton J. Hendrick, *The Life of Andrew Carnegie*, 2 vols. (Garden City, N.Y., 1932), is the standard biography.

The Carnegie Institution launched a new era in the history of scientific research agencies in the United States. Its antecedents, such as the dream of a national university, the example of the Royal Institution of London, the benefactions of James Smithson and others, and the repeated efforts of scientists to consolidate research funds, were all characteristic nineteenth-century methods of improving the social relations of science. Its final form and function, on the other hand, distinguished the Carnegie Institution from its predecessors and made it (along with the contemporaneous agencies established by John D. Rockefeller) a prototype of the modern research foundation.[76]

A number of conflicting influences shaped the Institution. There had been periodic agitation for a national university ever since George Washington's proposal in the 1790's. Never an actuality, over the years the university had been a conveniently formless ideal whose character changed with changing times. By the end of the nineteenth century, John W. Hoyt and other leaders of the National Education Association held that without such an institution, the American educational system would remain a "truncated pyramid." Patriotic ladies called it the only fitting memorial to the Father of His Country. Influential scientists saw it as the long-awaited agency to rationalize the nation's total scientific effort.[77]

Andrew Carnegie, now one of America's most conspicuous philanthropists as well as a man of unusual perception and broad interests, was well aware of the current university schemes. Ever since John Hoyt had approached him in 1899, Carnegie had pondered the problems confronting the higher learning in America.[78] In the spring of 1901, when his friend Andrew Dixon White broached the subject

---

[76] For an official but informative survey of the Rockefeller contributions to scientific research agencies, see Raymond B. Fosdick, *The Story of the Rockefeller Foundation* (New York, 1952).

[77] John W. Hoyt, "The Life of John Wesley Hoyt, A.M., M.D., LL.D.," pp. 369–70, 414–17, typescript autobiography in the John W. Hoyt Papers, State Historical Society of Wisconsin; Daniel Coit Gilman, "Another University in Washington and How to Secure It," *The Century Magazine*, LV (November 1897), 156–57; Simon Newcomb, "Why We Need a National University," *North American Review*, CLX (February 1895), 210–16; Charles D. Walcott, "Relations of the National Government to Higher Education and Research," *Science*, XIII (June 28, 1901), 1001–15; Susanna P. Gage, "A George Washington Memorial University," *The Outlook*, LVIII (February 26, 1898), 521–24. A convenient history and bibliography of the national university movement is Edgar B. Wesley, *Proposed, The University of the United States* (Minneapolis, 1936).

[78] Hoyt, "Life of John W. Hoyt," pp. 477–550, 456, Hoyt Papers, State Historical Society of Wisconsin.

of a Carnegie-endowed university in the District of Columbia, the millionaire already had concluded that George Washington's original conception was now outmoded. "You suggested [a] National University at Washington, Washington's desire," he told White. "Several have; but while this does, as you say, ensure immortality to the Founder, it has hitherto seemed to me not needed, and this puts immortality under foot."[79]

That summer at Skibo, his castle retreat in Scotland, Carnegie continued to confer with White, Daniel Coit Gilman, and John Shaw Billings. Late in November, after his return to the United States, he announced his decision to give $10 million for the advancement of learning. The Carnegie Institution would not be a university in the usual sense; it would strengthen rather than compete with existing facilities. Accordingly, the principal aim was "to increase the efficiencies of universities & other institutions . . . by seeking to utilize & add to their existing faculties & to aid their teachers in experimental work."[80] The scheme showed the influence of Geological Survey Director Charles D. Walcott, who now joined with White, Gilman, and Billings as Carnegie's closest advisors.[81] Though he sought expert counsel, Carnegie's decisions were always his own. As those close to him would learn, he had not bound himself to the November outline. Carnegie's deed of trust, dated January 28, 1902, relegated the university scheme to fourth place in the list of institutional objectives. Now the controlling principle was "to promote original research, paying great attention thereto as one of the most important of all departments."[82]

An article in the January number of the *North American Review* had prompted Carnegie to transform the still plastic institution. "I read last night an interesting article . . . which sums up our National Poverty in Science," he told Simon Newcomb on January 3. "To change

---

[79] Andrew Carnegie to Andrew D. White, April 26, May 2, 1901, Andrew Carnegie Papers, Library of Congress.

[80] Andrew D. White to Andrew Carnegie, May 13, June 21, 1901; Andrew Carnegie to Andrew D. White, May 28, 1901; "University in Washington," draft plan of organization, November, 1901; Andrew Carnegie to Theodore Roosevelt, November 28, 1901; all in the Andrew Carnegie Papers, Library of Congress. See also Hendrick, *Life of Andrew Carnegie*, II, 219, and Fabian Franklin, *The Life of Daniel Coit Gilman* (New York: Dodd, Mead & Co., 1910), pp. 390–97.

[81] The best, though brief sketch of Walcott is Nelson H. Darton, "Memorial of Charles D. Walcott," *Bulletin of the Geological Society of America*, No. 39 (1927), 80–116, which includes a bibliography of Walcott's extensive writings.

[82] Carnegie Institution of Washington, *Yearbook*, No. 1, vii–viii, xiii; Franklin, *Daniel Coit Gilman*, pp. 400–401.

our position among the Nations is the Aim I have in view."[83] In the article in question, Carl Snyder, a free-lance journalist and editorial writer for the Washington *Post*, had presented a dreary picture of "America's Inferior Position in the Scientific World." Snyder suggested that much of the vigor of European science stemmed from its solid institutional base. American scientific men had nothing to compare with the Collège de France, the Pasteur Institute, or the Royal Institution of London. It was time, concluded Snyder, for someone to establish an equivalent agency "in the chief city of the New World."[84] Future historians would frequently cite Snyder's article as an informed estimate of American science at the turn of the century. Actually, it was better interpreted in the light of its immediate purpose, which was directive rather than didactic. Snyder's article, strategically placed in Carnegie's favorite magazine, was too timely to have been entirely coincidental.

As a pioneer in its field, the Carnegie Institution was one of the first to explore a number of issues which would continue to concern private scientific agencies in the twentieth century. One of Carnegie's principal goals was to locate and assist exceptional men. "How is it that knowledge is increased," he asked, "how can rare intellects be discovered in the undeveloped stages?"[85] After a searching eight-month study of American scientific institutions, the Carnegie trustees answered that the best procedure was to give priority to large research projects. "Hitherto, with few exceptions," read the first policy statement, dictated by Secretary Charles D. Walcott, "research has been a matter of individual enterprise, each man taking up that problem which chance or taste led him to." But in modern times the stakes were too high to risk chance success. Modern science, like modern business, required centralized planning and direction. "The most effective way to find and develop the exceptional man is to put promising men at work . . . under proper . . . supervision. The men who can not fulfill their promise will soon drop out, and by the survival of the fittest the capable, exceptional man will appear."[86] Walcott's

---

[83] Andrew Carnegie to Simon Newcomb, January 3, 1902, Simon Newcomb Papers, Library of Congress.

[84] Carl Snyder, "America's Inferior Position in the Scientific World," *North American Review*, CLXXIV (January 1902), 59–72.

[85] Franklin, *Daniel Coit Gilman*, pp. 393–97.

[86] Carnegie Institution, *Confidential Report of the Executive Committee*, pp. xi–xiii; Charles Walcott to Andrew Carnegie, June 19, 1902, Andrew Carnegie Papers, Library of Congress. Walcott's orientation is clear in his address on the "Outlook of the Geologist in America," *Bulletin of the Geological Society of America*, No. XIII (February 2, 1902), 117–18.

approach ran counter to one of the scientific community's most cherished traditions, that of the unfettered scientific genius seeking knowledge according to his own dictates. Older scientists like astronomer Lewis Boss feared that "machine-like organization" was a preliminary step to a "scientific dictatorship."[87]

Machine-like or not, organization in research and manpower procurement was as necessary in modern society as was organization in business enterprise and social welfare. In the 1840's, American science had been transformed by specialization and professionalization. Now, at the beginning of the twentieth century, yet another generation of scientists was riding the wave of a new organizational revolution. Charles Walcott offered Andrew Carnegie an unusually keen analysis of the process. There were two basic approaches to scientific discovery, he explained in 1903: individualism, "the old view that one man can develop and carry forward any line of research"; and collectivism, "the modern idea of cooperation and community of effort." Walcott indicated that most of the younger American scientists, thirty-five to fifty years old, were thoroughgoing collectivists, while their elders remained loyal to the individualistic traditions of an earlier day. "In my opinion," he advised, "we might as well try to make a great research institution of the C. I. by pure individualism, as to expect success in great industrial enterprises by the individualism of 1850 to 1870."[88]

During the succeeding years, the Carnegie Institution evolved slowly, but decisively, along "collectivist" lines. Like the Rockefeller Institute for Medical Research, it was more an operating than a grant-making institution. In its research departments, teams of specialists tackled major scientific problems. The nonmagnetic brigantine *Carnegie* crisscrossed the oceans charting the earth's magnetic field. At Cold Spring Harbor, New York, Charles B. Davenport supervised far-reaching studies of experimental evolution in plants, animals, and man. Atop Mt. Wilson in California, George Ellery Hale directed a great solar observatory, recalling to life a project which had lain dormant since the collapse of the southern California land boom in the 1880's.[89]

---

[87] Lewis Boss to Andrew Carnegie, April 7, 1902, Andrew Carnegie Papers, Library of Congress.

[88] Charles D. Walcott to Andrew Carnegie, January 25, 1903, Andrew Carnegie Papers, Library of Congress. See also Simon Newcomb, "The Organization of Research," *North American Review*, CLXXXII (January, 1906), 32–43.

[89] The annual *Yearbook* of the Carnegie Institution is the authoritative statement of institutional policy and programs. See especially *Yearbook*, No. 10

Eventually a host of private agencies appeared to assist in promoting scientific research. After World War I, when the National Research Council widely publicized the vital importance of scientific research in American life, an increasing number of scientific societies and philanthropic foundations took an active interest in the increase as well as the diffusion of knowledge. The tax-exempt status of contributions to such agencies was an added reason for their mushroom growth.[90] Between 1920 and 1934, the National Research Council's comprehensive check list of research funds in America doubled. By 1953, the seventy-seven largest American foundations were devoting 16 percent of their total expenditures, or $26 million out of $142 million, to scientific research.[91]

The amount of money supplied by private agencies was a small percentage of the total national research budget, which reached $5 billion in 1953, but mere dollars were no just measure of their effect. The timely investment of small sums had often yielded great returns, as in the 1930's when a $700 Rockefeller Foundation grant materially aided Howard W. Florey in proving the clinical value of penicillin.[92] In a society witnessing a phenomenal expansion of industrial and government science, furthermore, private scientific agencies had a critical responsibility. Military, political, and economic considerations tended to give research and development projects a utilitarian bent. Long ago Frank B. Jewett, President of the Bell Telephone Laboratories, had warned that such a tendency could become self-defeating. "As

---

(Washington, D.C., 1911), 8–13. Mark H. Haller, *Eugenics: Hereditarian Influences in American Thought* (New Brunswick, 1963), is an insightful study of the work at Cold Spring Harbor. On Carnegie's personal interest in the Mt. Wilson observatory, see Hendrick, *Andrew Carnegie*, II, 237–41.

[90] A useful introduction to the work of the National Research Council is the official *History of the National Research Council, 1919–1933* (Washington, D.C., 1933). Helpful discussions of taxation factors are Berien C. Eaton, Jr., "Charitable Foundations, Tax Avoidance and Business Expediency," *Virginia Law Review*, XXXV (November 1949), 809–61, (December 1949), 987–1051, and Franklin C. Latcham, "Private Charitable Foundations: Some Tax and Policy Implications," *University of Pennsylvania Law Review*, XCVIII (April 1950), 617–53.

[91] Callie Hull *et al.*, comps., "Funds Available in 1920 in the United States of America for the Encouragement of Scientific Research," *Bulletin of the National Research Council*, No. 9 (Washington, D.C., 1921); Callie Hull *et al.*, comps., "Funds Available in the United States for the Support and Encouragement of Research in Science and its Technologies," 3rd ed., *Bulletin of the National Research Council*, No. 95 (Washington, D.C., 1934); F. Emerson Andrews, *Scientific Research Expenditures by the Larger Foundations* (Washington, D.C., 1956), p. 5.

[92] Fosdick, *The Rockefeller Foundation*, p. 165.

we meet with added success in turning scientific discoveries to practical account," he explained, "we are confronted with the strong temptation to seek knowledge because it is useful, and not simply for the sake of knowledge itself. We are thus in danger of losing the true perspective, for it becomes increasingly easy to pass from seeking knowledge because it is useful, to seeking what we may consider, from a priori reasons, to be useful knowledge."[93]

Private agencies were in a unique position to avoid myopic utilitarianism. Like individual patrons of science in the nineteenth century, twentieth-century agencies were free to venture capital on the unknown, to channel their resources at crucial moments into areas of research critical for further advance. Their special function, as Dean Rusk, President of the Rockefeller Foundation, explained it in 1952, was "to prime the pump, to look for germinal ideas, and to help establish standards that will lead to continuous improvement in the quality of research and scholarship."[94]

[93] Frank B. Jewett, "Motive and Obligation," *Reprint and Circular Series of the National Research Council*, No. 68 (Washington, D.C., 1926), 7.

[94] *Hearings Before the Select* (Cox) *Committee to Investigate Tax-Exempt Foundations and Comparable Organizations* (82 Cong., 2nd sess., House of Representatives [Washington, D.C., 1953]), p. 485.

Science and Government Agencies

Carroll W. Pursell, Jr.*

Today scientific research and development receives about $.5 billion in support from universities, $5 billion from private industry, and a staggering $15 billion from the federal government, which has become its principal patron. This predominant role, only recently assumed, has had a large impact on the government itself, on the national economy, and on the very body of science.

Only two really important scientific activities took root within the government before the Civil War, and both of these were officially considered to be temporary, since they were tied to the taming of a great and newly acquired empire.[1] The first, the Coast Survey, got off to a false start in 1807, was reactivated in 1832, and then became the most important scientific agency of the federal government, partly because of the real need of commercial interests for accurate charts and maps, and partly through the superb political-scientific leadership of its chief, Alexander Dallas Bache. The second was the exploration of the West, carried on by the Army. From the Lewis and Clark expedition of 1803 through the Pacific railroad surveys of 1853, the systematic exploration of the West was consigned to the military. In part, this was because the use of men already on the government's

---

* CARROLL W. PURSELL, JR., was born in Visalia, California, in 1932. He took his B.A. at the University of California, Berkeley, in 1956, his M.A. at the University of Delaware in 1958, and his Ph.D. at the University of California, Berkeley, in 1962. He is currently Assistant Professor of History at the University of California, Santa Barbara. He is one of the editors of *The Politics of American Science: 1939 to the Present* (Chicago, 1965), and has published articles on American science and technology, as well as on other subjects, in *Delaware History; Agricultural History; Journal of the Presbyterian Historical Society; Technology and Culture; William and Mary Quarterly;* and the *Proceedings of the American Philosophical Society.* Professor Pursell is currently at work on a study of federal science policy during the Great Depression, 1929–39.

[1] A. Hunter Dupree, *Science in the Federal Government: A History of Policies and Activities to 1940* (Cambridge, Mass., 1957).

payroll appealed to economy-minded congressmen. In part, it was because military discipline was necessary for meeting the exigencies of exploration, because West Point graduates formed a reliable pool of academically trained engineers, and because activities designed to "provide for the common defence" were clearly constitutional in a period when internal improvements were highly suspect.[2]

After the Civil War, there were many in the military who hoped that their antebellum domination of government science would be perpetuated. To some degree it was. The Naval Observatory, established surreptitiously in 1842 as an adjunct to the testing and setting of naval charts and instruments, was probably the nation's leading observatory during the several decades following the war. Its long-time director, Simon Newcomb, was acclaimed internationally for his work. This golden age was short-lived, however, and between 1894 and 1929, no major new instruments were added to the observatory's equipment. By and large, such routine matters as timekeeping were the only activities encouraged.[3]

Before the Civil War, the beginnings of meteorological activities were found in the Army Medical Corps, the Naval Observatory, the Patent Office, and the Smithsonian Institution. During the years 1870–90, this duty was primarily the obligation of the Army Signal Corps. This activity was taken, in large part, to afford something for the corps to do after the war. Despite the efforts of General William B. Hazen, chief signal officer after 1881, to establish a sound scientific bureau combining research and service, the military saw little use for the corps' activities, and scientists tended to want both the weather service and the Naval Observatory removed from an uncongenial military context. In 1890 the weather service was finally removed to the Department of Agriculture, where it remained until 1940. By that time, commercial aviation had replaced farming as the most important user of the service, and the bureau was moved to the Department of Commerce.[4]

The greatest blow to the scientific pretensions of the military was the loss of its preeminence in western exploration. To a large extent,

---

2 William H. Goetzmann, *Army Exploration in the American West, 1803–1863* (New Haven, 1959).

3 Gustavus A. Weber, *The Naval Observatory: Its History, Activities, and Organization* (Baltimore, 1926); Simon Newcomb, *The Reminiscences of an Astronomer* (Boston, 1903).

4 Donald R. Whitnah, *A History of the United States Weather Bureau* (Urbana, 1961).

this resulted from the fact that gross facts of geography, the very type of information best discovered by the military, were nearly all known. Furthermore, as territories were divided into states, these new jurisdictions usually set up their own fact-finding scientific bodies. The late war had killed off the topographical engineers as a separate group and had hastened the conversion of West Point from a largely engineering school. The Corps of Engineers, with quickly increasing river and harbor appropriations to spend, was being turned into a routine practitioner of civil engineering.

The postwar explorations were, instead, carried on by a series of civilian agencies. The first of these began in 1867 as the Geological Survey of the Fortieth Parallel, under the leadership, not of a military officer, but of Clarence King, geologist and literator. Significantly, King had learned his science at Yale's Sheffield Scientific School rather than at West Point and had done his graduate work with J. D. Whitney's California state survey rather than with the Army. His survey was administered by the Corps of Engineers, but King had a free hand in planning the science involved. Congress thought it was supporting a survey of practical (economic and military) importance to the nation, and, in fact, King did make exhaustive studies of the various western mining regions. At the same time, however, King concentrated on producing sound scientific data and, in some cases, even contributed in important ways to geologic theory. King finished his survey in 1872 and completed the publication of results in 1880—at a total cost to the government of $386,711.[5]

While still involved with the King survey, the Corps of Engineers began its own survey in 1869 under the direction of Lieutenant George M. Wheeler. The survey started as a military reconnaissance of Nevada and Utah, but Congress soon extended its scope to include the hundredth meridian. It began to show signs of permanence. Using both civilians and military officers to make observations of natural history, Wheeler's survey differed little from others typical of the pre-Civil War period.

During these same years, the General Land Office roused itself long enough to begin a survey of its own, the third in the field. Led by Ferdinand V. Hayden, who termed himself "U.S. Geologist," the Geological and Geographical Survey of the Territories (as it was called after 1873) threatened to duplicate much of the work of both

---

[5] Thurman Wilkins, *Clarence King; A Biography* (New York, 1958).

King and Wheeler, since it covered part of the same territory and cultivated most of the same scientific interests.[6]

Extensive and expensive as these three surveys were, they were hardly sufficient to exhaust the willingness of the Congress to do something for the new West, or the willingness of scientists to participate in its taming. In 1870 John Wesley Powell persuaded Representative James A. Garfield to sponsor a bill appropriating $10,000 for a Geological and Topographical Survey of the Colorado River of the West. In 1874 the "mission" of the Powell survey was extended to include the Geographical and Geological Survey of the Rocky Mountain Region. Powell's genius for discovering problems to be solved led him to a major interest in the disappearing Indian tribes of the West and a concern for the classification of arid lands.[7]

Besides these new surveys, the old Coast Survey of Bache, now under the leadership of the Harvard mathematician Benjamin Peirce, began to run lines overland to connect east and west coast maps. When, in 1878, this agency's name was changed to the Coast and Geodetic Survey, it was clear that it, too, was a contender for the honor of mapping the West. By the end of the fiscal year 1886, it was estimated that the federal government had, from the beginning, spent some $68 million on surveys of one kind or another.[8]

This plethora of survey parties crossing and recrossing the West was symptomatic of several important facts. First, Congress, in refusing to face the need for a permanent surveying effort, had failed to designate any single agency to carry on this important housekeeping task. Second, in the absence of any clear policy or even intention on the part of Congress, established bureaus and hopeful newcomers to Washington had only to be convincing about their own pet schemes to win support. And lastly, the great West was so much at the core of American concern, and offered such high rewards for the accom-

---

[6] Adelaide R. Hasse, *Reports of Explorations Printed in the Documents of the United States Government* (Washington, D.C., 1899); L. F. Schmeckebier, "Catalogue and Index of the Publications of the Hayden, King, Powell and Wheeler Surveys," U.S. Geological Survey *Bulletin* (1904), p. 222.

[7] Everett W. Sterling, "The Powell Irrigation Survey, 1883–1893," *Mississippi Valley Historical Review*, XXVII (1940–41), 421–34; Wallace Stegner, *Beyond the Hundredth Meridian: John Wesley Powell and the Second Opening of the West* (Boston, Mass., 1954).

[8] Martha J. Lamb, "The Coast Survey," *Harper's New Monthly Magazine*, LVIII (March 1879), 506–21; George M. Wheeler, *Report upon the Third International Geographical Congress and Exhibition at Venice, Italy, 1881* (Washington, D.C., 1885), pp. 473–74; Morgan B. Sherwood, *Exploration of Alaska, 1865–1900* (New Haven, 1965).

plishment of necessary tasks, that it could not escape being the object of rival attentions. The taming of the West was the overriding purpose of the nation, and whoever best served that purpose stood in the mainstream of American scientific effort.

Five surveys, all at work mapping the West and collecting information on natural history, were a scandal to many in the government. The problem was more than merely one of unnecessary duplication. Restricting each to a different territory would not produce one complete map, since each was using different methods and, to some extent, emphasizing different sciences. The only other alternative was to choose between them. In 1874 Congress set out to investigate the government's surveying effort. Testimony was taken, but no action. In 1878 Congress called upon the National Academy of Sciences to study and report on the situation. Formally neutral, the Academy was in fact dominated by an antimilitary bias, and its recommendation called for civilian science within the government.

It was the recommendation of the Academy, following the suggestions of Powell, that the western survey should concern itself primarily with collecting sufficient information to classify properly the western public lands. With this scientific information in hand, the government could then rewrite its land laws to conform to rational standards. The revolutionary nature of this proposal was not lost upon western congressmen, who effectively resisted the passage of an organic act to create such an agency. Not without their own resources, the scientists worked with Representative Abram Hewitt to create a Geological Survey through the simple expedient of appropriating money for a director. Leaning on this frail reed, Powell, who became the second director of the Survey, built what was to be the most powerful scientific bureau in the government at the time.

Before the Civil War, science in the government occupied an uncertain constitutional position. Although such scientific agencies as the Coast Survey could grow to immense size and great importance by serving the needs of some influential constituency, such activities could be looked on as internal improvements and hence perhaps unconstitutional. The Coast Survey stayed alive by being responsible for an important job and doing it well, but it always lived under the shadow of someday completing its mapping task and being closed out. This uncertainty promised to continue as long as southern congressmen raised constitutional objections to internal improvements in particular and the growth of the federal government in general.

Upon the withdrawal of the southern states from the Congress at the time of the Civil War, however, the way was cleared for the government to take a forthright stand in favor of supporting scientific research on a permanent basis. In 1862 the nation's farmers received institutional support for a scientific attack on their problems through the establishment of a Department of Agriculture and the passage of the Morrill Act for land-grant colleges.[9]

The proper institutional support did not translate itself immediately into spectacular results. By 1870 the Department contained divisions of chemistry, horticulture, entomology, statistics, seeds, and botany. The subsequent creation of a division of microscopy emphasized the limits of thus organizing work around particular fields of competence or interest. Added to the organizational problem was that of political interference. On the latter count, Civil Service reform proved to be a two-edged sword which, while it helped to protect scientists from capricious political action, also made it difficult for the Department to hire particular men whom outside scientists considered most competent. Appropriations for the Department were $199,770 in 1864 and were still at the same level in 1880.

It is instructive that at the very time that America was being converted into a modern industrial nation, and its farmers were growing restive under the burden of a changing economy which they could neither understand nor control, the Department of Agriculture evolved into a tool of unprecedented effectiveness for dealing with rural problems. The cutting edge of this tool was to be science, and it was in the future to be directed against specific problems. What in fact happened was that the Department gave birth to that organizational form that was to prove so fruitful for government science in the future—the bureau.

Ideally, a scientific bureau had as its foundation an organic act from the Congress, defining its duties and obligations in terms of some specific problem or "mission," such as soil conservation, pure food and drug regulation, or space exploration. Having the long-term stability of a direct congressional mandate, the bureau would be able to build up a staff of professional scientists and put them to work in teams attacking aspects of the problem assigned. It was equally important that the bureau serve some definite constituency which was itself organized beyond the reach of normal politics. In this way, the bureau was able to depend upon some extragovernmental body for continuous support and guidance. In 1881 the old division of ento-

---

[9] Gladys L. Baker *et al.*, *Century of Service: The First 100 Years of the United States Department of Agriculture* (Washington, D.C., 1963).

mology was reorganized to become the Department's first modern bureau of this type.

While the Department was hitting upon its own proper internal arrangement, the passage of the Hatch Act in 1887 gave it the opportunity to create a nationwide network of agricultural experiment stations, coordinated and partially financed from the Department in Washington. In 1906 the Adams Act increased federal support and control and at the same time restricted some of the funds to the execution of original research. These growing relations between the Department and scattered land-grant colleges and experiment stations not only strengthened the resources of the Department but served also to complicate federal-state relations generally and offered the most compelling precedent before World War II for federal support of nongovernmental research and involvement in higher education.[10]

One of the problems faced by the new science bureaus was the proper relationship, within their areas, of research, service, and regulatory activities. This problem can best be seen in those agencies dedicated to some type of conservation work. With the closing of the frontier came a growing realization that the resources of even this wealthy continent were not inexhaustible. At the same time, there was a growing concern by business for the rationalization of the economy, from resources (conservation) through markets (trusts). A simple survey was sufficient to allow lands to be settled willy-nilly. Settlement in a controlled and rational manner demanded sound and extensive data so organized as to aid desirable use and regulate harmful exploitation.[11]

The beginnings of scientific conservation antedated the conservation crusade of the Progressives. In 1888 John Wesley Powell received congressional authority to begin an extensive irrigation survey to

---

[10] H. C. Knoblauch *et al.*, *State Agricultural Experiment Stations: A History of Research Policy and Procedure*, U.S. Department of Agriculture Miscellaneous Publication No. 904 (Washington, D.C., 1962); Charles E. Rosenberg, "The Adams Act: Politics and the Cause of Scientific Research," *Agricultural History*, XXXVIII (January 1964), 3–12; T. Swann Harding, *Two Blades of Grass: A History of Scientific Development in the U.S. Department of Agriculture* (Norman, Okla., 1947).

[11] Samuel P. Hays, *Conservation and the Gospel of Efficiency: The Progressive Conservation Movement, 1890–1920* (Cambridge, Mass., 1959); Richard T. Ely, "Conservation and Economic Theory," *Transactions*, American Institute of Mechanical Engineers, LIV (1916), 458–73; Samuel P. Sadtler, "Conservation and the Chemical Engineer," *Transactions*, American Institute of Chemical Engineers, II (1909), 105–14; John Birkinbine, "The American Institute of Mining Engineers and the Conservation of Natural Resources," *Transactions*, American Institute of Mining Engineers, XL (1909), 412–18.

identify, locate, and conserve the fast disappearing water resources of the arid West. Western interests turned on him and trimmed the power of his activities when they learned that distribution of the public domain was to be halted until properly classified. In fact, so much resentment was raised against this intrusion of science into a traditionally political situation that Congress made drastic cuts in the budgets of even the Coast Survey, Lighthouse Commission, Smithsonian Institution, and the Naval Observatory. The irrigation survey was shifted to the Department of Agriculture, where it was safely shoved into the background; but Powell, on his resignation as director of the Geological Survey, left behind a cadre of conservation-minded scientists who were already thinking in terms of scientific classification and integrated use.

Gradually, the new conservation bureaus began to take shape. During the 1860's, commercial fishing interests, and Spencer F. Baird of the Smithsonian, began to worry about the progressive disappearance of fish off the coast of New England. In 1871 Congress set up a Fish Commission to carry on research on the problem. Two years later, service joined research as a function of the bureau, when artificial propagation and operation of hatcheries became a large part of the bureau's responsibilities. During the 1880's, the government became concerned with the fauna of the continent, both as destructive pests and economic potential. It was still the age of mass slaughter of wild birds and animals, but by 1896, when the old Department of Agriculture Division of Economic Ornithology and Mammalogy became the Division of the Biological Survey, the federal government was firmly committed to a broad-scale research effort in fundamental natural history.[12]

It was the Forest Service, however, which came to epitomize the new conservation agency. After a decade of agitation by scientists, forestry became a division of the Department of Agriculture in the mid-1880's. Its activities were directed by the German-trained Bernhard E. Fernow, who concentrated his limited resources on background research, deliberately rejecting any idea of regulation and depending upon the example of well-run forests to spread the practice. Fernow's activities, however, had little relevance to the nation's problem of fast-disappearing forests. In 1891 Congress authorized the President to withdraw forest lands from sale, to be held by the gov-

---

[12] William H. Dall, *Spencer Fullerton Baird* (Philadelphia, 1915); Jenks Cameron, *The Bureau of Biological Survey, Its History, Activities, and Organization* (Baltimore, 1929).

ernment. Within two years, 17,500,000 acres were so withdrawn but without provisions being made for management or protection. Neither the passivity and scholarly aloofness of Fernow nor the aesthetic preservationism of men like John Muir was able to solve the problem of what should be done.[13]

It was Gifford Pinchot who hit upon the combination for success. Rejecting the intensive methods of European foresters and the wilderness ideals of Muir, he advocated rational and businesslike exploitation. In 1895 he was among a handful of scientists who planned the intervention of the National Academy in the problem. Secretary of the Interior Hoak Smith was induced to ask the Academy to study the matter, and the whole problem was thus turned over to the scientists who had a plan. The Academy's report, and compromise legislation in 1897, laid the groundwork for a forest-management policy and gave hope that the Department of Interior would have the chance to do some real long-range scientific planning for the West.[14]

Starting in Interior, Pinchot was induced to switch to Agriculture to replace Fernow in the Division of Forestry. By cutting back on his predecessor's elaborate research emphasis, the new Forester succeeded in producing enough immediate results in forest management to win over the largest and most influential segments of the lumber industry. Yale's new school of forestry, financed by Pinchot family money and headed by the former chief assistant to the Forester, gave the Division a firm academic base. By 1901, when Vice President Theodore Roosevelt succeeded President McKinley, the stage was set for a massive governmental assault on the problems of conservation. The key men were in the government's service, the necessary agencies were established, the fundamental nature of both the problem and its solution was known. The only things previously lacking had been the legal authority to carry out their plans and an administration which would back them to the hilt.

Theodore Roosevelt, the first President since John Quincy Adams to have a personal knowledge of, and interest in, science, made conservation a keystone of the Progressive Era. In no other area of governmental concern could disinterested scientific fact displace political prejudice with such startling results. It was a time for government

13 Andrew Denny Rodgers, III, *Bernhard Eduard Fernow* (Princeton, N.J., 1951); Sylvester Baxter, "The Forestry Work of the Tenth Census," *Atlantic Monthly*, XLVIII (November 1881), 682–88.

14 Gifford Pinchot, *Breaking New Ground* (New York, 1947); M. Nelson McGeary, *Gifford Pinchot: Forester-Politician* (Princeton, N.J., 1960).

by expert, and no one was more obviously expert than the scientifically trained man, whether forester or engineer-turned-city-planner. There was considerable opposition from those aspiring politicians or business men who had not yet arrived, but the controlled, rational resource-use policies of such Progressive conservationists as Pinchot won the admiration and support of big businessmen and bureaucrats.[15]

Because of their responsibility for the public domain, the conservation bureaus, which were essentially stabilized by 1916, brought science into more direct contact with major social, political, and economic considerations than had any of the earlier scientific agencies. Whether initially established to provide service, research, or regulation, it was soon discovered that the bureaus would necessarily have to provide all three. Service was inadequate without power, and power meant regulation. But regulation was itself impossible without research. Yet the three, while always necessary, were not always completely compatible. The Forest Service, for example, could not wait for research but had to offer service immediately. When service alone proved inadequate, regulation was required. By this time, research might discover that decades of service had been misdirected and that regulations were based on erroneous assumptions. Research, it was found, was a two-edged sword which could undermine as well as provide foundations for service and regulation.[16]

As American industry moved out of the free-swinging nineteenth century and began to face the problems of modern industrialism which it had itself created, it, too, turned to government science for help. Many industries, especially the newer ones based on electricity and chemicals, were already beginning to support their own industrial research laboratories, but there were certain functions which were either clearly unprofitable or impossible for industry to provide for itself.[17]

The government's constitutional responsibility concerning weights and measures had for many years been handled by the Coast and

[15] J. Leonard Bates, "Fulfilling American Democracy: The Conservation Movement, 1907 to 1921," *Mississippi Valley Historical Review*, XLIV (June 1957), 29–57; James L. Penick, Jr., "The Age of the Bureaucrat: Another View of the Ballinger-Pinchot Controversy," *Forest History*, VII (Spring-Summer 1963), 15–21.

[16] Ashley L. Schiff, *Fire and Water: Scientific Heresy in the Forest Service* (Cambridge, Mass., 1962).

[17] C. E. Skinner, "Industrial Research and Its Relation to University and Governmental Research," *Transactions*, American Institute of Electrical Engineers, XXXVI (1917), 871–904.

Geodetic Survey on the theory that surveying had a close connection with standard measures. With the rising need for such exotic new standards as the ohm, henry, and watt, this rationale was clearly inadequate. An American economy which was becoming truly national, increasingly technological, and incredibly complex stood in urgent need of all kinds of standards from screw threads to drug purity. When Henry S. Pritchett became head of the Coast Survey in 1897, he began a careful, and eventually successful, campaign to have a special bureau set up to handle national standards. After study of foreign laboratories and consultations with interested executive bureaus, a bill was presented to Congress and was passed in 1901 with the endorsement of such organizations as the National Academy of Sciences, the American Association for the Advancement of Science, and the American Institute of Electrical Engineers.[18]

The organic act of the new National Bureau of Standards authorized it not only to care for the standards themselves but to enter into research to determine such things as physical constants and properties of materials. The Bureau was permitted to conduct research and provide standards for private firms and professional societies, and a visiting committee of civilian scientists was established to insure that the nature and quality of work undertaken would conform to the best thinking of the scientific community. Eventually, the Bureau established standards for, and tested materials purchased by, the federal government, thus providing measures of quality which could be used by civilian consumers as well.

During these same years, the nation's mineral industry, already important as the center of industrial prosperity, came more and more to the attention of conservationists concerned with nonrenewable resources as well as those who sought to prevent the dramatic and tragic mine disasters which took an enormous toll of workers. The Geological Survey had been interested in the industry since the days of King, and it now received some funds for specific investigations of mine safety, testing of coals, and the like. Just as the Bureau of Reclamation had spun off from the Survey with a cluster of responsibilities more or less related, so now it appeared reasonable that a Bureau of Mines should do the same. Congress set up such a Bureau in 1910, giving it an emphasis on mine safety. However, Joseph A. Holmes,

18 Lyman J. Briggs, "Early Work of the National Bureau of Standards," *Scientific Monthly*, LXXIII (September 1951), 166–73; Gustavus A. Weber, *The Bureau of Standards: Its History, Activities, and Organization* (Baltimore, 1925).

the first bureau chief, raised prevention of waste to equal importance.[19]

The newly born aviation industry received early support from government-sponsored research. Although the Smithsonian Institution's role as a research center was handicapped by growing curatorial duties and its relatively paltry endowment, the work of Secretary Samuel Pierpont Langley in aeronautics gave the government an early interest in that field. After Langley's death, Secretary C. D. Walcott helped organize a Smithsonian advisory committee on aeronautics and, after the start of World War I in France, succeeded in getting it formalized as a government body. The National Advisory Committee for Aeronautics (NACA), established in 1915, presided over aeronautical research in the United States for over 40 years, and its unusual structure made it a model for later scientific agencies within the government.[20]

Except for facilities to encourage military research, the federal scientific establishment was virtually complete by 1916. Government science in this country, however, was no more prepared for a large-scale European war than was any other governmental interest. Many of the bureaus such as the National Bureau of Standards, the National Advisory Committee for Aeronautics, and the Bureau of Mines, had interests pertinent to wartime needs but were essentially organized around peacetime problems. Within the military itself, the strong scientific interest of the early nineteenth century had nearly died out. A few people saw the danger in such a situation early in the century. In 1902 it was suggested that the American Institute of Electrical Engineers might find it "proper to constitute a committee whose sole purpose should be to cooperate with the various bureaus of the army and navy in connection with the development of electrical war projects." Little progress was made along these lines, however, until after the war had broken out in Europe.[21]

Pushed finally to preparedness, the government set up a whole galaxy of temporary groups such as the Council for National Defense, the War Industries Board, and the Food Administration. While these all needed some kind of expert advice from scientists, it was the Navy

---

[19] Fred Wilbur Powell, *The Bureau of Mines: Its History, Activities, and Organization* (New York, 1922).

[20] George W. Gray, *Frontiers of Flight: The Story of NACA Research* (New York, 1948); J. C. Hunsaker, "Forty Years of Aeronautical Research," *Annual Report of the . . . Smithsonian Institution . . . 1955* (Washington, D.C., 1956), pp. 241–71.

[21] Caryl D. Haskins, "Civilian Co-operation in the Development of Electrical Devices for Military Purposes," *Transactions*, American Institute of Electrical Engineers, XIX (1902), 559–62.

Department which moved with the most firmness to strengthen its scientific facilities. Recalling the old Permanent Commission of the Civil War, which had been the most effective science agency of the time, the Navy, in 1915, appointed Thomas A. Edison as chairman of a Naval Consulting Board. The Board, made up of some of the leading industrial scientists and inventors of the day, recommended the establishment of a facility for carrying on naval research. Money was appropriated, but the scheme was not carried out until the building of the Naval Research Laboratory in 1923. Meanwhile the Consulting Board, like its Civil War predecessor and its World War II successor the National Inventors Council, spent most of its efforts in evaluating the volunteered ideas of civilian inventors: a task which, in World War I, produced only one item put into actual production from 110,000 ideas sent in.[22]

The National Academy of Sciences, at least on paper, seemed to be ideally situated to provide the government with the kind of central scientific direction which it so badly needed in time of crisis. In actual fact, its history and structure militated against its usefulness in this context. The almost moribund Academy had for years been little more than an honorary society. Its membership reflected not the broad spectrum of modern scientific interest in the nation but certain nineteenth-century preconceptions about that interest. In the first place, "pure" scientists, that is, academic research men rather than engineers or industrial scientists, were favored for membership. In the second place, academic science was probably overrepresented in comparison with government science. In point of fact, so great was the fear that membership of government men might make the Academy a political pawn, that a cabal had been formed in 1900 to prevent the election of Gifford Pinchot. The structure of the Academy was defective in that the membership was limited to a relatively small number of men, and these were permitted to give advice to the government only when asked to do so by some official agency.[23]

The scientific needs of the government were quite different. It needed a large number of scientists, it had a greater need for applied science and engineering than basic research, and it required an orga-

[22] Lloyd N. Scott, *Naval Consulting Board of the United States* (Washington, D.C., 1920); K. T. Compton, "Edison's Laboratory in Wartime," *Science,* LXXV (1932), 70–71; A. Hoyt Taylor, *The First Twenty-Five Years of the Naval Research Laboratory* (Washington, D.C., n.d. [1948]).

[23] Frederick W. True, *A History of the First Half-Century of the National Academy of Sciences, 1863–1913* (Washington, D.C., 1913); Richard H. Heindel, "From the Correspondence of Oliver Wolcott Gibbs," *Science,* LXXXIV (September 18, 1936), 268.

nization that could work with government agencies continually rather than merely being on call. The nation's engineering community, operating through some 32 advisory committees, was making a strong bid to become the primary technical advisors to the government. In 1916, however, a reform group within the Academy, led by George Ellery Hale, persuaded President Wilson to establish, by executive order, the National Research Council. This new agency, while firmly under Academy control, tried to provide that wide and useful representation which its parent organization lacked. Spending large amounts of private foundation funds and enjoying an appointment as the department of research for the Council of National Defense, the National Research Council supervised extensive work in such areas as submarine detection, carried on to a large extent by scientists quickly given commissions and put into uniform.[24]

All in all, the results of the American scientific war effort, in terms of hardware, were not very impressive. The late start in preparedness, the shortness of the war, and the sacrifice of research to immediate expedients, all militated against any very startling developments. Yet the great innovations of the battlefield—the airplane, tank, machine gun, and poison gas—were impressive enough. The fact that the government sponsored intensive and cooperative research attacks on these problems shows that a new type of warfare was present, calling for new institutional responses. The creation of a Chemical Warfare Service in 1918, staffed immediately by a team of top-flight university scientists, exemplified the needs and responses of the time. Indeed, this service and the need for helium, nitrates, and chemicals of many kinds earned the conflict the name of a "chemist's war."[25]

World War I left its mark on American science. Research, though not a complete stranger, was finally established as a strong partner of both industry and the military, and its position in the government generally was strengthened. Furthermore, the kind of cooperative

---

[24] *A History of the National Research Council, 1919–1933*, Reprint and Circular Series of the National Research Council, No. 106 (Washington, D.C., 1933); Gano Dunn, "The Engineering Societies in the National Defense," *Transactions*, American Society of Mechanical Engineers, XXXIX (1918), 464–73; William M. Black, "Engineers and the War," *Transactions*, American Institute of Electrical Engineers, XXXVII (1918), 945–56.

[25] Joseph S. Ames, "Science at the Front," *Atlantic Monthly*, CXXI (January 1918), 90–100; George K. Burgess, "Applications of Science to Warfare in France," *Scientific Monthly*, V (October 1917), 289–97; Henry P. Talbot, "Chemistry at the Front," *Atlantic Monthly*, CXXII (August 1918), 265–74, and "Chemistry Behind the Front," *Atlantic Monthly*, CXXII (November 1918), 651–63; Frank Parker Stockbridge, *Yankee Ingenuity in the War* (New York, 1920).

assault on large problems which had been the developing technique of government bureaus for decades, now became a common experience for many American scientists. And finally, the war had left behind a whole string of new institutions, from the National Research Council to the nearly aborted Naval Research Laboratory, which would have a vitalizing effect on government science in general. The whole war effort had been intense but so short that it had only a tangential effect on American society in general. But it taught lessons and provided experience which were to stand the nation in good stead in future emergencies.

The general letdown experienced by the nation after the war was reflected in the structure and activities of the government's scientific efforts. The National Research Council, established on a permanent basis in 1918, reorganized itself around scientific fields and peacetime problems of liaison. As such, it lost most of its usefulness to the military and declined generally in importance. The Naval Research Laboratory was finally set up in 1923 and, though hardly taken seriously by military circles, managed to do notable work, particularly in the area of radar. The various conservation agencies, while lacking the crusading support they enjoyed during the Progressive Era, continued to perform well and were even able to extend their efforts. The Chemical Warfare Service, suffering as it did from all the worst of wartime associations, found itself under heavy attack and threatened with imminent dissolution.[26]

Under Herbert Hoover the Department of Commerce during the 1920's attempted to relate itself to industry in somewhat the same way that the Department of Agriculture serviced agriculture. It was a reasonable analogy, which has persisted to the present, and Secretary Hoover pursued it with alacrity and imagination. Industrial standards, radio, aviation, and even conservation became objects of particular departmental concern, and all of them required the aid of science at some level. In keeping with his preference for voluntary self-help, Hoover also fought a losing battle to create a National Research

---

[26] E. W. Allen, *Cooperation with the Federal Government in Scientific Work.* Bulletin Series of the NRC, No. 26 (Washington, D.C., 1922); Edward B. Rosa, "The Economic Importance of the Scientific Work of the Government," *Scientific Monthly*, XI (July 1920), 5–24, (August 1920), 141–51, (September 1920), 246–53; Harold G. Bowen, *Ships, Machinery, and Mossbacks: The Autobiography of a Naval Engineer* (Princeton, N.J., 1954); Robert Morris Page, *The Origin of Radar* (New York, 1962); Donald C. Swain, *Federal Conservation Policy, 1921–1933* (Berkeley, Calif., 1963); Charles H. Herty, *The Reserves of the Chemical Warfare Service*, Reprint and Circular Series of the National Research Council, No. 16 (Washington, 1921).

Fund, financed by private industry, administered by the quasi-governmental National Research Council, and applied to the pursuit of basic research. The high position of Hoover as both Secretary and President, combined with his unique membership in the National Academy of Sciences, led most scientists to expect much from his tenure and some to be disappointed with his performance.[27]

When Hoover left office, the nation was facing the bitter reality of the Great Depression. Because of the delays involved in federal budgeting, it was not until 1932 that the budgets of the various science agencies felt the pinch. When the cutbacks came, however, they were in many cases substantial. So successful had been scientists in convincing the public that science and the common welfare were connected, that there were even demands for a moratorium on research. It seemed quixotic to many that money should be spent to increase farm crop yield while it was necessary to burn surplus crops already harvested. The first move of both President Hoover and President Franklin D. Roosevelt was to cut the normal expenditures of government. Among these, science budgets suffered severely, the Bureau of Standards receiving cuts of 50 percent. The first responsibility of government science, therefore, was just to stay alive, and in this it was successful. By 1936, budgets were back to normal and, in most cases, were even beginning to grow again.[28]

Having insured the existence of science in the government, the next chore was to attempt to bring scientific research to bear on the problems of the depression itself. This could take several tacks. First, increased government support of research could absorb some of the unemployed scientists and engineers who were either losing their jobs or were just graduating from college. Second, leading spokesmen for science, such as Karl T. Compton, held out the hope that sponsored research itself might turn up sufficient new devices and techniques to give the economy a much needed boost. The most ambitious such proposal was for a $16 million "Research Program of Science Progress," to be financed by the government and let out through grants and contracts administered by the National Research Council. This proposal, turned down by the administration as a special emergency

[27] Vernon Kellogg, "Herbert Hoover and Science," *Science*, LXXIII (February 20, 1931), 197–99.

[28] Herbert Hoover *et al.*, "The Scientific Work of the Government of the United States," *Scientific Monthly*, XXXVI (January 1933), 7–34; (February 1933), 97–130; (March 1933), 193–224; (April 1933), 291–317; (May 1933), 408–34.

measure, reappeared as a suggested program of the Bureau of Standards but failed in this guise as well.

The threat of unwise economy measures and the promise of new opportunities through emergency programs led to several attempts by civilian scientists to organize some central agency for the guidance of the government in scientific matters. The National Academy and Research Council were, once again, found wanting in the emergency and a reform group within these organizations won Secretary of Agriculture Henry Wallace's support for a Science Advisory Board. Envisioned originally as an adjunct of the National Industrial Recovery Act, the Board was established by executive order on July 31, 1933, under circumstances that did much to muffle its effectiveness. It never received the wholehearted support of the entire scientific community and was eventually killed.[29]

A second attempt to organize scientific advice came through the National Resources Board. Established in the Department of the Interior, this influential committee, numbering among its members the President's uncle, Frederic A. Delano, in 1935 invited the National Academy of Sciences, the Social Science Research Council, and American Council on Education to nominate two members each to form a tripartite Science Committee to advise the parent organization. This committee made several notable studies of scientific and technological interest, but its effectiveness, as a spokesman for the nation's physical scientists, was weakened by its working majority of social scientists, who considered their own fields equally worthy of government subvention.[30]

In actual fact, both the Science Advisory Board and the Science Committee suffered from insufficient support by both their scientific constituents and the government. Essentially, they lacked all of the criteria which contributed so much to the success of the scientific

---

[29] *Report of the Science Advisory Board, July 31, 1933 to September 1, 1934* (Washington, D.C., 1934) and *Second Report of the Science Advisory Board, September 1, 1934 to August 31, 1935* (Washington, D.C., 1935); Karl T. Compton, "Science Makes Jobs," *Scientific Monthly*, XXXVIII (April 1934), 297–300; John C. Merriam, "Some Responsibilities of Science with Relation to Government," *Science*, LXXX (December 28, 1934), 597–601; A. M. MacMahon, "Science and the Recovery Program," *Scientific Monthly*, XL (January 1935), 77–80; Karl T. Compton, "Science Advisory Service to the Government," *Scientific Monthly*, XLII (January 1936), 30–39.

[30] National Resources Committee, *Technological Trends and National Policy, Including the Social Implications of New Inventions* (Washington, D.C., 1937); National Resources Committee, *Research—A National Resource* (Washington, D.C., 1938–40); National Resources Committee, *Federal Relations to Research* (Washington, D.C., 1939).

bureaus, and their main success was in pointing up the need for some supra-bureaucratic coordination and in giving valuable experience to a generation of science administrators, who were soon to face an even greater challenge to their organizational resourcefulness. The importance of the 1930's to government science was that it strained and sometimes broke the old patterns of scientific organization, support, and relationships. The problems thus raised were not settled during the depression, but all the solutions later hit upon were suggested and debated during these prewar years.

The increased role of the federal government in the support of American science, which scientists could not bring themselves to accept during the depression, was forced upon them by the events of the forties. During World War I, the government had brought scientific men to Washington and put many of them into uniform. When the war was over, this whole effort could be rapidly abandoned because no basic alignments had been changed. In World War II, the government supported vast amounts of research *in situ*, leaving scientists on campuses and in industrial research laboratories. In the previous decade, serious doubts had been raised as to whether the government could devise ways in which to stimulate directly civilian science without ruining its unique structure. Under the pressure of war, ways were quickly found.

The main scientific effort of the government during the war was funneled through the National Defense Research Committee, set up in June 1940 and a year later absorbed into the Office of Scientific Research and Development (OSRD). Once again the traditional Academy-Research Council was by passed by reformers. A small group of scientists, including James Conant, president of Harvard University, Karl T. Compton, president of the Massachusetts Institute of Technology, and Vannevar Bush, president of the Carnegie Institution of Washington, decided, on the basis of World War I experience and subsequent developments, to bypass all existing agencies and establish an independent agency, patterned on the National Advisory Committee for Aeronautics which Bush had lately chaired. The resulting National Defense Research Committee was made up of part-time administrators capable of spending government money and authorized both to initiate research projects without being asked and to farm those projects out to the best available contractor. There was some small precedent in the government for each of these innovations, but each flew directly in the face of the great bulk of previous experience. It was the initial and critical decision of the National Defense

Research Committee to concentrate on that research in weaponry which would have a most decisive and immediate impact on the war effort, and secondly, to do this in a manner which would be least likely to disturb prewar arrangements in science and technology.[31]

The immense success of the National Defense Research Committee and the Office of Scientific Research and Development tended to overshadow the war efforts of the older science agencies. Members of the National Academy exercised their individual rather than their corporate leadership. The Smithsonian Institution, once the arbiter of government science, was reduced to playing a very minor role. The Weather Bureau, like many of its sister agencies, tended more to change its clientele than the nature of its services. Many of these scientific agencies were reorganized by executive order before the outbreak of hostilities in order to strengthen administration and liaison between bureaus. In some cases, like that of the Bureau of Standards, such new tasks as the development and production of proximity fuses tended to overshadow normal activities and remained on after the war as an incubus of dangerous proportions.[32]

Between the giant new agencies like the Office of Scientific Research and Development and the Manhattan District, and the old-line service agencies, there was established a group of new organizations to perform specific wartime functions not otherwise provided for.[33] A National Roster was set up to register, and hopefully allocate, specialized personnel throughout the country. The National Inventors Council was set up, in the tradition of the Permanent Commission

[31] James Phinney Baxter 3d, *Scientists against Time* (Boston, 1946); Irvin Steward, *Organizing Scientific Research for War: The Administrative History of the Office of Scientific Research and Development* (Boston, 1948); James B. Conant, "The Mobilization of Science for the War Effort," *American Scientist*, XXXV (April 1947), 195–210.

[32] "Review of the Years 1939–1947," *Report of the National Academy of Sciences—National Research Council. Fiscal Year 1946–1947* (Washington, D.C., 1948), pp. 1–3; "A Brief Summary of the Smithsonian Institution's Part in World War II," *Annual Report of the . . . Smithsonian Institution . . . 1945* (Washington, D.C., 1946), 459–72; U.S. Department of Commerce, *The Weather Bureau Record of War Administration: Part 10, World War II History of the Department of Commerce* (Washington, D.C., July 1948); U.S. Department of Commerce, *World War II History of the Coast and Geodetic Survey* (Washington, D.C., 1951).

[33] Arthur Holly Compton, *Atomic Quest: A Personal Narrative* (New York, 1956); H. DeW. Smyth, *Atomic Energy for Military Purposes: The Official Report on the Development of the Atomic Bomb . . . 1940–1945* (Princeton, N.J., 1945); Richard G. Hewlett and Oscar E. Anderson, *A History of the United States Atomic Energy Commission*, I, *The New World, 1939/1946* (University Park, Pa., 1962).

and the Naval Consulting Board, to provide a clearinghouse for the thousands of inventions submitted to the government by private citizens. After months of debate, an Office of Production Research and Development was organized within the War Production Board to give industry the kind of scientific aid that the Office of Scientific Research and Development was providing for the military. All of these agencies faced the same basic problem: the need to rationalize quickly the vast edifice of American science which had been built up over two centuries of salutary neglect, and to concentrate its efforts toward winning a war that none had wanted and for which few had prepared.[34]

Neither the new nor the old agencies attempted to provide any real overall supervision of America's scientific war effort. Even the powerful and effective Office of Scientific Research and Development operated to win the cooperation of the several estates of science rather than to dictate their various roles, and limited itself strictly to problems of medicine and weaponry. For some critics, it seemed that the disparate and individualistic nature of American scientific effort—an essential quality which the government tended to accept rather than challenge—was inherently too weak and inefficient to meet the challenge of world war, and perhaps after that, renewed depression. Led by Senator Harley M. Kilgore of West Virginia, these critics sought to make fundamental changes in the social structure of American science.[35]

This division of opinion as to whether the government could or should impose social controls upon scientific and technical research, which began under the pressure of depression in the 1930's and persists into our own day, underlay the debate over technological mobilization during World War II and much of the subsequent discussion over national science policy. Only on this one point could everyone agree: that the necessary and deep involvement of science in the war effort had brought about basic changes in the relationship between

---

[34] U.S. Department of Commerce, *Administrative History of the National Inventors Council* (Washington, D.C., n.d.); Leonard Carmichael, "The National Roster of Scientific and Specialized Personnel," *Scientific Monthly*, LVIII (February 1944), 141–47.

[35] Bruce Catton, *The War Lords of Washington* (New York, 1948); *Technological Mobilization*, Hearings before a Subcommittee of the Committee on Military Affairs, October, November, and December 1942 (77th Cong., 2nd sess.); *Scientific and Technical Mobilization*, Hearings by a Subcommittee of the Committee on Military Affairs, 1943–44 (78th Cong., 1st and 2nd sess.); Vannevar Bush, "The Kilgore Bill," *Science*, XCVIII (December 31, 1943), 571–77; Harry Grundfest, "The Utilization of Scientists," *Science and Society*, VII (Winter 1943), 24–31; Richard H. Heindel, *The Integration of Federal and Non-Federal Research as a War Problem*, Prepared for the Science Committee of the National Resources Planning Board (Washington, D.C., July 1, 1942).

science and the federal government. The latter had, from its earliest days, made use of science to promote the common welfare, but now had also to rely upon science to provide for the common defense.

As the war drew to a close, there was an almost unanimous consensus among leading scientists that, in the postwar years, the government would not only have to support a sizable scientific effort of its own but would also have to give massive support to science in industry and the universities. The nature and extent of this support was a matter of considerable debate. Through three years of hearings by the Kilgore committee of the Senate, sentiment had been building for a program of subvention, centering around a proposed National Science Foundation. The proposals of the Kilgore committee were considered to be somewhat radical by most of the powerful science administrators who centered around Vannevar Bush. In order to provide an alternative to this, Bush prevailed upon President Roosevelt, in November of 1944, to ask for answers to four questions involving postwar science policy. These questions were, of course, referred to Bush and offered him an opportunity to present a conservative plan for the federal support of science.

Bush's report, made public several days before that of Kilgore, also envisioned a central National Research Foundation. This foundation was to continue much of the good work of the Office of Scientific Research and Development, including independent supervision of medical and weapons research. The essential differences between the plans of Bush and Kilgore were that the former would support only physical and not social science, would create a foundation virtually independent of presidential control, would make no attempt to distribute funds on anything like a geographical basis, and would allow grantees to retain patent rights where applicable. Kilgore's plan would have preserved governmental control of research sponsored by government funds, while Bush's plan sought to limit the role of the government to merely that of paying the bill.[36]

The debate over the relative merits of these two plans dragged on in the Congress from 1945 until 1950. In 1948 a bill was passed creating a National Science Foundation free of political responsibility, but it was vetoed by President Truman. The essential question to be decided was whether the government should be able to use science

---

[36] *Government's Wartime Research and Development, 1940–1944*, Report from the Subcommittee on War Mobilization to the Committee on Military Affairs, U.S. Senate . . . Parts I and II, 1945 (79th Cong., 1st sess. [Washington, D.C., 1945]); Vannevar Bush, *Science—The Endless Frontier* (Washington, D.C., 1945).

as a tool for social conservation and reconstruction, or whether science should remain the exclusive property of the expert and essentially beyond the democratic control of society as a whole. It was not so much a matter of whether science would be free: it was more a matter of whether it should be responsible to the government or continue to be responsible only to big business and big education. It was universally agreed that the people should pay for it in either case.[37]

The National Science Foundation, which was finally established in 1950, was more a victory for the conservative than liberal faction but, on the whole, was quite different from what either Bush or Kilgore had anticipated. Had it been set up in 1945 it would have been of towering importance in the structure of all American science. But between 1945 and 1950, the perpetual realities of bureaucratic life and the new element of the East-West cold war sapped its incipient primacy. In actual fact, the Foundation became only another pillar in the edifice of government science rather than the capstone of the whole structure.

In the first place, several vital areas of research needed immediate attention and could not wait five years while the American people decided on the fundamental direction of the postwar nation. Less than a month after Bush and Kilgore had recommended their respective foundations, the United States dramatically brought the war to an end with the use of the atomic bomb. Neither Bush nor Kilgore had mentioned atomic research in his report: the former because he was bound by secrecy and the latter because he had never heard of it. The genie thus so percipitously loosed had just as quickly to be bottled up again in some kind of government agency. With the setting up in 1946 of an independent Atomic Energy Commission, the still unborn Foundation lost the most lucrative and dramatic field in all of science.[38]

---

[37] Lyman Chalkley, "Science, Technology and Public Policy," *Science*, CII (September 21, 1945), 289–92; John T. Connor, "The Role of the Federal Government in Postwar Scientific Activities," *The Chemist*, XXIII (December 1946), 463–75; George A. Lundberg, "The Senate Ponders Social Science," *Scientific Monthly*, LXIV (May 1947), 397–411; Alfred E. Cohn, "Federal Legislation in Support of Science," *Political Science Quarterly*, LXII (June 1947), 228–40; John R. Steelman, *Science and Public Policy*, 5 vols. (Washington, D.C., 1947).

[38] Morgan Thomas, *Atomic Energy and Congress* (Ann Arbor, Mich., 1956); Howard A. Meyerhoff, "Domestic Control of Atomic Energy," *Science*, CIII (February 1, 1946), 133–36; Brien McMahon, "U.S. Politics: A Legislator," *Air Affairs*, I (March 1947), 400–405; P. Morrison, "U.S. Politics: A Scientist," *Air Affairs*, I (March 1947), 406–12.

Medical research, which has been handled by the Medical Research Committee of the Office of Scientific Research and Development, had its own humanitarian urgency and the alert National Institutes of Health quickly took over a large number of wartime research contracts from the Office when the latter went out of business. The powerful medical profession, more used to doing business with the Public Health Service, had never been enthusiastic about submerging the identity of medical research within some giant multipurpose science agency such as the proposed foundation.[39]

Nor could military research long reside in an organizational limbo. All interested civilian scientists were determined that weapons research should not be turned back completely to the mercies of the military where it had languished between World War I and World War II. Nor, for that matter, was the military anxious to lose all contact with the men who had given them radar, penicillin, the proximity fuse, and the atomic bomb. The most obvious postwar solution, to perpetuate the Office of Scientific Research and Development, was vetoed by Bush himself, who wanted the National Research Foundation to carry on this work. A splinter group of scientists and military tried to make the National Academy the supervisor of military research, but this move was scotched by the White House. It was finally decided that the military services should carry on their own research, relying upon the use of contracts, grants, and numerous advisory panels (under the Research and Development Board) to provide for the direct participation of civilian scientists.[40]

By the time the National Science Foundation was finally established in 1950, control of medical, atomic, and military research (before Sputnik the three greatest scientific efforts of the government) had already been wrested from it. The mission of the new agency became, partly through default, the support of "basic research," a concern for science education, and a weak mandate to provide the government with a national science policy. Even these were not its exclusive re-

---

[39] Ralph Chester Williams, *The United States Public Health Service, 1798–1950* (Washington, D.C., 1951); Donald C. Swain, "The Rise of a Research Empire: NIH, 1930 to 1950," *Science*, CXXXVIII (December 14, 1962), 1233–37.

[40] Louis N. Ridenour *et al.*, "Symposium: Military Support of American Science, A Danger?" *Bulletin of Atomic Scientists*, III (August 1947), 221–30; Vannevar Bush, *Modern Arms and Free Men: A Discussion of the Role of Science in Preserving Democracy* (New York, 1949); *Research and Development*, Hearings before the Committee on Military Affairs . . . on H.R. 2946, May 22, 23, 29, 1945 (79th Cong., 1st sess.).

sponsibility. The postwar Office of Naval Research had early made a place for itself in the hearts of academic scientists by generously supporting a wide spectrum of basic research. The old Office of Education, never a very vigorous agency, was still the logical place for educational responsibilities, and it was apparent to all that very few people concerned, and certainly not civilian scientists or government scientific bureaus, would permit any agency to make a single scientific policy for the whole nation.[41]

By the end of the Truman Era, the postwar federal scientific establishment was virtually complete. The most important research tasks had been provided for in some manner, and if there was no overall policy, at least the most important jobs got done. The domestic issues which had dictated the lines of controversy in the late 1940's were, if not irrelevant, at least pushed into the background by the increasing tempo of cold war, already become hot in Korea. With the renewal of actual shooting war, such old World War II agencies as the National Inventors Council and National Roster were reactivated, and funds for military research and development reached new heights.

As the cold war expanded through the years, it raised fundamental questions for American science. In the first place, the prospect of peace breaking out, though unlikely, posed a real threat to the continuation of government subvention on such a high scale. It has never been established that the support of science for its own sake is something the government could or should do solely as a form of *noblesse oblige*. In the second place, cold war motivation has placed a strain on many of the most cherished myths of the scientific profession. It has been decisively demonstrated, for example, that unfree science (either Soviet or American) can flourish and produce astonishing results. Scientists have also demonstrated rather clearly that the "scientific method," except to the extent that it shares in the common virtues of honesty and fair-mindedness, provides no panaceas for the solution of complex political problems. In short, the scientist's picture of himself as suffering Prometheus no longer approximates the facts.[42]

---

[41] The Bird Dogs, "The Evolution of the Office of Naval Research," *Physics Today*, XIV (August 1961), 30–35; John E. Pfeiffer, "The Office of Naval Research," *Scientific American*, CLXXX (February 1949), 11–15.

[42] For some postwar problems of American science, see Arthur M. Schlesinger, Jr., "The Oppenheimer Case," *Atlantic Monthly*, CXCIV (October 1954), 29–36; Sidney Painter, H. A. Meyerhoff, and Alan T. Waterman, "The Visa Problem," *Scientific Monthly*, LXXVI (January 1953), 11–19; John G. Palfrey, "The AEC Security Program: Past and Present," *Bulletin of Atomic Scientists*, XI (April 1955), 131–33; "Loyalty and Research: Report of the Committee on Loyalty in Relation to Government Support of Unclassified Research," *Science*, CXXIII (April 20, 1956), 660–62. E. U. Condon, "The Duty of Dissent,"

The government's response to the launching of Sputnik in October of 1957 has placed some strain upon the accommodation reached in the postwar debates. The metamorphosis of the National Advisory Committee for Aeronautics into the first truly cold war science agency, the National Aeronautics and Space Administration (NASA), has created the latest in that long line of predominant agencies which, by virtue of the importance of their mission and scale of their support, have been able to warp the government's whole scientific effort.[43] The National Aeronautics and Space Administration has taken the spotlight from the National Institutes of Health, drained funds from the Atomic Energy Commission, and actively supported both science education and basic research in the face of the National Science Foundation. Despite objections from Republicans and disadvantaged scientists in other fields, the creation and support of the National Aeronautics and Space Administration represents a major science policy of the nation. It is not high-level policy making in the grand manner, but its effects are much the same.[44]

A more conscious and direct attempt to coordinate the vast structure of government science has also been a part of the post-Sputnik response. In 1957 President Eisenhower appointed James R. Killian as his personal science advisor and head of the President's Science Advisory Committee. Congressional talk of a Department of Science, going back at least as far as the Allison Commission of 1884, was revived, and the Office of Science and Technology was created as a separate entity within the Executive Office of the President, so that it might be answerable to Congress. A Congressional Office of Science and Technology has been proposed, and the National Academy of Science has been appointed as science advisor to the Subcommittee on Science, Research, and Development of the House Committee on Sciences and Astronautics.[45]

Science, CXIX (February 19, 1954), 227–28; Frank Freidel, "The Dynamite in AD-X2," *New Republic*, CXXVIII (April 13, 1953), 5–6. For the scientists' reaction to the atomic bomb, see Alice Kimball Smith, *A Peril and a Hope, The Scientists' Movement in America, 1945–1947* (Chicago, 1965).

[43] A. Hunter Dupree, "Central Scientific Organisation in the United States Government," *Minerva,* I (Summer 1963), 453–69.

[44] Eugene M. Emme, *Aeronautics and Astronautics: An American Chronology of Science and Technology in the Exploration of Space, 1915–1960* (Washington, D.C., 1961); Alison Griffith, *The National Aeronautics and Space Act: A Study of the Development of Public Policy* (Washington, D.C., 1962).

[45] *A Matter of Priority: An Examination of the Budget and Benefits of the Moon Shot in Relation to Other National Problems*, prepared by the Staff of the Senate Republican Policy Committee, Bourke B. Hickenlooper, Chairman (processed, May 10, 1963); *Scientists' Testimony on Space Goals*, Hearings be-

This burst of administrative and organizational ingenuity is symptomatic of a fundamental aspect of the history of governmental involvement in scientific activities. The government's need for science has frequently stimulated it to new organizational experiments. The basic problem has been that, much as the government needs science, science has, by and large, offered its services only on its own terms. Those terms have been support without control or, in other terms, power without responsibility. By and large, the government has refused to grant such terms, and the two have compromised in such a manner as to blur the traditional boundaries between the private and public sectors of American life.

The fundamental trend over the past century has been the rise of scientific research in the universities, private foundations, and industrial establishments of the nation, and the spinning of a web of mutual interest between these institutions and the federal government. The trend has been hastened by the steadily increasing need of the government for scientific data to aid it in discharging its growing responsibilities. As these scientific needs have increased, they have, in turn, exerted a growing influence on that scientific activity taking part outside the government. Both to protect their own interests and to influence federal science policy, civilian scientists have sought to create institutions through which they could effect policy but which would not allow politics to effect them. At the same time, government scientists have sought to create institutions through which they could benefit from the support of their civilian colleagues against their political masters. And finally, those vested with political responsibility sought to create institutions through which they could best accomplish their scientific purposes without abdicating their responsibility to the people as a whole. It is typical of the American political genius that all inter-

---

fore the Committee on Aeronautical and Space Sciences United States Senate, June 10, 11, 1963 (88th Cong., 1st sess.); Hubert H. Humphrey, "The Need for a Department of Science," *The Annals of the American Academy of Political and Social Science*, CCCXXVII (January 1960), 27–35; remarks by Sen. E. L. Bartlett, "Needed: A Congressional Office of Science and Technology," *Congressional Record*, CIX (July 30, 1963, 88th Cong., 1st sess., and also August 13, August 19, and August 23); "New Office of Science and Technology Proposed by Kennedy to Strengthen White House Advisory Setup," *Science*, CXXXVI (April 6, 1962), 32–34; *Government and Science*, Hearings before the Subcommittee on Science, Research, and Development of the Committee on Sciences and Astronautics, Oct. 15–Nov. 20, 1963 (88th Cong., 1st sess.); *Federal Research and Development Programs*, Hearings before the Select Committee on Government Research of the House of Representatives, 1964, 3 vols. (88th Cong., 1st and 2d sess.).

ested parties have settled for something less then they desired. The institutional maze produced by the interplay of history and necessity confounds the enemies as well as the friends of federal science.[46]

---

[46] For various aspects of these problems, see Don K. Price, "The Scientific Establishment," *Science*, CXXXVI (June 29, 1962), 1099–1106; National Academy of Sciences, Committee on Science and Public Policy, *Federal Support of Basic Research in Institutions of Higher Learning* (Washington, D.C., 1964); Dael Wolfle, *Science and Public Policy* (Lincoln, Nebr., 1959); Robert Gilpin and Christopher Wright, *Scientists and National Policy-Making* (New York, 1964); *Harvard and the Federal Government: A Report to the Faculties and Governing Boards of Harvard University* (Cambridge, Mass., 1961); Charles V. Kidd, *American Universities and Federal Research* (Cambridge, Mass., 1959). For selections from some of the more important documents, see James L. Penick, Jr., Carroll W. Pursell, Jr., Morgan B. Sherwood, and Donald C. Swain, eds., *The Politics of American Science: 1939 to the Present* (Chicago, 1965).

Science and the Military

Clarence G. Lasby*

In 215 B.C., the proud Roman legions approached from land and sea to destroy the opulent Greek city of Syracuse on Sicily. The Romans were confident of victory and the Greeks resigned to defeat. But antiquity was not without resources other than legions. Years before, a wise king had induced the renowned mathematician, Archimedes, to "reduce to practice some part of his admirable speculations in science" and bring it "more within the appreciation of people in general." Though "repudiating as sordid and ignoble the whole trade of engineering and every sort of art that lends to mere profit or use," the scientist succumbed to the entreaties of his king, and as the enemy approached, patriotically assumed command of his marvelous "engines." For three years he demoralized the Romans, until such terror had seized them "that if they did but see a little rope or a piece of wood from the wall . . . , they turned their backs and fled." Archimedes was a supreme commander, for the "rest of the Syracusans were but the body of [his] designs, one soul moving and governing all. . . ." Eventually, through treachery, the Romans entered the city, and Archimedes died in the melee that followed.[1]

Plutarch's account of the siege of Syracuse may be apocryphal; it is surely exaggerated. But it does suggest that the scientists of the mid-twentieth century are not the first to provide useful weapons for the field of battle. The application of science to warfare is venerable,

* CLARENCE G. LASBY, Assistant Professor of History at the University of Texas, was born in New York in 1933. He received his B.A. from the University of Redlands, and his M.A. and Ph.D. from the University of California at Los Angeles. He has received grants for his work in the social history of the United States from the Social Science Research Council and the Mershon Committee on National Security Studies. He will soon publish a history of the United States' program for the importation and utilization of German scientists following World War II.

[1] Plutarch, *Life of Marcellus*, ed. A. H. Clough (Boston, 1895), II, 252–60.

and throughout the centuries it has embraced the talents of the famous as well as the forgotten. Yet, historically, it has been an infrequent and haphazard process; as late as 1900, the scientist was still essentially above the battle. Not until World War II did the long and sporadic engagement of science and warfare culminate in harmonious and perilous union.

In the United States, the military utilization of science to improve or develop weapons was virtually nonexistent until World War I. Shielded by oceans, and sharing the benefits of general world stability after 1815, the nation gave little attention to its military security. The national interest centered instead on immediate and practical problems; it was in two such areas of challenge—westward expansion and overseas exploration—that science and the military were to form their initial partnership. Prior to the Civil War, the pragmatic quest for knowledge of the West as an aid to settlement, and of information about distant lands as an impetus to commerce, fostered a series of surveys and expeditions which united the scientist, soldier, and seaman in common national ventures.

The proclivities and policies of Thomas Jefferson were fundamental to the incipient relationship. As a devotee of science, aware of its theory and alert to its practical applications, Jefferson considered it an essential component of the national purpose. By supporting and organizing the Lewis and Clark expedition, he turned vision to reality and established precedent as well. The expedition blended the aims of empire and the desires for trade with the interests of science —the collection of flora and fauna, the acquisition of information concerning Indians, and astronomical observations. It also put into practice Jefferson's conviction that the military should be utilized as an instrument to advance civilian and scientific endeavors. Although he feared a regular standing Army dedicated to military purposes, Jefferson was not opposed to an armed society; he believed that every citizen should be a soldier. The corollary to this was that every regular soldier should be useful to society. To this end, he established the United States Military Academy in 1802; it was oriented to train officers in engineering and science, not to educate them in strategy, tactics and the art of warfare. West Point soon became a sort of national university rather than a professional academy. Many of its graduates sought civilian careers, and even those who remained in the Army were often more civilian than military in their expertise and their allegiance. The Jeffersonian emphasis on "technicism" persisted within the military services until the Civil War; its legacy was a corps of skilled engineers competent to serve science as well as the nation.[2]

The Topographical Engineers were the finest expression of that legacy. Existing initially as a bureau within the Army's Corps of Engineers, the Engineers served as escorts and managers of numerous expeditions following the tradition of Lewis and Clark. Typical of the early ventures was the expedition commanded by Major Stephen H. Long in 1819 to search for the headwaters of the Platte and Red Rivers. One observer's description gives a sense of the varied purposes and personnel of the expedition:

> Botanists, mineralogists, chemists, artisans, cultivators, scholars, soldiers; the love of peace, the capacity for war: philosophical apparatus and military supplies; telescopes and cannon, garden seeds and gunpowder; the arts of civil life and the force to defend them—all are seen aboard.[3]

Long's survey made only meager contributions to botany and zoology, but it did set a pattern of civilian-soldier teamwork that was to flourish during the 1840's and 1850's. By then, the Topographical Engineers had become an independent Corps responsible to the Secretary of War. Armed with more accurate techniques and equipment, consumed by an enthusiasm for inquiry, and fired by the spirit of Manifest Destiny, they provided scientific mapping for half a continent. Through this, they answered to the needs of settlement, diplomacy, and military operations. But they were also zealous observers and collectors, working nearly always with a retinue of scientists. The countless specimens gathered through this collaboration filled private institutions and made the Smithsonian one of the great museums of the world. From study of these specimens, careers were furthered or built: John Torrey and Asa Gray in botany; Spencer F. Baird in zoology; James F. Hall and Frederick V. Hayden in geology; and Joseph Leidy in vertebrate paleontology. The vast amount of accumulated data also had an impact on the cultural life of the nation and of

---

[2] For the impact of West Point upon science and engineering, see R. Ernest Dupuy, *The West Point Tradition in American Life* (New York, 1940); and Sidney Forman, *West Point: A History of the United States Military Academy* (New York, 1950). Jefferson's impact on "technicism" within the services is discussed in Samuel P. Huntington, *The Soldier and the State* (New York, 1954), pp. 195–203.

[3] This observation of a "man of long and distinguished public service" is quoted in Hiram M. Chittenden, *American Fur Trade of the Far West* (New York, 1902), II, 566.

the world, for it provided some of the indispensable evidence that would later support the theory of evolution.[4]

The Navy, after a belated start, also became a partner and patron of science. Despite the pleas of President John Quincy Adams for a naval academy, a national observatory, and overseas exploration, Congress refused to allocate the necessary funds. But science quickly gained votaries among the officers of the Navy. By 1836, Edgar Allen Poe could predict that

> the time is coming when, imbued with a taste for science and a spirit of research, they [seafarers] will become ardent explorers of regions in which they sojourn. Freighted with the knowledge which observation only can impart, and enriched with collections of objects precious to the student of nature, their return after the perils of a distant voyage will then be doubly joyful. The enthusiast in science will anxiously await their coming, and add his cordial welcome to the warm greetings of relatives and friends.[5]

Two years later the Navy fulfilled the prediction when Lieutenant Charles Wilkes sailed with the United States Exploring Expedition to Latin America, the Antarctic, and the South Sea Islands. After four years at sea, the flotilla returned with honor for the nation, charts for the Navy, and a spectacular treasure in anthropology, botany, zoology, meteorology, hydrography, and physics. During the following two decades, Lieutenant W. F. Lynch led an expedition to the Dead Sea; Lieutenant James Gillis to Chile; Captain John Rodgers to the North Pacific; and Commodore Matthew Perry to Japan. As the Navy broadened its horizons to virtually every part of the world, science received benefits in nearly every branch of its activity.

The practical needs of the Navy and the demands of commercial interests also led to the promotion of science through the establishment in 1830 of the Depot of Charts and Instruments, and in 1842 of the Naval Observatory. The Navy's choice of Lieutenant Matthew Fontaine Maury as its first superintendent of the Observatory initiated a glorious era of naval science. Maury made the oceans his province: he intensively studied their currents, tides, depths, temperatures, and the winds above them. His treatise on *Navigation* became the standard textbook for midshipmen; his *Wind and Current Charts* shortened the

---

[4] The definitive study of the Topographical Engineers is William H. Goetzmann, *Army Exploration in the American West* (New Haven, 1959).

[5] Edgar Allan Poe, *Southern Literary Messenger*, II, No. 7 (June 1836), 454–55.

sailing time for mariners throughout the world; his volume of astro-nomical observations was the first ever issued by an American obser-vatory; and his deep-sea research contributed to the laying of the Atlantic cable. Because of his pioneering investigations in navigation, hydrography, meteorology, and marine geology, he was considered by 1860 the world's foremost oceanographer.[6]

These early relationships between science and the military were extensive and fruitful; they were also superficial, based upon expedi-ency rather than upon any natural affinity. They had served the nation well in meeting its multifarious requirements in an age of rapid ex-pansion, but they did not establish a permanent bond between the two professions. In fact, the cooperation between science and the services was accompanied by continuous antagonism and tension. Although scientists wished to utilize the military for protection and transportation, they voiced a subdued but increasing criticism of the services' control and encroachment in scientific activities. The noted scientist and grandson of Benjamin Franklin, Alexander Dallas Bache, led a struggle for years against the Navy's attempt to win the Coast Survey from the Treasury Department; and the American scientific community stood alone in refusing to give credit to the accomplish-ments of Matthew Fontaine Maury.[7] On occasions, the military ag-gravated the tension by their attempts to exclude the scientists from research opportunities. Commodore Matthew Perry, for example, in-flexibly opposed the inclusion of any civilian scientists in his expedi-tion to Japan in 1852. He argued that a diplomatic mission should not be burdened with scientific objectives; that Naval officers could arrange the necessary observations; that civilians would not submit patiently to Naval discipline; and that scientists, accustomed to free-dom in correspondence, might jeopardize the mission through a breach of security.[8]

Persistent conflict rather than cooperation dominated the relation-ship of science and the military after the Civil War. Most of the old patterns of collaboration disappeared during the Gilded Age in the face of an overwhelming trend toward the separation of the military

---

[6] See Frances Leigh Williams, *Matthew Fontaine Maury, Scientist of the Sea* (New Brunswick, N.J., 1963); and Charles Lee Lewis, *Matthew Fontaine Maury: The Pathfinder of the Seas* (London, 1888).

[7] A. Hunter Dupree, *Science in the Federal Government* (Cambridge, Mass., 1957), pp. 145–46; and F. L. Williams, p. 472.

[8] A. Hunter Dupree, "Science vs. the Military: Dr. James Morrow and the Perry Expedition," *Pacific Historical Review*, XXII (1953), 29–37.

from scientific activities. This was most evident with regard to western exploration and meteorology. Although the Topographical Engineers disbanded in 1863, a victim of the war, the Army did not desert the field. In the late 1860's, the Corps of Engineers eagerly participated in two western ventures. But scientists were no longer willing to act as servants to the military. Geologist Clarence King, who administered the scientific functions of the Army's survey of the Fortieth Parallel, expressed the prevailing sentiment:

> Eighteen hundred and sixty seven . . . marks, in the history of national geological work, a turning point, when the science ceased to be dragged in the dust of rapid exploration and took a commanding position in the professional work of the country.[9]

Agitation against military control reached a crescendo in the 1870's, as scientists fought to exclude the military from jurisdiction over the United States Geological Survey. The leading lobbyist, geologist John Wesley Powell, argued that

> whenever the scientific works of the General Government fall out of the control of scientific men, and into the hands of officers or function-aries whose interest is not in all research . . . science at once becomes severed from the great body of scientific men; it no longer takes a proper part in the great work to be done, and it speedily decays in influence and value.[10]

The civilians were victorious in 1879 when the Department of the Interior supplanted the military in exploration by winning control of the Survey.

A similar exertion by advocates of civilian control eventually elim-inated the Army from concern with weather forecasting and mete-orological research. Congress had sanctioned forecasting within the Signal Corps in 1870 in order to aid agriculture and commerce. Under the enlightened leadership of Colonel Albert J. Myer and his succes-sor, General William B. Hazen, the Signal Service produced practical results and inspired some basic research in atmospheric electricity and solar radiation. Myer employed Cleveland Abbe, formerly the director of an astronomical observatory in Cleveland, to administer a group of

---

[9] Quoted in Thurman Wilkins, *Clarence King* (New York, 1958), p. 111.

[10] *Testimony before Joint Commission to Consider the Present Organization of the Signal Service, Geological Survey, Coast and Geodetic Survey, and the Hydrographic Office of the Navy Department* (49th Cong., 1st sess., Senate Misc. Doc. No. 82, March 16, 1886), p. 179.

civilian scientists; and Hazen later established a "study room division" to conduct basic research. However, there was constant tension between civilian and military personnel. The officers resented the scientists, who in turn protested that military intrusion was adversely affecting their research.[11] Abbe argued that it was not

> a wise policy for the Army and Navy . . . to endeavor to build themselves up and attain an appearance of activity and superficial popularity through the country on the basis of the work done in any other department except that for which they were specifically commissioned.[12]

Following a congressional investigation in 1886, during which the Secretary of War as well as the scientific community opposed putting the meteorological program under the Army, the Department of Agriculture assumed responsibility for it.[13]

There was one notable exception to the pattern of civilian displacement of the military in scientific pursuits. In spite of the desires of eminent scientists, the Naval Observatory remained with the Navy, and continued to promote outstanding research. Matthew Fontaine Maury chose to place his loyalty with the South in 1861, but his successor, astronomer Simon Newcomb, gave even greater prestige to the Observatory. Harvard University had offered Newcomb the directorship of its observatory, but he "did not believe that, with the growth of intelligence in our country, an absence of touch between the scientific and literary classes on the one side, and 'politics' on the other, could continue."[14] His primary research emphasis was in celestial mechanics, and during a period of thirty-six years with the Navy, he made a colossal effort to give precision to calculations of the positions and motions of heavenly bodies. He published fundamental tables of the motion of Neptune, Uranus, Mercury, Venus, Earth, and Mars, and impressive studies of the motion of the moon. In 1877, as Superintendent of the *Nautical Almanac*, he embarked upon a project to

---

[11] See Nathan Reingold, "Science and the United States Army," unpublished manuscript, Washington, D.C. (The manuscript is filed at the National Science Foundation.)

[12] Quoted in Reingold, p. 58.

[13] The decline of science in the military services was hastened not only by civilian antagonism but also by military acquiescence. After the Civil War, the central trend within the services was toward the replacement of technicism with military professionalism. In order to concentrate on what they conceived to be their single purpose—increased efficiency in war—the services de-emphasized their former civilian technical functions. See Huntington, pp. 230–56.

[14] Simon Newcomb, *The Reminiscences of an Astronomer* (Boston, 1903), p. 213.

summarize all of the worthwhile observations of the position of the sun, moon, planets, and certain fixed stars made throughout the world since 1750. The scientific splendor of his work won universal acclaim, including that of Albert Einstein, who considered it "of monumental importance to astronomy."[15]

By the turn of the century, the separation of science from the services was nearly complete, and to search for a continuity of the former relationship after 1900 is to pursue shadows in history. The Naval Observatory survived, but after the retirement of Simon Newcomb, it was a pale replica of its earlier days, performing only routine functions. The military academies continued as permanent institutions, but their emphasis had shifted from the technical to the professional —they taught less science and more strategy. The Army and Navy Bureaus maintained a lingering attachment to technology, but they existed as subordinates to the needs of the line.[16] Most significantly, a profound transformation within science and the military had extinguished the once vibrant spirit of teamwork: both had reached maturity as professions with distinctive and diametrically opposed interests, attitudes, and values.[17] The scientist was no longer an amateur, probing inchoate fields of interest; he was a specialist devoting his life to pure rather than applied science, proud of his profession and self-conscious about his beneficial role in society. The soldier and sailor were no longer the Jeffersonian citizen-servants, expert in a scientific skill and devoted to essentially civilian pursuits; they were professional fighters, isolated from society, loyal and obedient to their calling, and wholly dedicated to the art of war. The former collaborators were not only separated in fact; they were isolated in spirit.

[15] "Einstein's Appreciation of Simon Newcomb," *Science*, LXIX (March 1, 1919), p. 249. There is no biography of Simon Newcomb. For his life and career see W. W. Campbell, "Biographical Memoir, Simon Newcomb, 1835–1909," *Memoirs of the National Academy of Sciences*, XVII (Washington, D.C., 1924), 1–18; Raymond C. Archibald, "Simon Newcomb, 1835–1909: Bibliography of His Life and Work," *Ibid.*, pp. 19–69; and *DAB*, XIII (New York, 1943), 452–55.

[16] The Army Medical Corps continued to emphasize scientific methods, especially after the Spanish-American War. See E. E. Hume, *Victories of Army Medicine: Scientific Accomplishments of the Medical Department of the United States Army* (Philadelphia, 1943).

[17] There is great need for a study of the rise of the scientific profession in the United States and of the characteristics of the scientific elite. Suggestive beginnings are Bernard Barber, *Science and the Social Order* (New York, 1952); Max Weber, "Science as a Vocation," in H. H. Gerth and C. W. Mills, eds., *From Max Weber: Essays in Sociology* (New York, 1946), pp. 129–56; and Anne Roe, *The Making of a Scientist* (New York, 1952). The military profession has been carefully studied in Huntington, *op. cit.*, and Morris Janowitz, *The Professional Soldier* (Glencoe, Ill., 1960).

It is this isolation that gives meaning to the twentieth-century pattern of scientific-military relations in weapons research. The astonishing feature of the pattern is not that science revolutionized warfare but that the revolution occurred so slowly. The cultural lag in weapons development has the elements of a tragicomedy; it reflects the consuming and antagonistic illusions of two tough professions. The scientist viewed man as essentially good and improving, posed a future of limitless potentiality for progress, insisted on the untrammeled independence of the individual, and spoke of international brotherhood. The militarist saw man as basically evil and unchanging, posed a future of limitless possibility for catastrophe, adhered to an unquestioned subordination to the group, and spoke of national solidarity. One accepted peace as normal, sought scientific innovation, and would share the benefits of research; the other considered war as inevitable, resisted technical change, and would conserve the advantage of secrets. The scientist was striving to fulfill his promise of utopia through faith in reason; the military to forestall its foreboding of disaster through faith in power. Such entrenched parochialism created an enduring barrier to communication, vulnerable only to the demands of national security. Patriotism was a powerful catalyst to cooperation in time of war, isolation a prevailing constant during intervals of peace.

There were few precedents for the brief encounter of science with weapons during World War I. The nation's steadfast aversion to military affairs had offered no inspiration for improving the instruments of warfare, and military doctrine was inordinately slow to embrace the thesis that superior arms favor victory.[18] Inventors plagued the services with alleged innovations throughout the nineteenth century; they were greeted with callous disfavor by officers forced by economy to standardize those arms already proven in the field. Scientists remained generally indifferent; they did offer their services during the Civil War, and were able to induce Congress to establish the National Academy of Sciences as an advisory group.[19] The results of the liaison were negligible, and during the next fifty years the War Department sought the Academy's advice on only five matters: the question of tests for the purity of whiskey; the preservation of paint on Army

---

[18] I. B. Holley, Jr., *Ideas and Weapons* (New Haven, 1953), pp. 10–13.

[19] The primary impetus for the founding of the National Academy of Sciences appears to have been the desire of American scientists to achieve the same recognition from their government as had their European colleagues. See Frederick W. True, *A History of the First Half-Century of the National Academy of Sciences, 1863–1913* (Washington, D.C., 1913), pp. 7–15.

knapsacks; the galvanic action from association of zinc and iron; the exploration of the Yellowstone; and meteorological science and its applications.[20] Occasionally a high-level officer recognized that "the valor of great masses of men, and even the genius of great commanders in the field, have been compelled to yield the first place in importance to the scientific skill and wisdom in finance which are able and willing to prepare in advance the most powerful engines of war."[21] Seldom did they translate rhetoric into research. They did not innovate; they waited passively for industrial technology throughout the world to present advances in armament. By 1914, conservatism in weapons technology and doctrine had become a part of the profession's tradition.

"Victory smiles upon those who anticipate changes in the character of war," wrote the Italian military philosopher, Giulio Douhet, "not upon those who wait to adapt themselves after the changes occur."[22] There was a hint of such anticipation within the Navy in 1915, when Secretary Josephus Daniels asked Thomas Edison to lead "a department of development and invention, to which all ideas and suggestions, either from the service or from civilian inventors, can be referred for determination as to whether they contain practical suggestions for us to take up and perfect."[23] Yet the choice of the 68-year-old inventor, and the screening task assigned to the Naval Consulting Board displayed the military's limited comprehension of the potential value of science for warfare. The results which stemmed from the wartime service of the Board explicitly proved the failure of such an approach: out of 110,000 suggestions presented to it, only one went into production. Scientists alone were aware and confident of their usefulness, and it remained for members of the National Academy of Sciences to prompt the organization of the National Research Council in July 1916. Spurred by a desire to help in the war and to advance the cause of science, astronomer George Ellery Hale and physicist

---

[20] U.S. Congress, Staff Study of the Senate Committee on Government Operations, *Science and Technology Act of 1958* (85th Cong., 2nd sess. [Washington, D.C., 1958]), p. 110.

[21] John McAllister Schofield, *Forty-six Years in the Army* (New York, 1897), p. 457. Schofield was Commanding General of the Army from 1888 to 1894.

[22] Giulio Douhet, *The Command of the Air*, trans. Dino Gerrari from 1921 Italian ed. (New York, 1942), Bk. I, p. 30.

[23] L. N. Scott, *Naval Consulting Board of the United States* (Washington, D.C., 1920), p. 186; see also Josephus Daniels, *The Wilson Era* (Chapel Hill, N.C., 1946), pp. 133–34.

Robert Millikan provided the nation with its first organization to promote military research.[24]

The rapprochement of scientist and soldier offered little promise of startling achievements; it fulfilled expectations. The "confusion," as Millikan recalled, was "in the situation."[25] The military, burdened with great responsibilities for which it was unprepared, quite naturally emphasized mass production and mobilization rather than weapons innovation. When problems arose, it called upon the scientific pool of talent; there was little opportunity for the scientists to assume the initiative and insufficient time to bring ideas to fruition even if they had. Equally restrictive was the practice of placing civilian scientists in uniform under direct military control; the relationship was one of commander and subordinate, not of equals.

During World War I, only a few contributions emerged from the organizational and administrative chaos, none of which was of crucial importance to the victory: submarine sound-detecting tubes, sound-ranging equipment for the location of guns, and superior airplane cameras.[26] Perhaps the most obvious failure was in the field of aeronautics. This country made no advances in creative design for aircraft, and provided no exclusively American plane for use in the war. The ultimate impression made by science on the military was meager. In 1919, General P. C. March, the War Department's Chief of Staff, wrote, "Nothing in this war has changed the fact that it is now, as always heretofore, the Infantry with rifle and bayonet that, in the final analysis, must bear the brunt of the assault and carry it on to victory."[27]

There were a few observers to whom the wartime relationship, though tenuous and short-lived, augured a new age. Elihu Root cautioned that "the most civilized nation will be as helpless as the Aztecs were against Cortez" if it ignores scientific preparation for defense; and the National Advisory Committee for Aeronautics warned that

---

[24] The best account of the origin of the National Research Council is Robert A. Millikan, *Autobiography* (New York, 1950).

[25] Noted in I. Bernard Cohen, "American Physicists at War: From the First World War to 1942," *American Journal of Physics*, XIII (October 1945), 337.

[26] There is no suitable account of science during World War I. For general surveys see R. M. Yerkes, ed., *The New World of Science, Its Development During the War* (New York, 1920); and George C. Reinhardt and William R. Kintner, *The Haphazard Years: How America Has Gone to War* (New York, 1960). The development of the air arm during the war is carefully studied by I. B. Holley, *Ideas and Weapons*.

[27] *Annual Reports of the War Department, 1919* (Washington, D.C., 1919), I, 473–74.

aeronautics must be encouraged, for it would be the first arm of offense and defense in any future war.[28] These sibylline judgments were alien to a nation crusading for peace and denouncing war. They were especially so because of the worldwide reaction against the foremost scientific innovation of the struggle—poison gas. Civilians and soldiers alike expressed abhorrence at the barbaric, inhuman use of toxics, which for centuries had been disavowed by civilized nations. President Wilson clearly expressed the public temper; bemoaning the German use of chemistry for destruction, he counseled at Paris "that only the watchful, cautious cooperation of man can see to it that science, as well as armed men, is kept within the harness of civilization."[29]

No caution was required to keep the American effort within harness during the following two decades. An apathetic public, a myopic government, a disinterested science and a conservative military were all remiss with respect to weapons and war. The nation sought peace, settled for isolation and neutrality, struggled with the great depression, and expressed its traditional antimilitarism with increased fervor. Its watchword was economy; it confirmed it each year by reducing military appropriations. In addition, executive and congressional leaders limited the sphere of military strategy to defense of the homeland and excluded the architects of that strategy from deliberations on national and foreign policy. Following its hopes and delusions, the nation rejected the possibility of conflict and ignored the necessity of strength.[30]

The scientists, patriotic volunteers in 1917, made it clear that their descent from Olympus was for the duration only. Their retreat from the vulgar application of knowledge to weapons after the war ended was immediate and, they trusted, eternal. "Do not think for a moment that I fancy that we are ever going to abolish force in human affairs . . . ," wrote Robert Millikan, "but this I do believe, that since Man is essentially a rational being and since he has found that international war conducted along modern lines is likely to annihilate him, he will find a way to settle most of his international differences over the council tables. . . ."[31] Many scientists worked to ensure a peaceful

---

[28] Elihu Root, "Industrial Research and National Welfare," *Science*, XLVIII (1918), 532.

[29] State Department, *Papers Relating to the Foreign Relations of the United States, The Peace Conference*, 13 vols. (Washington, D.C., 1942–1947), III, 179.

[30] For the effect of budgetary restrictions on military research and development between wars, see Mark S. Watson, *Chief of Staff: Prewar Plans and Preparations* (Washington, D.C., 1950).

[31] Millikan, *Autobiography*, p. 223.

future through participation in international scientific organizations; many others nourished the bonds of fellowship as eager students in Europe.[32] Their efforts to create a community of nations were combined with exertions to enhance the prestige and value of science at home. In 1918 they prompted President Wilson to sanction a permanent National Research Council to stimulate the application of scientific resources for the public welfare. By 1924, a Carnegie Corporation grant had provided a new headquarters for the peacetime organization in Washington; the edifice was a worthy tribute to science—"pilot of industry, conqueror of disease, multiplier of the harvest, explorer of the universe, revealer of nature's laws, eternal guide to truth."[33] The encomium was an apt description of the role of science during the interwar period; there was no place among such lofty pursuits for weapons research.

The military, sensitive to recurring criticism, muted its warnings of disaster and its demands for funds. Most of the leaders remained unaware of the potential of research; and the few who did appreciate the wisdom of large-scale scientific research in weaponry were forced to spend most of their limited budgets to maintain equipment on hand. Some useful work continued, especially within the Naval Research Laboratory, the Ordnance and Signal Corps, and the National Advisory Committee for Aeronautics, but the results were not such as to elicit enthusiasm. At the same time, military conservatism prevented exploitation of the most obvious lessons. The Tank Corps, for example, was abolished in 1918, and the development of heavy models was not revived until 1940. For the most part, the services began World War II with the same weapons as they ended World War I.

The interwar isolation of science and the military was costly. The basic knowledge and techniques for the development of all the weapons used after Pearl Harbor, with the exception of the atomic bomb, were available before the conflict began. To view the time lapse between innovation and its application to national defense is to see pathos in history. On the eve of war, when science had revolutionized communications, the Signal Corps was still maintaining its homing pigeon lofts. And at the same time that Hitler was preparing his modernized tanks for a deadly assault, Colonel George S. Patton was

---

[32] The period before 1932 has been described by Robert Jungk as the "beautiful years" due to the fellowship between American and European physicists. See *Brighter Than a Thousand Suns* (New York, 1958), pp. 10–28.

[33] *Annual Report of the National Academy of Sciences, 1923–1924* (Washington, D.C., 1925), p. 53.

standing, with tears in his eyes, to watch his old cavalry regiment stack their sabers. The horse cavalry, symbol of tradition and competitor of the tank, survived until after the war—a monument to professional and public irresponsibility.[34]

In the autumn of 1939, Albert Einstein wrote, in his famous letter to President Roosevelt, "Some recent work by E. Fermi and L. Szilard . . . leads me to expect that the element of uranium may be turned into a new important source of energy in the immediate future." Years later, Einstein said with deep regret, "If I had known that the Germans would not succeed in constructing the atom bomb, I would never have lifted a finger."[35] These disparate comments by the world's most eminent physicist suggest in bold outline the technological history of World War II. Inspired by foreign colleagues and motivated by fear, American science translated the forces of nature into such instruments of destruction as to revolutionize warfare and redirect the course of history.

The rapid transition was possible because scientists made prudent use of the past. They rejected the earlier arrangement whereby talent existed simply as a tool for use by the military and insisted on an organization "which could make its own assessment of what the armed services needed and which could then, preferably with the assistance of the Services but over their opposition if necessary, go about the business of getting the necessary weapons developed."[36] The Office of Scientific Research and Development (an expansion of the National Defense Research Council of 1940), headed by the shrewd and spry Yankee, Vannevar Bush, had access to the President, controlled its own budget, and mobilized the resources of science through contracts with industry and universities. At the outset, the military accepted the novel partnership with some reluctance. They were impatient with the academic assumption that theories could be converted into weapons, and feared that some scientific superagency might attempt to deprive them of their research and development functions. Eventually the bold and imaginative accomplishments of the Office of Scientific Research and Development led to an effective liaison; but in spite of the many postwar panegyrics on the friendship and cooperation of the scientific and military professions, friction was always present.

---

[34] Edward L. Katzenbach, Jr., "The Horse Cavalry in the Twentieth Century: A Study in Policy Response," *Public Affairs*, VIII, 120–49.

[35] Einstein's letter is quoted in Gordon Dean, *Report on the Atom* (New York, 1953), pp. 247–49; his later statement is in Jungk, p. 87.

[36] Irvin Stewart, *Organizing Scientific Research for War* (Boston, 1948), p. 6.

Scientists looked upon the military with disdain, and as one officer noted, ". . . those of us who had been working in applied science for years cannot be blamed for not always enthusiastically endorsing all the efforts of the Johnny-come-latelys who inevitably stream into Washington at the beginning of a war."[37]

Although they repudiated former patterns of organization, the scientists systematically exploited the accumulated knowledge of the previous years. Their triumphs were not in the realm of pure science—the creation of new knowledge of the physical world—but in applied research—the application of known discoveries to military hardware. This is true of the three major innovations of World War II: radar, the proximity fuse, and the atomic bomb. Radar had a history extending as far back as 1886, when the German physicist Heinrich Hertz proved that radio waves were reflected from solid objects. During the 1920's, the Naval Research Laboratory and the Signal Corps made some refinements on his discovery; the British made a great step forward by the development of a special magnetron tube that permitted the use of wave lengths at considerable distances. Thus in 1940, American scientists were able to use the English magnetron as a basis for the creation of 150 radar systems.[38] The proximity fuse was also feasible because of earlier British research. The final result —a fuse which exploded the shell as a result of reflected radio waves when it reached a certain proximity to a target, rather than on the basis of a time setting—was so valuable that it was not used over land until 1944 in order to prevent its duplication by the enemy.[39]

The most remarkable achievement of applied science, the atomic bomb, was such a gigantic design and production undertaking that it was placed under the administration of the Army's Corps of Engineers and the joint leadership of Colonel Leslie R. Groves and physicist Robert Oppenheimer. Designated the "Manhattan Project," it constituted a unique relationship between science and the military, and it raised one problem—secrecy—that was to plague every future effort in weapons research. The need for secrecy was apparent to the military during the 1930's, and had been so restrictively applied that it delayed the full exchange of information on radar between

---

[37] Harold G. Bowen, *Ships, Machinery and Mossbacks* (Princeton, N.J., 1954), p. 178.

[38] For the development of radar, see James Phinney Baxter, 3rd, *Scientists Against Time* (Boston, 1964); and Sir Robert Watson-Watt, *The Pulse of Radar* (New York, 1959).

[39] Baxter, pp. 221–42.

the Army and Navy.[40] Although the scientists, themselves, had imposed a ban on information about the uranium project, they chafed at the later restrictions which compartmentalized their work into tight units and allowed no one to know more than he needed to perform his special task. Despite such restrictions, the military-scientific-industrial team created the ultimate weapon. The dramatic climax at Hiroshima proved for all time that science could be effectively applied to warfare.

Victory followed the bomb. But what of the future? In his Farewell Address to the Manhattan Project, General Groves spoke of both as he eulogized the achievements of his team:

> Five years ago, the idea of Atomic Power was only a dream. You have made that dream a reality. You have seized upon the most nebulous of ideas and translated them into actualities. . . . You built the weapon which ended the War and thereby saved countless American lives. With regard to peacetime applications, you have raised the curtain on vistas of a new world.[41]

It was only just that the General should have his moment of oratory; he had performed well. But his words did not fit his achievement— they defied historical realities. It would have been more apt could he have cited the warning of the young Henry Adams nearly a century before: "Some day science may have the existence of mankind in its power, and the human race commit suicide by blowing up the world." And it would have been more prescient could he have mentioned the comment of the same young critic grown old, still having visions of disaster, but observing that "bombs educate vigorously."[42] For this was the real challenge forced upon the postwar world: could mankind learn and change enough in time to prevent its annihilation.

The men who had become partners in 1939 were to continually address themselves to that challenge after 1945, but not as professionals existing on the fringe of society. Success in war had its rewards; both the scientist and the soldier gained unprecedented prestige and influence. The public image of the scientist, particularly the phys-

---

[40] Dulany Terrett, *The Signal Corps: The Emergency* (Washington, D.C., 1956), p. 43.

[41] Quoted in Richard G. Hewlett and Oscar E. Anderson, Jr., *The New World, 1939–1946* (University Park, Pa., 1962), p. 655.

[42] Adams' statements are in Worthington C. Ford, *Cycle of Adams Letters*, I, 135; and Henry Adams, *The Education of Henry Adams* (Boston, 1918), p. 496.

icist, took on aspects of the heroic. Samuel K. Allison, director of the Manhattan Project's Metallurgical Laboratory recalled that suddenly physicists were

> exhibited as lions at Washington tea parties, were invited to conventions of social scientists, where their opinions on society were respectfully listened to by life-long experts in the field, attended conventions of religious orders and discoursed on theology, were asked to endorse plans for world government, and to give simplified lectures on the nucleus to Congressional committees.[43]

The military, too, blessed by the nation's gratitude and graced by a coterie of heroes, enjoyed exceptional popularity. Military officers moved into important civilian posts within the government, participated in domestic politics, and for the first time in history, developed close associations with the business elite.[44]

The widespread attention lavished upon the partners in victory represented more than natural and spontaneous adulation. It expressed a realization that both had emerged from the war as strategic elites—groups with special knowledge, skills, and values who could not be excluded from increased responsibility for the direction of postwar policy.[45] During the war, the military, and to a lesser extent the scientists, had participated in political decisions; in the immediate postwar world, they renounced their previous isolation from society and insisted upon a larger share in the determination of national policy. They derived from their wartime experience not only enhanced pride and power but, above all, purpose. They felt compelled to project their conceptions of the nature of society, to define its ends and goals, and to influence the crucial decisions that would ensure its security or salvation. Thus the war had engendered two revolutions: one in the relationship of scientists and the military to each other as progenitors of new weapons; the other in the relationship of both to society. The latter was to have a profound impact, for as they endeavored to shape the future of the nation, the two elites were often in grave and fundamental disagreement. Though the demands of national security impelled them toward cooperation, their training and

---

43 Samuel K. Allison, "The State of Physics; Or the Perils of Being Important," *The Bulletin of the Atomic Scientists* (hereafter cited as *BAS*), VI, No. 1 (January 1950), 3. . . .

44 See Samuel P. Huntington, pp. 354–73.

45 For a brilliant theoretical analysis of strategic elites in modern society, see Suzanne Keller, *Beyond the Ruling Class* (New York, 1963).

traditions inclined them toward conflict. Theirs was still an unnatural alliance, marked by increasingly awesome success but enduring frustration.

The roots of that frustration become starkly visible during the brief hiatus between war and cold war. The political uncertainty between 1945 and 1947 precluded a sharp definition of national goals and provided a timely opportunity for emerging elites. Spokesmen for the scientists and the armed services rushed eagerly into the ideological vacuum with confident prescriptions for the future. It was immediately apparent as they faced the issue of primary mutual importance—that of defining the nature of their peacetime relationship—that they were seeking a similar end through opposite means. The military, professionally alert to history, took a position which gave full meaning to Santayana's advice that "those who cannot remember the past are condemned to repeat it." Looking back to the interwar period, they deduced that military weakness had been an invitation to war. Intensely aware of the technological revolution, they made it clear that they had abandoned their traditional antagonism toward weapons innovation. As Secretary of War, Robert Patterson, summarized to a congressional committee, "Since the laboratories of America have now become part of our first line of defense, I cannot make too strong, or too emphatic, the interest of the War Department in the promotion of scientific research and development for new weapons."[46]

Thus the services, reaffirming their traditional axioms that the nature of man is evil and acquisitive, and that the essence of international politics is rivalry, moved forcefully to ensure the continued development of weapons. In 1945 the War Department vigorously supported the May-Johnson bill, which provided for civilian control of atomic energy, but which at the same time ensured the future development of atomic power for military purposes. In the same year, the Air Force signed a contract with the Douglas Aircraft Company to establish Project RAND in order to retain scientific manpower for the study of intercontinental warfare; and in 1946 the Navy established the Office of Naval Research, which lured scientists into its laboratories through a sincere dedication to basic research. The military displayed their concern for scientific preeminence in weaponry even more impressively by their program to import German and Austrian scientists. Well before the ultimate demise of the Third

---

[46] *Science Legislation* (Hearing before a Subcommittee of the Committee on Military Affairs, U.S. Senate, 79th Cong., 1st sess. [Washington, D.C., 1945]), p. 229.

Reich, a host of scientific intelligence teams had followed in the wake of the invading armies in search of "intellectual reparations." In July 1945, the War Department General Staff approved a plan whereby not more than 350 "chosen, rare minds" would be brought to the United States for temporary residence and exploitation. As the Soviet Union challenged the United States in competition for the minds of the vanquished, the services altered their original intentions in order to provide for the long-range exploitation of up to 1,000 scientists. The program was ironic but imperative; as a general officer candidly noted: "Pride and face-saving have no place in national insurance."[47]

Through argument and action, the military insisted upon a role as the nation's guardian; they assumed that strength, not weakness, was essential to future security, and genius, not geography, the means of attaining it. Most of the scientists, convinced that history had been rudely interrupted, and that a new world began with the ashes of Hiroshima, were not eager to enter into a permanent alliance. Peace, not preparedness, was their consuming passion. They, too, were determined to remember the past in order to renounce it. They remembered that as patriots they had abandoned their traditional commitment to beneficial research to work on weapons; that they had forsaken fundamental research to serve as applied technologists; and that they had sacrificed free and full publication to advance the cause of security. Their precipitate exodus to university and industrial laboratories after the Japanese surrender acted out their renunciation. Above all, their memories focused on Hiroshima. The scientists, however reluctantly, had opened the nuclear Pandora's box. They had hoped that whatever evil resided therein might be restrained, and that they could save the world from its affliction. In this they failed, although some of them made a noble effort to prevent the use of the atomic bomb.[48]

It was this failure that provided the impetus for their entry into the world of politics; for however much the politicians and the soldiers explained their decision as a means to hasten peace and save lives, to most of the scientists the bomb was a peacemaker tarnished by its own destructiveness. "When we thought of it, of what occurred," said

---

[47] See Clarence G. Lasby, "German Scientists in America: Their Importation, Expoitation and Assimilation, 1945–1952," unpublished doctoral dissertation, University of California at Los Angeles, 1962.

[48] On the use of the bomb, see especially Herbert Feis, *Japan Subdued, the Atomic Bomb and the End of the Pacific War* (Princeton, N.J., 1961); and Robert Batchelder, *The Irreversible Decision, 1939–1950* (Boston, 1961).

a Cornell physicist, "not from the angle of statistics, but in terms of little Matsuos, as well as little Noris going to school that morning with their black oilcloth bags, the nature of the war that we were making became clear."[49] Out of sorrow and guilt came anger. "Our conscience rebels," asserted an Oak Ridge physicist, "against a social system" which forces the scientist "by moral pressure and the instinct of self-preservation to develop one of the greatest discoveries of all time into an instrument for mass murder."[50]

The physical scientists who had created the bomb did rebel; obsessed by their cursed miracle, they resolved, deeply and sincerely, to create a "new world" in which it would be controlled. Albert Einstein insisted that "a world authority and an eventual world state are not just *desirable* in the name of brotherhood, they are necessary for world survival."[51] "Unite or perish" were their words of warning. "Other men have spoken them, in other times, of other wars, of other weapons," said Robert Oppenheimer. "They have not prevailed. They are misled by a false sense of human history who hold that they will not prevail today. It is not for us to believe that. By our works we are committed to a world united, before this common peril, in law, and in humanity."[52] To fulfill their commitment, they educated, they pleaded, they carried their message to the people and lobbied in Congress; they became preachers and then politicians. Their spontaneous fears and hopes led them to organize, and by January of 1946, their independent groups had coalesced to form the Federation of American Scientists, which thereafter was to serve as the nucleus of their movement.

There was, however, a tragic weakness in the argument of the crusading scientists: it required a radical alteration in the behavior of men and nations. Their naïve belief in the possibility of such a miracle in world politics now seems incredible. Even then, their spiritual ally, Senator William Fulbright, protested that "we can't control things like you can in a laboratory; if you have a test tube and there is a certain bug in there, you can make him do things . . . and you can't do that

---

[49] *The Social Task of the Scientist in the Atomic Era* (Princeton, N.J.: Emergency Committee of Atomic Scientists, 1947), p. 7. Statement by Dr. Philip Morrison.

[50] *Science Legislation Hearings*, p. 323. Statement by Dr. H. J. Curtis.

[51] Albert Einstein, "The Real Problem is in the Hearts of Men," *New York Times Magazine* (June 23, 1946), p. 7.

[52] Quoted in Leslie R. Groves, *Now It Can Be Told* (New York, 1962), p. 355.

in the political field. You can't do it. It is purely a matter of persuasion in this field."[53] But the scientists believed that they possessed unique attributes to bring about the transformation. As "citizens of the world," they could resurrect the international brotherhood of science and extend it to encompass all humanity. As perennial optimists accustomed to solving problems, they were convinced "that if physicists would only make others see their own wider vision, their ultimate influence will transcend that of any possible technological contribution."[54]

The scientists' primary political objective was the international control of atomic energy, a goal embodied in the Baruch Plan. On other issues where science conjoined with national security policy, they assumed the position of critics of the military's programs. Convinced that the May-Johnson bill was a military "conspiracy," they lobbied for a competing bill to exclude the services from the atomic energy field. They dramatized the issue of civilian versus military control and denounced General Groves as a martinet intent upon operating a permanent Manhattan Project. Certain that science could never progress under military auspices, they generalized about a "military mind" incompatible with the scientific spirit. Distressed by the "German scientist" program, they opposed it as immoral, imprudent, and inconsistent with the nation's domestic and foreign policy. To many of the scientists, the foremost enemies of society throughout the world were the generals and admirals; they were of the opinion that "to permit these individuals to continue their irresponsible careers of deliberately planning and thereby often provoking war, had become intolerable."[55]

But by the end of 1946, following the Russian rejection of the Baruch Plan, it was clear that mankind, not the military, was subverting the scientists' hopes. Their illusions of world government shattered against the reality of Soviet intransigence; once again, it was necessary for them to make an accommodation with the reality of power politics. Slowly and reluctantly, spurred by the ensuing shocks of the Berlin blockade, the Korean war, and Russian scientific accomplishments, they returned to weapons research. They did not withdraw from their stated positions; they accepted military preparedness as a temporary

---

[53] *Science Legislation Hearings*, p. 327.

[54] Percy W. Bridgman, *The Reflections of a Physicist* (New York, 1950), p. 318.

[55] Lawrence K. Frank, "Can We Curb the Irresponsibles?" *Science*, CIII (March 22, 1946), 350.

expedient, but only in the belief that "our diplomatic agents will have a far wider field in which to maneuver for peaceful ends if we have a wide variety of countermeasures."[56] They did not abandon their hopes; they merely gave greater concentration to their fears.

The scientists' unyielding fidelity to the belief that their actions must somehow benefit mankind has had momentous import, for after 1947 they acquired increasing and unprecedented influence at every level from the laboratory to the Pentagon to the White House. They claimed, and were conceded, unique competence as weapons innovators. They alone could advance the basic knowledge upon which many systems depend, and their opinions were indispensable in determining when the "state of the art" was such that a new weapon was feasible. They confidently and continuously impinged upon this former special province of the soldier. Less obvious, but equally persistent, has been the encroachment of a scientific elite into the realm of strategy and policy. An elite gains ascendancy in proportion to the relevance of its function to the problems confronting society. In a world of nuclear arms, scientists are "men in the know" without whose knowledge and skills there can be no adequate defense, but also without whose judgment there may be no judicious policy. Consequently, scientists have become intimately involved in the cardinal decisions that affect the nation and the world. Whenever possible they have used their enhanced power and prestige to their own advantage; whether as technologists or strategists, they have striven to project the attitudes and assumptions of their profession.[57] The extension of scientific values has affected both the character of weapons and the nature of strategy.

The renewed relationship of the scientists and the military in the development of weapons reflected the lessons of the war. Above all, the military forsook its traditional opposition to technological innovation and accepted the principle that a future war could not be fought

---

[56] Frederick Seitz, "Physicists and the Cold War," *BAS*, VI, No. 3 (March 1950), 85–86.

[57] This is not to say that all scientists expressed the same views on policy issues. Scientists, like other professionals, differ in their ideas because of personal as well as professional biases. Indeed, the scientific profession has experienced intense internal schisms during the postwar period—schisms which are carefully documented in Robert Gilpin, *American Scientists and Nuclear Weapons Policy* (Princeton, N.J., 1962). Nevertheless, the majority of scientists expressed certain predispositions which are closely related to the values of their profession. For an astute discussion of some of these policy predispositions, see Warner R. Schilling, "Scientists, Foreign Policy, and Politics," in Robert Gilpin and Christopher Wright, eds., *Scientists and National Policy-Making* (New York, 1964), pp. 144–73.

with old weapons. They accepted the scientist as an indispensable partner and hoped, as General H. H. Arnold expressed it, to get "the most advanced weapons quicker."[58] Their reliance upon the scientist has been fruitful; its legacy is a stunning array and variety of novel weapons, the nomenclature of which has become part of the vocabulary of the nuclear age. More enlightening than the accomplishments in weapons innovation, however, are the disappointments and delays. At the end of the war, the United States held undisputed weapons superiority; in the decades that followed, it saw that superiority lapse into relative equality with the Soviet Union.

There are many reasons for this subdued impact of science upon the art of warfare. For one thing, national leadership has often been indecisive. Yearning for peace, our government has not always been alert to the necessity, or amenable to the expense, of preparing for war. Yet, even when national intensions were clear and forceful, the effort has faltered. A prominent explanation, endlessly voiced by scientists, has been that the services have failed to create a congenial atmosphere for scientific research; indeed, that they are incapable of ensuring the development of radically new weapons because "military organization, military customs, practices, and rules, military traditions are all made for fighting and not for research. . . ."[59] That the services have hindered innovation in fact, despite their dedication to it in theory, is incontestable. They have harassed scientists in military laboratories with needless restrictions and irritations and have on occasions directed research as they would a field platoon.[60] They have sacrificed imaginative new ideas in their legitimate quest for the improvement of existing weapons for maximum, immediate readiness.[61] They have fought among themselves as rivals for a particular weapons system and a larger share of the budget. Sometimes they have merely been conservative. "The very nature of the animal is involved," suggested one Assistant Secretary of Defense; the scientist "is a man

[58] *Science Legislation Hearings*, p. 357.

[59] Statement by Dr. Lee A. Dubridge, "Current Comment: Science and Government," *BAS*, IX, No. 4 (May 1953), 151.

[60] U.S. Congress, House Subcommittee of the Committee on Government Operations, *Organization and Administration of the Military Research and Development Program* (83d Cong., 2nd sess. [Washington, D.C., 1954]). Some scientists have insisted that military research should be accomplished under complete civilian control. See Lloyd V. Berkner, "Science and National Strength," *BAS*, IX, No. 5 (June 1953), 154–55, 180.

[61] See J. Sterling Livingston, "Decision Making in Weapons Development," *Harvard Business Review*, XXXVI, No. 1 (January-February 1958), 128.

that is a nonconformist and . . . he is searching new fields and exploring new avenues, and the military man is pretty much on the opposite side."[62]

The Assistant Secretary's simple dichotomy has been universally accepted; it is only partially true. The record suggests that the titans of innovation—the explorers and searchers of science—have been as responsible as the military for the lethargic application of knowledge to weapons. If judged by the "most advanced weapons quicker" criterion, they have been surprisingly derelict. Two reasons are evident: they have been human in the sense that they have occasionally failed in vision, and they have been hesitant because they have often been disturbed by values. The startling example of the human is their lack of anticipation regarding intercontinental ballistic missiles. At the end of the war, there was considerable interest among some military officers for a program to develop long-range rockets—an interest that inspired the Army to import the German creators of the V-2. No support for such a program was forthcoming from the scientists. In December 1945, Dr. Vannevar Bush expressed annoyance at those persons who were writing about "a 3,000 mile high-angle rocket, shot from one continent to another, carrying an atomic bomb . . ." and added: "I say, technically, I don't think anybody in the world knows how to do such a thing, and I feel confident it will not be done for a very long period of time to come."[63] During the same month, an Air Force Scientific Advisory Board headed by the renowned Hungarian scientist, Dr. Theodore von Karman, issued a less conservative but equally discouraging report.[64] As late as 1949, Bush was berating "some eminent military men exhilarated perhaps by a short immersion in matters scientific," who had asserted that high-trajectory guided missiles spanning thousands of miles to hit a target were feasible.[65] It was not until 1953, when it was clear that a smaller and lighter thermonuclear bomb could be produced, that the Air Force initiated a forceful program. Surveying the absence of scientific foresight, one admiral, his pride ruffled by criticism of the military, remarked: "It

---

[62] Statement by Donald Quarles, *Organization and Administration of the Military Research and Development Program*, pp. 29–30.

[63] U.S. Congress, Senate, Special Committee on Atomic Energy, *Hearings* (79th Cong., 1st sess. [Washington, D.C. 1945]), p. 179.

[64] Theodore von Karman, *Toward New Horizons: Science the Key to Air Supremacy*, report to General H. H. Arnold (Washington, D.C., 1945).

[65] Vannevar Bush, *Modern Arms and Free Men* (New York, 1949), pp. 84–85.

appears we can find a congealed area of contented smugness in the high reaches of the scientific world as [well as] in the lofty regions of the Military mind." [66]

The admixture of values with technical judgment in weapons innovation is apparent in the role of certain scientists with respect to the hydrogen bomb. The possibility of a fusion bomb was recognized during the war, but little effort was made to explore its potentialities until after the explosion of the Russian atomic bomb in September 1949. The shock of the Soviet accomplishment prompted several scientists at the University of California to initiate a crash program to develop the "Super." [67] But the scientists of the General Advisory Committee to the Atomic Energy Commission recommended against a crash program, citing among other reasons: "We all hope that by one means or another, the development of these weapons can be avoided. We are all reluctant to see the United States take the initiative in precipitating this development." A majority of the members of the Committee attached an annex to the report which asserted that in not proceeding with the super bomb, "we see a unique opportunity of providing by example some limitations on the totality of war and thus of eliminating the fear and arousing the hope of mankind." A minority annex, signed by physicists Dr. Enrico Fermi and Dr. Isidor Rabi went further in stating that the bomb's "very existence and the knowledge of its construction [is] a danger to humanity as a whole. It is necessarily an evil thing considered in any light." [68] In the case of the H-bomb, the protesting scientists were overruled, but their reluctance to construct such a weapon in 1949 indicates their unwillingness to explore the possibilities during the previous four years.

Scientists have also been reluctant to exploit the military potentialities of outer space because of value judgments. In this area it is the military who have shown imagination. To be prepared for any eventuality, many officers have taken the position that the development of space technology is essential to national security and have expressed a desire for the most visionary weapons. They have envisaged a moon

---

[66] Statement by Admiral D. S. Fahrney (Ret.), "The History of Pilotless Aircraft and Guided Missiles," unpublished manuscript, Department of the Navy, 1960, p. 432.

[67] For the best discussions of the decision to construct the hydrogen bomb, see U.S. Atomic Energy Commission, *In the Matter of J. Robert Oppenheimer* (Washington, D.C., 1954); and Warner R. Schilling, "The H-Bomb Decision," *Political Science Quarterly*, LXXVI (March 1961), 24–46.

[68] U.S. Atomic Energy Commission, *In the Matter of J. Robert Oppenheimer*, pp. 79–80.

base, nuclear-armed satellites, and laser beams that could sweep through space to destroy enemy missiles or detonate their bombs. Their assumption is that we cannot "look at the problem of tomorrow in terms of weapons of today and just automatically say that there will be no military uses of space way out, including the moon."[69] Most scientists have urged that the space program be directed toward the acquisition of useful knowledge and the search for peace. Their assumption is that space activities can provide a basis for international cooperation; and conversely, that military activities might expand the arms race by inciting a Russian response. They do not want to jeopardize their goal of international harmony through a speculative venture for exotic weapons.[70]

The steady enlargement of the role of scientists in strategic decisions—those concerned with the management of the instruments of violence for the national purpose—issued naturally from their vital expertise. Strategy could not be left solely to the military or political leaders, because it was far more complex than ever before. It involved an assessment of the future military potential of both the United States and the Soviet Union; as such, it had to provide for unseen contingencies, made more baffling by a cunning and competent enemy. Scientists qualified as seers. In addition, they have benefited from special attributes that embellish their prestige. Their public image has generally been that of "miracle workers," inspired by creativity and imagination, predisposed to quick and beneficial solutions, and free from the personal ambitions that motivate the members of other elites.[71] This prestigious image has been translated into heightened political power and representation at the highest levels in government. Following Sputnik, it was acknowledged by the appointment of a Special Assistant to the President for Science and Technology and the establishment of the President's Science Advisory Committee. Once within the "corridors of power," the scientists have enjoyed a singular status. "They walk into a room where lay administrators still stand in awe

---

[69] Statement by Roy W. Johnson, at that time Director of the Advanced Research Projects Agency of the Department of Defense, in U.S. Congress, House, Select Committee on Astronautics and Space Exploration, *Astronautics and Space Exploration* (85th Cong., 2d sess. [Washington, D.C., 1958]), p. 1180.

[70] For the views of scientists and the military with respect to space, see Vernon Van Dyke, *Pride and Power: The Rationale of the Space Program* (Urbana, Ill., 1964).

[71] For a perceptive analysis of the scientists' public image and the benefits that derive from it, see Robert C. Wood, "The Rise of an Apolitical Elite," in Gilpin and Wright, pp. 41–72.

of imagined mystery. That myth of science, the picture of the infallible specialist in immutable fact, lingers on in the minds of administrators."[72]

Neither scientists nor soldiers determine strategic policy; they influence it, but they are only two of a congeries of groups and individuals who compete and compromise to achieve their goals. Nor do they have a monopoly on the abilities and experience requisite for decision making; the special knowledge of social scientists is indispensable to the process.[73] During the postwar period, however, due to the extent of their complicity in weapons development, they have exerted a pervasive effect upon policy. Although they do not approach problems as monolithic professions, and sometimes agree on alternatives, the general influence of each has been directed toward winning acceptance of contradictory strategic programs.

The military faced an entirely novel strategic situation in 1945. The existence of modern weapons meant that the former bulwark of the oceans and naval power was inadequate for defense, and that there would be no time to mobilize industrial and military strength for a future conflict. The development of the atomic bomb also dictated a reliance on strategic bombing as the primary factor in policy. Until the Korean war, the military responded by stressing continual mobilization and a powerful Air Force. Slow to react to the implications of nuclear weapons, they assumed that war, if it came, would be total; thus they prepared for a general conflict with the Soviet Union. Following the Russian acquisition of nuclear bombs, and until 1960, the predominant military thinking aimed at the creation of, and dependence upon, a massive retaliatory force of nuclear-armed bombers, so awesome that it would deter aggression. Throughout this period, the services placed nearly complete emphasis on the importance of military factors in international politics.[74]

Within this purview, the large majority of scientists attempted to complement or change the accepted military strategy in several different ways, all of which were explicit applications of ideas expressed

---

[72] James L. McCamy, *Science and Public Administration* (Tuscaloosa, Ala., 1960), pp. 204, 208.

[73] Social scientists, especially economists, have been influential through such organizations as the RAND Corporation. See Saul Friedman, "The RAND Corporation and Our Policy-Makers," *The Atlantic Monthly*, CCXII, No. 3 (September 1963), 61–68.

[74] Studies of postwar military strategy are found in M. Janowitz, *The Professional Soldier*; Bernard Brodie, *Strategy in the Missile Age* (Princeton, N.J., 1959); and Samuel P. Huntington, *The Common Defense* (New York, 1961).

in their earlier crusade. To mitigate the effect of a Soviet attack, they induced the Eisenhower administration, in 1953, to adopt a continental defense system based upon improved interceptor planes and missiles and an early warning radar system. This, they believed, would reduce the nation's vulnerability, and by doing so, would offer increased opportunities for negotiation. They were also convinced that complete dependence upon the doctrine of massive retaliation might prove fatal. Deploring such dependence, Robert Oppenheimer noted, "It is the only military instrument which brings the Soviet Union and the United States into contact—a most uncomfortable and dangerous contact—with one another."[75] To allow for the existence of conflict without its leading to a total nuclear war, they argued for the acquisition of capabilities to wage limited war. Not until the Kennedy administration was this alternative policy fully accepted. With regard to both continental defense and limited warfare, the scientists proceeded against the opposition of the prevailing military view. They received virtually no support in their most devoted effort—that of successfully negotiating a disarmament or arms-control agreement with the Soviet Union. Without their continuous labor, the limited nuclear test ban treaty of 1963 would not have been possible. Through an impressive impact upon strategic policy, the scientists were able in part to offset the terrifying implications of their weapons creations.[76]

The changing and complex nuclear world has been a bitter crucible for science and the military. In answering the peacetime call to arms, both groups entered an arena that required a compromise of traditional values, ideals, and goals. They have had to abandon their parochial allegiance to a unique way of life for homage to diverse and unpleasant responsibilities. The adjustment has been accompanied by intense professional frustration, marked by a division within the ranks, an altered self-image, and the agony of public disapproval. The scientific revolution in warfare has placed the military under immense stress. Its new mission to prevent war is in conflict with its long-held belief that war is inevitable; its pursuit of limited ends is radically different from its former dedication to total victory; its need to be prepared for conflict at all times does not allow for the previous reliance on mobilization; interservice rivalry has destroyed much of the unity

---

[75] J. Robert Oppenheimer, "Atomic Weapons and American Policy," *BAS*, IX, No. 6 (July 1953), 203.

[76] The scientists' role in the test ban agreement is briefly considered in Donald Cox, *America's New Policy Makers* (New York, 1964), pp. 249–63.

of the past; and in a world of nuclear arms, there can be no heroes. While suffering the torment of swift transition, the military has also experienced a challenge to its special expertise. Scientists and social scientists have seized a large share in creating arms and devising strategy, and the executive branch has greatly extended its authority to encompass military policy. Since 1945, the power of the military profession has steadily and continuously declined.[77]

The adaptation of the services to the new conditions has been surprisingly rapid. They have recognized the contributions of civilian experts; they have accepted the policy of deterrence; and they have encouraged advanced education for young officers. Although there has been resistance, especially among retired and reserve officers, a "new military" is in the ascendance.[78] Still, there has been no escape from frustration; there has been no gain in prestige. To the contrary, a host of critics has revitalized the nation's habitual antimilitary sentiment and expressed it in myriad ways. The sophisticated warn of a "garrison state" dominated by a bellicose military, and of a "power elite," in which the soldier seeks allies to control the nation.[79] The naïve merely portray the militarist as a warmonger, and seek rigid control over him as our one way to salvation.[80] Even the entertainers have considered it worthwhile to vilify the officers, as in the ludicrous and vicious movie, Dr. Strangelove. Criticism of any elite group is essential and valuable in a democratic society, but it should be based upon factual information and directed toward real problems. The anomaly here is that the critics have confused the nation's vast increase in armament with an augmentation of professional influence. Even more, they are unable to overcome their liberal prejudice; they, more than the military, are prisoners of the past. They continue to flay the shadows of an ancient samurai.

---

[77] See Samuel P. Huntington, "Power, Expertise and the Military Profession," *Daedalus,* 92, XCII, No. 4 (Fall 1963), 785–807; and Colonel Robert N. Ginsburgh, "The Challenge to Military Professionalism," *Foreign Affairs,* XLII, No. 2 (January 1964), 225–68.

[78] Morris Janowitz, ed., *The New Military: Changing Patterns of Organization* (New York, 1964).

[79] See Harold Lasswell, "The Interrelations of World Organization and Society," *Yale Law Journal,* LV (1946), 889–909, and "The Prospects of Cooperation in a Bipolar World," *University of Chicago Law Review,* XV (1948), 877–901; and C. Wright Mills, *The Power Elite* (New York, 1956).

[80] See especially Fred J. Cook, *The Warfare State* (New York, 1962); Tristram Coffin, *The Passion of the Hawks* (New York, 1964); John M. Swomley, Jr., *The Military Establishment* (New York, 1964).

Science, too, has suffered the anguish of forsaking traditional values to the insistent demands of the cold war. There have been ironic compensations; never before has the nation been willing to bestow such popularity upon scientists or such patronage upon the discipline. In 1961 the government spent $8.5 billion on research and development for national defense; approximately $200 million of this supported basic research in universities.[81] For many scientists, there is little solace in the statistics. Military research has generated its peculiar kind of pressures; the insistence on secrecy has been especially disturbing. Following their self-censorship during World War II, the scientists argued that the cost of secrecy had been greater than its benefits and that the results of future basic research should be published freely. This, they contended, was necessary to inspire our own scientific progress. At the same time, they were completely in favor of the stringent safeguarding of engineering and production techniques. The public and congressional reaction to this view reflected the unusual postwar insecurity and the obsession with spies. "Baiting" the scientists served as an outlet for emotions and "security clearances" as an assurance of safety. After 1954, the issue of secrecy diminished markedly. There has never been complete agreement in all military laboratories or with regard to university contracts, but there has been a sincere attempt to establish a delicate balance between the benefits of security and the advantages of unlimited discussion.[82]

A source of much greater distress to the scientists has been their unprecedented association with power. Those who have offered their talents to the development of weapons have had to face the charges of those who have remained pure through abstention. Dr. Harrison Brown of the California Institute of Technology berates the new "paramilitary," the younger generation of scientists who "are convinced that weaponry is a way of life" and to whom "it is easy to forget the monstrous machines of destruction to which their work is contributing."[83] A management consultant has similarly argued that today there are fourth and fifth generations of scientists who "are

---

[81] National Science Foundation, *Federal Funds for Science X* (Washington, D.C., 1962).

[82] The problems of secrecy are studied in Walter S. Gellhorn, *Security, Loyalty and Science* (Ithaca, N.Y., 1950); Ralph S. Brown, *Loyalty and Security* (New Haven, 1958); and Edward A. Shils, *The Torment of Secrecy* (Glencoe, Ill., 1956).

[83] Ralph Lapp, *Kill and Overkill* (New York, 1962), p. 21.

permanently dedicated to the invention and construction of what may appear to be a succession of weapons systems stretching through foreseeable time. In a real sense, these men are institutionalized, captive to their narrow specialties and to the paymaster, the grant, and the contract."[84]

If the association with power has led to the corruption of some, the attempt to make it amenable to professional values has led to the agony of others. The government, as it had throughout history, enlisted scientists in response to pragmatic needs; it was seeking expertise. Those who insisted upon intruding into the realm of policy, and thus in sharing in the direction of the power that devolved from their efforts, were not accepted graciously by either the politicians or the military. The appalling treatment of Robert Oppenheimer is a symbol of the painful adjustment. Even those scientists who successfully encroached into the positions of power have not escaped censure. President Eisenhower's warning in his farewell address that the "public policy could itself become the captive of a scientific-technological elite" allied with the military and industrial powers brought no peace to the conscience of science.[85] The pathway from the sacred to the profane has been marked with frustration.

Two decades after Hiroshima it is obvious that the dual relationship between scientists and the military—as partners in the creation of new weapons and as strategic elites participating in basic policy decisions—has been of momentous significance to American society. The joint research and development effort has provided the nation with an amazing destructive potential, and the two professions have helped to fashion a policy of deterrence that, contrary to the fears of 1945, has successfully avoided war for an extended period. There is less agreement as to the future of the relationship; some ask that it be dissolved, others that it be strengthened; the demands of international politics require that it be perdurable. It is likely, however, that both the military and scientists will be overshadowed in the future by the diplomats and politicians. The stalemate of mutual deterrence affords some opportunity for negotiation. Even in this process science is now indispensable; arms control requires its expertise, and diplomacy can benefit from its international orientation. Writing of the scientist, a member of the Army Medical Corps observed that the

---

[84] Statement by James Real, Center for the Study of Democratic Institutions, *Science, Scientists and Politics* (The Fund for the Republic, 1963), p. 11.

[85] New York *Times*, January 22, 1961.

world never had "more need of him, and there never was a time when more care was needful lest his torch should prove a firebrand and destroy more than it illuminates."[86] These words are more true today than when written in 1886.

---

[86] J. S. Billings, "Scientific Men and Their Duties," *Science*, VIII (1886), 547.

Bibliographical Guides: A Selective List*

EDITORS' NOTE: The following list of bibliographical guides and the bibliographical essays are highly selective, meant as suggestions for further reading. There is some repetition in titles, but since each author compiled his own list, the editors decided such repetition was permissible, as it calls attention to the scope and value of certain works.

GENERAL GUIDES

American Philosophical Society. *Classified Index to the Publications of the American Philosophical Society*. Philadelphia, 1940. 173 pp.

British Museum. Natural History Library. *Catalogue of the Books, Manuscripts, Maps and Drawings in the British Museum*. 5 vols. London, 1903–1915. *Supplement*. 1922–1940. 3 vols.

Conant, James B., ed. *Harvard Case Studies in Experimental Science*. 2 vols. Cambridge, Mass., 1957.

Downs, Robert B. *American Library Resources, A Bibliographical Guide*. Chicago, 1951. 428 pp. *Supplement, 1950–1961*. 1962. Lists guides to the holdings of individual libraries.

Griffin, Grace G., *et al.*, eds. *Writings on American History for 1902–1957*. 1904——. Published by the American Historical Association. Attempts to include all articles and books relating to all phases of American history published during the year. Beginning in the compilation for 1918, science has a separate section; but indexes for each volume should be consulted. There is also an Index volume for the *Writings* from 1902–1940.

John Crerar Library. *A List of Books on the History of Science*. Chicago, 1911. 297 pp. *Supplement*. 1917. *Second Supplement*. 1942.

Sarton, George. *A Guide to the History of Science*. New York, 1952. 316 pp. Very useful in any research.

U.S. National Museum of History and Technology. *Contributions. Papers* 1——. Washington, D.C., 1959——. Alternate citation: U.S. National Museum. *Bulletin* Nos. 218, 225, 228, 235, 240——.

TOPICAL GUIDES

Crane, Evan J., *et al. A Guide to the Literature of Chemistry*. 2d ed. New York, 1957. 397 pp.

---

* Compiled by Michele Aldrich.

Dalton, Blanch H. *Sources of Engineering Information.* Berkeley, Calif., 1948. 109 pp.

Edwards, Everett E. *A Bibliography of the History of Agriculture in the United States* (U.S. Dept. of Agriculture *Miscellaneous Publication* No. 84). Washington, D.C., 1930. 307 pp.

Engineering Index, 1884—. New York, 1892—. Cumulations of several years mark the coverage for 1884–1906; 1907—, annually compiled. Title varies occasionally, and there is little consistency in the place where historical material is cited.

Garrison, Fielding H., and Leslie Morton. *Medical Bibliography: An Annotated Check-list of Texts Illustrating the History of Medicine.* London, 1961. 655 pp.

John Crerar Library. *A List of Books on the History of Industry and Industrial Arts.* Chicago, 1915. 486 pp.

Karpinski, Louis. *Bibliography of Mathematical Work Printed in America Through 1850.* Ann Arbor, Mich., 1940. 697 pp.

La Rocque, Aurele. *Bibliography of the History of Geology.* Columbus, Ohio, 1964. Unpaged.

———. *Biographies of Geologists.* Columbus, Ohio, 1961. Unpaged.

———. *Contributions to the History of Geology: Biographic Index.* Columbus, Ohio, 1964. 217 pp. To obtain these valuable unpublished guides, write their author at The Ohio State University, Department of Geology.

Larson, Henrietta M. *Guide to Business History* (Harvard Studies in Business History, XII). Cambridge, Mass., 1948. 1181 pp. Excellent on technology, industry, and parts of practical science.

Meisel, Max. *A Bibliography of American Natural History; the Pioneer Century, 1769–1865.* 3 vols. New York, 1924–1929.

Miller, Genevieve. *Bibliography of the History of Medicine of the United States and Canada, 1939–1960.* Baltimore, 1964. 428 pp.

Merrens, H. Roy. "Historical Geography and Early American History," *William and Mary Quarterly,* XXII (October 1965), 529–48. A bibliographical, critical essay, focused on the treatment of the Atlantic seaboard.

Nickles, John M. *Geological Literature of North America, 1785-1918* (U.S. Geological Survey *Bulletin* 746 and 747). 2 vols. Washington, D.C., 1923 1924.

Parke, Nathan. *Guide to the Literature of Mathematics and Physics.* 2d ed. New York, 1958. 436 pp.

Pearl, Richard. *Guide to Geological Literature.* New York, 1951. 239 pp.

Southeastern Research Institute, Atlanta. *Directory of Engineering Data Sources; A Guide to American Literature in Engineering.* Atlanta, 1948. 63 pp.

[U.S. Geological Survey.] *Bibliography of North American Geology for 1908—.* A continuation of Nickles, *op. cit.,* issued as irregular *Bulletins* until commencing as annual in 1948.

U.S. Surgeon-General's Office. Library. *Index-Catalogue of the Library, Authors and Subjects.* 58 vols. in four series. Washington, D.C., 1880–

1955. Continued by the Library of Congress, *National Library of Medicine Catalog.* 1956—.

Wheat, Carl Irving. *Mapping the Transmississippi West, 1540–[1879].* 5 vols. in 6 pts. San Francisco, 1957–1963. Much information on geographic techniques, and excellent bibliographies of maps.

Wright, John K., and Elizabeth Platt. *Aids to Geographical Research.* 2d ed. New York, 1947. 331 pp.

BIOGRAPHY

Crowther, James Gerald. *Famous American Men of Science.* London, 1937. 414 pp.

Ireland, Norma Olin. *Index of Scientists of the World, from Ancient to Modern Times.* Boston, 1962. 662 pp.

National Academy of Sciences. *Biographical Memoirs.* Washington, D.C., 1877—.

MANUSCRIPTS

Academy of Natural Sciences of Philadelphia. *Guide to the Manuscript Collections in the Academy.* . . . Venia and Maurice Phillips, compilers. Philadelphia, 1963. 553 pp.

Lurie, Edward. "Some Manuscript Resources in the History of Nineteenth Century American Natural Science," *Isis,* XLIV (December 1953), 363–70.

Reingold, Nathan. "The National Archives and the History of Science in America," *Isis,* XLVI (March 1955), 22–28.

U.S. Library of Congress. *National Union Catalog of Manuscript Collections, 1959–1961.* Ann Arbor, Mich., 1962. 1061 pp. . . . *1962.* Hamden, Conn., 1964. . . . *Index, 1959–1962.* Hamden, Conn., 1964.

U.S. National Historical Publications Commission. *A Guide to Archives and Manuscripts in the United States,* Philip M. Hamer, ed., New Haven, Conn., 1961. 775 pp.

SCIENTIFIC SOCIETIES

Bates, Ralph S. *Scientific Societies in the United States.* 2d ed. New York, 1958. 297 pp.

Caullery, Maurice. *Universities and Scientific Life in the United States.* Cambridge, Mass., and London, 1922. 269 pp. See especially chap. xvii, "Academic and Scientific Societies."

National Research Council. *Scientific and Technical Societies of the United States and Canada.* 6th ed. Washington, D.C., 1955. 447 pp. The earlier editions are useful for now-defunct groups.

Thompson, James David, ed. *Handbook of Learned Societies and Institutions: America* (Carnegie Institution *Publication* No. 39). Washington, D.C., 1908. 592 pp.

SCIENTIFIC JOURNALS

Bolton, Henry C. *A Catalogue of Scientific and Technical Periodicals, 1665–1895* (Smithsonian Institution *Miscellaneous Collections*, XL). 2d ed. Washington, D.C., 1897. 1247 pp.

Brown, Peter, and George B. Stratton, eds. *World List of Scientific Periodicals Published in the Years 1900–1960*. 3 vols. 4th ed. Washington, D.C., and London, 1963–1965.

Index Medicus. Quarterly. New York and Washington, D.C., 1879–1927. Continued as *Quarterly Cumulative Index Medicus*. Chicago, 1927—.

Mott, Frank Luther. *A History of American Magazines, 1741–1905*. 4 vols. Cambridge, Mass., 1938–1957. Excellent annotation on scientific journals.

Royal Society of London. *Catalogue of Scientific Papers, 1800–1900*. 19 vols. London, 1867–1925. Subject indexes for mathematics, mechanics, and physics.

[Royal Society of London and the International Council.] *International Catalogue of Scientific Literature*. London, 1902–1917. A continuation of the previous, with separate annual volumes for each science, stopped with World War I.

JOURNALS USEFUL IN THE HISTORY OF SCIENCE

Agricultural History. Quarterly. Chicago. I—. January 1927—.

American Quarterly. Minneapolis. I—. Spring 1949—. Increasing numbers of articles on social history of science appear in later issues.

Bulletin of the History of Medicine. 10 issues per year. Baltimore. I—. January 1933—. Beginning April 1940, an annual bibliography of American history of medicine appears, cumulated to 1960 in G. Miller, *op. cit.*

Chronica Botanica. Annual. Leiden, Netherlands, and Waltham, Mass. I—. 1935—. Gradually became devoted to history of American botany.

Chymia. Annual. Philadelphia. I—. 1948—. Occasional articles on the history of American chemistry.

Current Work in the History of Medicine. Quarterly. London. I—. January 1954—.

Isis. Quarterly. Bruges, Belgium, and Cambridge, Mass. I—. January 1913—. The critical bibliographies are justly renowned in the history of science.

Journal of the History of Ideas. Quarterly. New York. I—. January 1940—.

Journal of the History of Medicine and Allied Sciences. Quarterly. New York. I—. January 1946—.

Journal of World History (*Cahiers d'Histoire Mondiale*). VIII:4 (1965). The entire issue is devoted to "Science in the American Context" and has some very provocative articles.

Minerva: A Review of Science, Learning and Policy. Quarterly. London. I—. Autumn 1962—.

Popular Astronomy. Frequency varied. Northfield, Minn. I:59. September 1893–December 1951.

Popular Science Monthly. New York. I—. May 1872—. See especially the biographies by Youmans.

Science. Weekly. Cambridge, Mass. I—. February 9, 1883—.

Scientific American. Monthly (weekly until 1859). New York. I—. August 28, 1845—.

Scientific Monthly. New York. I—. October 1915—. Similar to the earlier format of *Popular Science Monthly.*

Technology and Culture. Quarterly. Detroit. I—. Winter 1959—. Covers the history of engineering.

BIBLIOGRAPHICAL ESSAYS

Science in American Industry—*Kendall Birr*

To study the relationship between American science and industry one must begin with the general histories of science and technology. There are a number of good, brief histories of modern science. Stephen F. Mason, *A History of the Sciences*, rev. ed. (New York, 1962) is one of the best and has the added virtue of being in paperback. There is, unfortunately, no general history of science in America; Donald Fleming of Harvard will hopefully rectify that lack in the near future. A high standard for histories of technology has been established by *A History of Technology*, 5 vols., ed., Charles Singer, *et al.* (New York and London, 1954–1958); Volumes IV and V cover the period 1750 to 1900. See *Technology and Culture*, I (Fall 1960), 299 ff. for an extended evaluation of this work. T. K. Derry and Trevor I. Williams, *A Short History of Technology* (New York and Oxford, 1961) is a sound, well-written summary of the five-volume Singer work with some new material. For a very brief, incisive essay see F. B. L. Wilson, "The Evolution of Technology," *The Nineteenth Century World*, ed., Guy S. Métraux and Francois Crouzet (New York, 1963), pp. 132–76. Such works as James Kip Finch, *Engineering and Western Civilization* (New York, 1951) are also helpful. On the American scene, John W. Oliver, *History of American Technology* (New York, 1956) is a recent but not wholly satisfactory survey. Dirk J. Struik, *Yankee Science in the Making*, rev. ed. (New York, 1962) is a stimulating study of New England science and technology before 1860, though not everyone will agree with all of Struik's interpretations.

There are some general works on technological innovation in American industry. W. Paul Strassmann, *Risk and Technological Innovation: American Manufacturing Methods during the Nineteenth Century* (Ithaca, 1959) analyzes the iron and steel, textile, machine-tool, and electric power industries. John Jewkes, David Sawers, and Richard Stillerman, *The Sources of Invention* (New York, 1958) demonstrates the complexity of the innovative process and warns against drawing too sharp a contrast between nineteenth-century empiricism and individualism and twentieth-century science and institutionalism; it is particularly useful for brief sketches of some 50 significant twentieth-century inventions. National Bureau of Economic Research, *The Rate and Direction of Inventive Activity: Economic and Social Factors* (Princeton, 1962) contains some important essays, while *Technology and Social Change*, ed., Eli Ginzberg (New York, 1964) tries to estimate some of the consequences of modern technological changes.

Industrial histories contain much useful information on this subject. Victor S. Clark, *A History of Manufactures in the United States*, 3 vols.

(New York, 1929) is still fundamental. Harold I. Sharlin, *The Making of the Electrical Age* (New York, 1963) provides an excellent brief survey despite some erroneous details. Harold C. Passer, *The Electrical Manufacturers, 1875–1900* (Cambridge, Mass., 1953); Arthur A. Bright, Jr., *The Electric-Lamp Industry: Technological Change and Economic Development from 1800 to 1947* (New York, 1949); and W. Rupert Maclaurin, *Invention and Innovation in the Radio Industry* (New York, 1949) are splendid studies concerned with technological innovation in the electrical industry. For chemistry, see F. Sherwood Taylor, *A History of Industrial Chemistry* (New York, 1957) for a survey of both science and technology. L. F. Haber, *The Chemical Industry during the Nineteenth Century* (Oxford, 1958) provides an excellent brief analysis of both the European and American industries. Williams Haynes, *American Chemical Industry: A History*, 6 vols. (New York, 1945–1954) is impressively detailed; Volume VI provides brief historical sketches of American chemical firms. The oil industry has been fortunate in its historians. Harold F. Williamson and Arnold R. Daum, *The American Petroleum Iudustry: The Age of Illumination, 1859–1899* (Evanston, 1959) and many of the company histories demonstrate a thorough grasp of oil technology.

There is a brief sketch and a substantial bibliography on the history of organized industrial research in Kendall Birr, *Pioneering in Industrial Research* (Washington, D.C., 1957), chap. i, and more detail in Howard R. Bartlett, "The Development of Industrial Research in the United States," *Research—A National Resource*, 3 vols. (Washington, D.C., National Resources Planning Board, 1938–1941), II, 24 ff. W. David Lewis has prepared an unpublished manuscript on the history of the American industrial research laboratory for the Eleutherian Mills Historical Library, and is working on a general history of the subject with John Beer.

Technology and Culture (1959–   ) reviews the most important books in the history of industrial science, and its articles often deal with the American scene. Some of the best contemporary writing on industrial science and technology has appeared in *Fortune*; a number of the essays from that magazine are gathered in *The Mighty Force of Research*, Editors of Fortune (New York, c. 1953–1956).

Science and American Agriculture—*Reynold M. Wik*

The best source of information concerning science in American agriculture is the publications of the United States Department of Agriculture. From 1837 to 1862, farm statistics were presented in the Patent Office *Reports*. From 1862 to 1889 appeared the *Reports* of the Commissioner of Agriculture, and, after 1889, the annual *Reports* of the Secretary of Agriculture, each being published by the Government Printing Office in Washington, D.C. In 1894 the federal government introduced the annual *Yearbook* of the Department of Agriculture, a practice which has continued to the present time. The Yearbook for 1899, for example, included 880 pages devoted to 26 articles dealing with agriculture from 1607 to 1900. Since 1936 the *Yearbook*s have concentrated on the comprehensive treatment of one subject. The purpose of these books is to make available an authorative and comprehensive treatment of research work on important agricultural subjects. Some of the most valuable *Yearbooks* dealing with scientific agriculture would include: *Better Plants and Animals*, 1936; *Soils and Men*, 1938; *Food and Life*, 1939; *Farmers in a Changing World*, 1940; *Science in Farming*, 1943–1947; *Grass*, 1948; *Trees*, 1949; *Insects*, 1952; *Plant Diseases*, 1953; *Water*, 1955; *Animal Diseases*, 1956; *Soil*, 1957; *Land*, 1958; *Food*, 1959; *Power to Produce*, 1960; *Seeds*, 1961; and *After a Hundred Years*, 1962.

In addition, the annual report of the Secretary of Agriculture is published each year. Likewise, many bureaus, such as the Bureau of Animal Industry, have issued their own reports. The most significant bulletins of the agricultural experiment stations are available in the *Bulletins of the Experiment Stations*, issued by the U.S. Department of Agriculture. Department Bulletin No. 1199 (Washington, D.C., 1924), includes 12,500 references. Statistical materials appear in *Agricultural Statistics*, a volume devoted to farm prices, income, farm workers, food consumption, weather conditions, fisheries, forestry, and related subjects.

Unfortunately, there is no scholarly history of science in American agriculture. The subject is so vast that no one has attempted to master the material and to make a reliable synthesis. This monumental task remains for the dedicated scholars of the future. Neither do we have a sound history of technology in the United States. Before these fields can be treated in reliable fashion, there must be more research and specialized studies to form the basis of any definitive work.

However, some excellent monographs have appeared in recent years which give promise for the future. A. Hunter Dupree, in *Science in the Federal Government* (1957), has a valuable chapter on the evolution of research in American agriculture. His *Science and the Emergence of Modern America, 1865–1916* (1963), is likewise most helpful.

Other significant monographs would include, Byron T. Shaw, *Soil, Physical Conditions and Plant Growth* (1952); Nelson Klose, *America's Crop Heritage: the History of Foreign Plant Introductions by the Federal Government* (1950); T. Swann Harding, *Two Blades of Grass: A History of Scientific Development in the United States Department of Agriculture* (1947); Ernest B. Babcock and R. E. Clausen, *Genetics in Relation to Agriculture* (1918); H. C. Sherman, *Chemistry of Food and Nutrition* (1911); Henry H. Dukes, *The Physiology of Domestic Animals* (1933); and Hugh H. Bennett, *Soil Conservation* (1939).

In the field of applied science to technology, the relation of engineering to improved farm machinery is discussed in such books as: William T. Hutchinson, *Cyrus Hall McCormick* (1930); Leo Rogin, *The Introduction of Farm Machinery in its Relation to the Productivity of Labor in the Agriculture of the Nineteenth Century* (1931); and Reynold M. Wik, *Steam Power on the American Farm* (1953). It is significant to note that we still do not have a comprehensive book on the American farm tractor, the machine which made power farming possible and which caused the demise of the horse in rural America.

Considerable scientific material is found in *Agricultural History*, a quarterly published by the Agricultural History Society since 1927. Similarly, the farm journals in each of the states include articles featuring the latest discoveries in scientific farming. Most of the state experiment stations publish bulletins reflecting the age of science. Some of the titles are: *Iowa Farm Science*; *Utah Science*; *Tennessee Farm and Home Science*; *Frontiers of Plant Science* (Connecticut Experiment Station); *South Dakota Farm and Home Research*; *Maine Farm Research*; *Georgia Agricultural Research*; and *Illinois Research*. These publications discuss recent developments in agricultural engineering, animal science, bacteriology, botany, dairy science, entomology, horticulture, poultry science, biochemistry, and veterinary research.

Needless to say, it is obvious that virtually all of the writing on scientific farming has been done by specialists, most of whom are working for government agencies. As a result, their work is factual and extremely important. However, these materials should be handled by people who have a literary imagination and style which would present the drama of modern agriculture with a finesse and charm which it well deserves.

Science and Medicine—*John Duffy*

There is no plethora of books on the history of science or the history of medicine, and of the existing ones, only a few attempt to deal with the relationship between medicine and science. The one medical historian who has been exceptionally successful in placing medicine in its social and scientific milieu is Richard H. Shryock. Three of his books are essential to any understanding of American medical history: *The Development of Modern Medicine, an Interpretation of the Social and Scientific Factors Involved* (New York, 1947); *American Medical Research, Past and Present* (New York, 1947); *and Medicine and Society in America, 1660–1860* (New York, 1960).

Among the general medical histories, the best narrative account is that of Arturo Castiglioni, *A History of Medicine*, trans. and ed. by E. B. Krumbhaar, 2nd ed., revised and enlarged (New York, 1947). An incredibly detailed history which makes a first-rate reference work is Fielding H. Garrison, *An Introduction to the History of Medicine*, 4th ed. (Philadelphia and London, 1929). Garrison has also written a useful chapter on American medicine in Charles A. Beard, ed., *A Century of Progress* (New York and London, 1933). A fine brief medical history by an outstanding modern historian is Erwin H. Ackerknecht, *A Short History of Medicine* (New York, 1955). The only comprehensive study of American medicine is Francis R. Packard, *History of Medicine in the United States*, 2 vols. (Reprinted, New York and London, 1963). Originally published in 1929, this work is outdated, but it does contain a wealth of information. A good supplement to it is Felix Marti-Ibanez, ed., *History of American Medicine* (New York, 1959). Three useful monographs on specialized aspects of early American medicine are: John Duffy, *Epidemics in Colonial America* (Baton Rouge, La., 1953); William F. Norwood, *Medical Education in the United States Before the Civil War* (Philadelphia, 1944); and Henry

Burnell Shafer, *The American Medical Profession, 1783–1850* (New York, 1936).

State medical histories, where they exist, often are quite useful, but their quality varies considerably. Among the better older works are: Wyndham B. Blanton's three volumes, *Medicine in Virginia in the Seventeenth Century* (Richmond, 1930), *Medicine in Virginia in the Eighteenth Century* (Richmond, 1931), and *Medicine in Virginia in the Nineteenth Century* (Richmond, 1933); Henry R. Viets, *A Brief History of Medicine in Massachusetts* (Boston and New York, 1930); and James J. Walsh, *History of Medicine in New York, Three Centuries of Medical Progress*, 3 vols. in 1 (New York, 1919).

In recent years several good state histories have appeared: David L. Cowen, *Medicine and Health in New Jersey: A History* (Princeton, N.J., 1964); John Duffy, ed., *The Rudolph Matas History of Medicine in Louisiana*, 2 vols. (Baton Rouge, La., 1958–1962); and Joseph Ioor Waring, *A History of Medicine in South Carolina, 1670–1825* (Columbia, S.C., 1964).

Studies on the history of public health are only beginning. The sole general history is George Rosen, *A History of Public Health* (New York, 1958). For the United States, Wilson G. Smillie briefly surveys the scene in his *Public Health, Its Promise for the Future, A Chronicle of the Development of Public Health in the United States, 1607–1914*. Two fine monographs which bear on medicine and public health are John B. Blake, *Public Health in the Town of Boston, 1630–1822* (Cambridge, Mass., 1959), and Charles E. Rosenberg, *The Cholera Years, the United States in 1832, 1849 and 1866* (Chicago, 1962).

For the colonial period, Brooke Hindle's fine study, *The Pursuit of Science in Revolutionary America, 1735–1789* (Chapel Hill, N.C., 1956), given a good account of the physician-naturalists. Another useful work is Dirk J. Struik, *Yankee Science in the Making* (Boston, 1948). Two monographs, one old and one relatively new, are quite valuable: William Pepper, *The Medical Side of Benjamin Franklin* (Philadelphia, 1911); and Otho T. Beall, Jr., and Richard H. Shryock, *Cotton Mather: First Significant Figure in American Medicine* (Baltimore, 1954).

The best analysis of twentieth-century American medicine can be found in the previously cited writings of Richard H. Shryock. A particularly good survey of the present state of medical research which contains excellent brief historical summaries can be found in volume one of the American Foundation study, *Medical Research: A Midcentury Survey*, subtitled, *American Medical Research: In Principle and Practice* (Boston and Toronto, 1955). Another informative book dealing with the methodology of present-day medical science is David E. Green and W. Eugene Knox, eds., *Research in Medical Science* (New York, 1950).

Three excellent articles covering medical developments in the past hundrd years are: David L. Belding, "Fifty Years of Medical Progress, Medicine as a Science: Microbiology," *New England Journal of Medicine*, CCXLIV, No. 14 (April 5, 1951), 511–20; Frederick G. Kilgour, "Modern Medicine in Historical Perspective," *Bulletin of the Medical Library*

Association, L, No. 1 (January 1962), 42–56; and George Rosen, "The Bacteriologic, Immunologic and Chemotherapeutic Period, 1875–1950," *Bulletin of the New York Academy of Medicine*, XL, No. 6 (June 1964), 483 94.

Science and American Social Thought—*Charles E. Rosenberg*

There exist several useful bibliographic sources for the location of materials relating to the role of science in the development of American social thought. For medical and biological thought the several series of the *Index-Catalogue of the Library of the Surgeon-General's Office* are indispensable. Fransisco Guerra's *American Medical Bibliography, 1639–1783* (New York, 1962) may be profitably consulted as well for the colonial period. An excellent place to begin in any study of the relationship between science and religion in the United States is Nelson Burr's *A Critical Bibliography of Religion in America*, one volume bound in two (Princeton, 1961), pp. 1043–1109. *Isis*, the journal of the History of Science Society, prints a classified annual bibliography of writings in the field.

There is, unfortunately, no single study which attempts to evaluate and synthesize the role of science in American social thought. There are, of course, many pertinent monographic works. Particularly useful for the colonial period are the writings of Perry Miller, especially *The New England Mind*, 2 vols. (Cambridge, 1939, 1953) and his *Jonathan Edwards* (New York, 1949). The works of Cotton Mather and modern studies of Mather also contain revealing glimpses into the place of science in the Puritan world view. Whitfield J. Bell's *Early American Science. Needs and Opportunities for Study* (Williamsburg, 1955) not only suggests needed studies but is an excellent source of bibliographical references. Monographic materials become increasingly abundant with the early national and middle periods of American history. Particularly useful and/or meritorious are: Brooke Hindle, *The Pursuit of Science in Revolutionary America* (Chapel Hill, 1956); Daniel J. Boorstin, *The Lost World of Thomas Jefferson* (Boston, 1960); Edwin T. Martin, *Thomas Jefferson: Scientist* (New York, 1952); Arthur A. Ekirch, Jr., *The Idea of Progress in America, 1815–1860* (New York, 1951); Richard J. Storr, *The Beginnings of Graduate Education in America* (Chicago, 1953); William and Mabel Smallwood, *Natural History and the American Mind* (New York, 1941); Ethel M. McAllister, *Amos Eaton* (Philadelphia, 1941); William Stanton, *The Leopard's Spots. Scientific Attitudes toward Race in America 1815–1859* (Chicago, 1960); Daniel H. Calhoun, *The American Civil Engineer, Origins and Conflict* (Cambridge, Mass., 1960); Richard H. Shryock, *Medicine and Society in America, 1660–1860* (New York, 1960); Norman Dain, *Concept of Insanity in the United States, 1789–1865* (New Brunswick, N.J., 1964).

Spanning the Civil War are A. Hunter Dupree's *Science and the Federal Government* (Cambridge, Mass., 1957) and *Asa Gray* (Cambridge, Mass., 1959); Edward Lurie, *Louis Agassiz. A Life in Science* (Chicago, 1960); Nathan Reingold, *Science in Nineteenth-Century America. A Documen-*

tary History (New York, 1964); Charles Rosenberg, *The Cholera Years. The United States in 1832, 1849 and 1866* (Chicago, 1964); Arthur E. Fink, *Causes of Crime. Biological Theories in the United States. 1800–1915* (Philadelphia, 1938); Albert Deutsch, *The Mentally Ill in America*, 2nd ed. (New York, 1949).

The following studies of post-Civil War and recent America are similarly of value. Mark H. Haller, *Eugenics. Hereditarian Attitudes in American Thought* (New Brunswick, N.J. 1963); Hugh Hawkins, *Pioneer. A History of the Johns Hopkins University, 1874–1889* (Ithaca, N.Y., 1960); Milton Berman, *John Fiske. The Evolution of a Popularizer* (Cambridge, Mass., 1961); Samuel P. Hays, *Conservation and the Gospel of Efficiency* (Cambridge, Mass., 1959); Edward A. White, *Science and Religion in American Thought. The Impact of Naturalism* (Stanford, Calif., 1952); Morton White, *Social Thought in America. The Revolt Against Formalism* (Boston, 1957); Richard Hofstadter, *Social Darwinism in American Thought* (Boston, 1955); Stow Persons, ed., *Evolutionary Thought in America* (New Haven, 1950); William Jordy, *Henry Adams. Scientific Historian* (New Haven, 1952); Norman Furniss, *The Fundamentalist Controversy. 1918–1931* (New Haven, 1954). Students of American history should also be alert to studies of parallel intellectual currents in England and the Continent. Good examples are Richard S. Westfall, *Science and Religion in Seventeenth-Century England* (New Haven, 1958); D. G. Charlton, *Positivist Thought in France During the Second Empire. 1852–1870* (Oxford, 1959); Charles C. Gillispie, *Genesis and Geology* (Cambridge, Mass., 1951).

For historians interested in the approach of the sociologist of science, there is probably still no better introduction than Robert Merton's *Social Theory and Social Structure*, rev. ed. (Glencoe, Ill., 1957), Part IV, "Studies in the Sociology of Science," pp. 531–627. Bernard Barber and Walter Hirsch have edited a useful sampling of current work in the sociology of science: *The Sociology of Science* (New York, 1962). A similar and equally useful survey of medical sociology has been edited by E. Gartly Jaco: *Patients, Physicians and Illness* (Glencoe, Ill., 1958). This may be supplemented by Stanley H. King, *Perceptions of Illness and Medical Practice* (New York, 1962), which provides a useful survey of the literature in this field.

The preceding bibliography is merely suggestive; many excellent studies have not been mentioned, though some are noted in the footnotes. Articles in journals and unpublished doctoral dissertations are not mentioned at all, my assumption being that books are more readily available.

Science and Higher Education—*Charles Weiner*

The history of science education in the United States has yet to be written. Another pending project on the historian's agenda is the history of the impact of the changing role of science in American society on higher education in general. True, the increasing recognition of the need to document, interpret, and analyze critically the development of science in American culture has resulted in greater appreciation of the importance of questions related to science and higher education. Yet there are still no major studies of science and higher education per se. Many opportunities exist for such studies, and the major categories of materials available will be described below.

The educational aspects of science must be related to the larger scientific environment. Interpretations of this environment and suggestions for how it may be studied are provided by: Whitfield J. Bell, *Early American Science: Needs and Opportunities for Study* (Williamsburg, Va., 1955); Edward Lurie, "An Interpretation of Science in the Nineteenth Century: A Study in History and Historiography," *Journal of World History*, VIII (1965), 681–706; I. Bernard Cohen, *Some Early Tools of American Science* (Cambridge, Mass., 1950) and his "Science in America: The Nineteenth Century," in A. M. Schlesinger, Jr., and M. White, eds., *Paths of American Thought* (Boston, 1963), and Nathan Reingold, ed., *Science in Nineteenth Century America: A Documentary History* (New York, 1964).

Despite the excellent example set by I. Bernard Cohen in his pioneering study of science education at early Harvard (see above), very few studies have been made of the facilities for instruction in science, the financial support given, and the place of science in the curriculum of American colleges and universities. Donald Fleming, *Science and Technology in Providence 1760–1914: An Essay in the History of Brown University in the Metropolitan Community* (Providence, 1952). Louis W. McKeehan, *Yale Science: The First Hundred Years 1701–1801* (New York, 1947); Russell H. Chittenden, *History of the Sheffield Scientific School of Yale University 1846–1922* (New Haven, 1928); and Palmer C. Ricketts, *History of the Rensselaer Polytechnic Institute 1824–1934* (New York, 1934), are starting points for the history of science education at these institutions. For the great majority of educational institutions in the United States, the only account of the scientific component of their development can be found in the general history of the college, if one exists. Too often, these references to science are contained in a few paragraphs, and only in a few institutional histories do they exceed a chapter. However, even though direct references to science are scarce, good general histories of an institution can illuminate other related aspects, including the intellectual tone of the campus and long-term trends in the curriculum.

Louis Franklin Snow, *The College Curriculum in the United States* (New York, 1907), and Theodore Hornberger, *Scientific Thought in the American Colleges 1638–1800* (Austin, 1945) provide valuable information on science courses offered up to the nineteenth century. F. W. Clarke, *A Report on the Teaching of Chemistry and Physics in the U.S., Circular of the Bureau of Education, 1880* (Washington, D.C., 1881), C. Riborg Mann, *The Teaching of Physics for Purposes of General Education* (New York, 1912) provide data on the last decades of the century. *The Journal of Chemical Education* has published a number of articles on specific aspects of the history of chemistry in the college curriculum.

The following offer a viable general framework for evaluating the place of science in the curriculum, its relation to other studies, and its influence on the intellectual community: Richard Hofstadter and Walter P. Metzger,

The Development of Academic Freedom in the United States (New York, 1955) and Frederick Rudolph, *The American College and University* (New York, 1962), Metzger's reexamination of the German influence on American higher education has special relevance for the history of science education as does Richard J. Storr's study of graduate education, *The Beginnings of Graduate Education in America* (Chicago, 1953).

The relations between teaching and research are placed in the context of the development of professionalism in science in Edward H. Beardsley, *The Rise of the American Chemistry Profession, 1850–1900* (Gainesville, 1964) and in Everett Mendelsohn, "The Emergence of Science as a Profession in Nineteenth Century Europe," in Karl Hill, ed., *The Management of Scientists* (Boston, 1964). From the 1870's until the second decade of the twentieth century, *Popular Science Monthly* provided a platform for American scientists' public statements regarding their conception of the role of the college teacher of science. These statements are excellent sources, but the accounts they give of the state of science in America should not be accepted uncritically.

College catalogs, annual reports of college presidents, addresses delivered at the dedication ceremonies of new libraries and laboratories are all valuable sources that can further illuminate the whys, whats, and hows of science teaching in a specific academic institution or department. Although it is difficult to determine what textbooks were in use at specific institutions during specific periods, the effort is worthwhile, because study of the content of textbooks can indicate whether the science courses were up-to-date and on what level they were taught. Thomas Kuhn has discussed the conservative function of the textbook and its role in scientific change, in his *The Structure of Scientific Revolutions* (Chicago, 1962).

The unpublished materials in college archives or in manuscript collections provide essential information and insight into all of these questions. Yet these sources are virtually unexplored from the standpoint of the history of science and its relations with higher education. The Benjamin Peirce papers at Harvard, the Benjamin Silliman papers at Yale, and the Thomas C. Mendenhall papers at the American Institute of Physics are only a few of the more obvious examples of source materials indispensable for the study of science in higher education in the nineteenth century.

Not only is relatively little known about the whys, whats, and hows of science teaching, but we are also limited in our knowledge of *who* taught science. Who were the teachers of science, how were they trained, what were their motivations, and how did these factors affect their approach to the subject matter and their relation to the larger social and intellectual environment? Further, how did they affect their students? Many of these questions are answered in biographies of scientists such as the following: John F. Fulton and Elizabeth H. Thompson, *Benjamin Silliman, 1779–1864, Pathfinder in American Science* (New York, 1947); Edward Lurie's *Louis Agassiz: A Life in Science* (Chicago, 1960); and A. Hunter Dupree, *Asa Gray* (Cambridge, Mass., 1959); Ethel McAllister, *Amos Eaton: Scientist and Educator* (Philadelphia, 1941). Such questions are also dealt with in autobiographies of academic administrators such as

Daniel C. Gilman, *Launching a University* (New York, 1960). However, the researcher cannot afford to overlook the correspondence, diaries, lecture notes, and notebooks of science professors and their students scattered throughout manuscript collections at university and private libraries in the United States.

Major issues in the development of academic science in twentieth-century America have been and are currently discussed in the American Association for the Advancement of Science's journal *Science*, as well as in other contemporary scientific journals. In recent years *Daedalus*, the journal of The American Academy of Arts and Sciences, has devoted special issues to such topics as "Education in the Age of Science" (Winter 1959), "The Professions" (Fall 1963), "The Contemporary University: U.S.A." (Fall 1964), "Science and Culture" (Winter 1965), and "Creativity and Learning" (Summer 1965), all of which contain valuable contemporary interpretations of the role of science in higher education. James B. Conant's outstanding role as a scientist, educator, and social critic and p'anner is expressed in his suggested solutions to major problems concerning scientific education: *On Understanding Science* (Cambridge, Mass., 1947) and his *Science and Common Sense* (Cambridge, Mass., 1951).

The scientific community's increasing interest in history has provided a wealth of primary source materials for the history of twentieth-century physics, including its relation to higher education. Histories of academic physics departments, lecture notes, tape-recorded interviews, personal papers, and autobiographies are among the relevant materials that have been collected and made available for scholarly research by the American Institute of Physics through its Center for History and Philosophy of Physics.

Science and Private Agencies—*Howard S. Miller*

Much of the history of private scientific agencies is buried in little-used manuscript collections. Whitfield J. Bell, Jr., *Early American Science, Needs and Opportunities for Study* (Williamsburg, Va., 1955), and Edward Lurie, "Some Manuscript Sources in the History of Nineteenth Century American Natural Science," *Isis*, XLIV (December 1953), 363–70, are important guides. A growing concern for the preservation and use of science manuscripts is indicated by the "Conference on Science Manuscripts [May 5–6, 1960]," *Isis*, LIII (March 1962).

The leading nineteenth-century serials dealing with the scientific community as a whole are *The American Journal of Science*, often called simply *Silliman's Journal* (1818 to date), Edward L. Youmans' *Popular Science Monthly* (1872 to date), and *Science* (1883 to date), the weekly organ of the A.A.A.S. General magazines, such as the *North American Review* (1815–1940) and *The Atlantic Monthly* (1857 to date) also published considerable scientific material before the rise of specialized periodicals.

The publications of scientific and learned societies are a principle source of information and insight. Ralph Bates catalogs these agencies and their publications in *Scientific Societies in the United States*, 2nd ed. (New York, 1958). For technical papers, Max Meisel's *Bibliography of American Natural History: The Pioneer Century, 1769–1865*, 3 vols. (Brooklyn, 1924–1929), and the Royal Society of London, *Catalogue of Scientific Papers, 1800–1900*, 19 vols. (London, 1867–1925) are invaluable. The *Proceedings of the American Association for the Advancement of Science* (1848 to date) are especially significant because of the annual addresses of retiring presidents, a series of frequently nontechnical observations on the current state of science in America. The voluminous publications of the Smithsonian Institution can be located with the help of William J. Rhees, comp., *List of Publications of the Smithsonian Institution, 1846–1903*, Smithsonian Publication No. 1376 (Washington, D.C., 1903).

The principal guides to private scientific agencies and their research funds are Addison Brown, "Endowment for Scientific Research and Publication," *Annual Report of the Smithsonian Institution, 1892* (Washington, D.C., 1893), Carnegie Institution of Washington, *Confidential Report of the Executive Committee to the Board of Trustees, November 11, 1902* (Washington, D.C., 1902), Callie Hull *et al.*, comps., "Funds Available in the United States for the Support and Encouragement of Research in Science and its Technologies," 3rd ed., *Bulletin of the National Research Council*, No. 95 (Washington, D.C., 1934), and National Academy of Sciences, *Scientific and Technical Societies of the United States and Canada*, 6th ed. (Washington, D.C., 1955).

Ralph Bates' volume, cited above, is a useful introduction to the many brief, often "official" histories of American scientific agencies. George Brown Goode, "The Origins of the National Scientific and Educational Institutions of the United States," though dated, is still suggestive. It appears with a number of other valuable papers in the *Annual Report of the United States National Museum, 1897*, Pt. 2 (Washington, D.C., 1901). There is no solidly documented, interpretive history of the whole of American science. Richard Shryock's influential essay, "American Indifference to Basic Research in the Nineteenth Century," *Archives Internationales d'histoire des Sciences*, No. 5 (October 1948), and I. Bernard Cohen, "Science in America: The Nineteenth Century," in Arthur Schlesinger, Jr., and Morton White, eds., *Paths of American Thought* (Boston, 1963), pp. 167–89, treat special themes, while Nathan Reingold ties his volume of documents, *Science in Nineteenth Century America: A Documentary History* (New York, 1964), together with a general interpretive scheme. Donald Fleming's study of *Science and Technology in Providence, 1760–1914* (Providence, R.I., 1952) should stimulate similar investigations of other communities.

Biographers have slighted both scientists and their patrons. Except for Donald Fleming, *John William Draper and the Religion of Science* (Philadelphia, 1950), A. Hunter Dupree, *Asa Gray* (Cambridge, Mass., 1959), and Edward Lurie, *Louis Agassiz, A Life in Science* (Chicago, 1960), most biographies of nineteenth-century scientists are either superficial or of the life-and-letters variety. David Starr Jordan, ed., *Leading American Men of Science* (New York, 1910), and Bernard Jaffe, *Men of Science in America* (New York, 1944), are of uneven quality. *The Biographical Memoirs of the National Academy of Sciences* (Washington, D.C., 1877 to date) have noticed over 500 deceased members thus far, often with a complete bibliography of the subject's published works. Burton J. Hendrick, *The Life of Andrew Carnegie*, 2 vols. (New York, 1932), and Allan Nevins, *Study in Power, John D. Rockefeller*, 2 vols. (New York, 1953), treat the leading practitioners of wholesale giving. Most patrons of science lived quiet lives; biographical details must be pieced together from scattered eulogies, obituaries, and standard biographical dictionaries.

Most modern philanthropic foundations are reluctant to open their files to historians, and there is no satisfactory historical analysis of the foundation as a social institution. The Russell Sage Foundation, *Report of the Princeton Conference on the History of Philanthropy in the United States* (New York, 1956), contains an extensive bibliography. Frederick P. Keppel's discussion of *The Foundation, Its Place in American Life* (New York, 1930), is valuable but brief. The leading studies of twentieth-century foundations and their policies are F. Emerson Andrews, *Scientific Research Expenditures by the Larger Foundations* (Washington, D.C., 1956), and the same author's more inclusive *Philanthropic Foundations* (New York, 1956).

Science and Government Agencies—*Carroll W. Pursell, Jr.*

A. Hunter Dupree, *Science in the Federal Government: A History of Policies and Activities to 1940* (Cambridge, Mass., 1957) is the indispensable beginning point for any study of this subject. Those already familiar with it will realize how much the present study depends upon it. For the period after 1940, one may consult National Academy of Sciences, Committee on Science and Public Policy, *Federal Support of Basic Research in Institutions of Higher Learning* (Washington, D.C., 1964), which is actually a short history of science in the federal government since 1940, and the collection of papers titled "Perspectives on Government and Science," *The Annals of the American Academy of Political and Social Science*, CCCXXVII (January 1960). Other general studies, made from the perspective of political science and concentrating on the post-World War II years are Don K. Price, *Government and Science: Their Dynamic Relation in American Democracy* (New York, 1954); J. Stefan Dupre and Sanford A. Lakoff, *Science and the Nation: Policy and Politics* (Englewood Cliffs, N.J., 1962); United Nations Conference on the Application of Science and Technology for the Benefit of the Less Developed Areas, *Scientific and Technological Policy, Planning, and Organization* [U.S.], IX (Washington, D.C., n.d.); and Mary E. Corning, *OECD Scientific Research; Country Reports on the Scientific Research—United States* (Paris, 1963).

Several official assessments of government science have been made in this century, the most important of which are *Conduct of Scientific Work under the United States Government*, H.R. Doc. 1337 (January 18, 1909) (60th Cong., 2nd sess.); National Resources Committee, *Research—A*

National Resource (Washington, D.C. 1938–1940); Vannevar Bush, *Science, The Endless Frontier* (Washington, D.C., 1945); *Government's Wartime Research and Development, 1940–1944*, Report from the Subcommittee on War Mobilization, pursuant to S. Res. 107 (January 23, 1945) (79th Cong., 1st sess.); and President's Scientific Research Board, *Science and Public Policy*, 5 vols. (Washington, D.C., 1947), also known as the Steelman Report.

There are few recent studies of individual scientific agencies, but, for their histories before the mid-1920's, the so-called Service Monographs, issued in 66 volumes between 1918 and 1930 by the Institute for Government Research, are quite useful. All agencies were requested by the Bureau of the Budget to write histories of their activities during World War II, and these are available in forms ranging from multivolume published works to typescripts available only in agency libraries. No other period is so well covered, although several agencies now employ historians to record events as they happen.

Standard periodical sources are useful for information on government science. Besides these, perhaps the two most important for this purpose are *Science* (1883 to the present) and *Scientific Monthly* (1915–1917). The bulk of manuscript resources are housed in Washington, D.C. The papers of the government agencies themselves are now in the National Archives. Besides these, the personal and professional papers of many prominent government (or part-time government) scientists are available at the Library of Congress, such as those of Gifford Pinchot and John Campbell Merriam. The Presidential libraries, of course, will contain materials for their several periods.

In addition to the various monographs and articles cited in footnotes, useful titles on particular subjects include: Oscar E. Anderson, Jr., *The Health of a Nation: Harvey W. Wiley and the Fight for Pure Food* (Chicago, 1958); Robert Gilpin, *American Scientists and Nuclear Weapons Policy* (Princeton, N.J., 1962); Walter Sullivan, *Assault on the Unknown: The International Geophysical Year* (New York, 1961); Lloyd V. Berkner, "Wanted: A National Science Policy," *Atlantic Monthly*, CCI (January 1958), 40–44; Robert W. King, "A Tax Credit Plan for Reestablishing Private Support for Pure Science," *Science*, CV (June 6, 1947), 593–94; G. B. Kistiakowsky, "Science and Foreign Affairs," *Science*, CXIII (April 8, 1960), 1019–24; Simon Newcomb, "Science and Government," *North American Review*, CLXX (May 1900), 666–78; George K. Burgess, "Governmental Research," *Scientific Monthly*, XI (October 1920), 341 - 52; President's Science Advisory Committee, *Scientific Progress, The Universities, and the Federal Government* (Washington, D.C., 1960); National Academy of Sciences, *The Role of the Department of Commerce in Science and Technology* (Washington, D.C., 1960); Carroll W. Pursell, Jr., "The Anatomy of a Failure: The Science Advisory Board, 1933–1935," *Proceedings of the American Philosophical Society*, CIX (December 10, 1965), 342–51. Some of the problems and possibilities associated with studying the history of science and government since World War II are discussed in A. Hunter Dupree, "The Structure of the Government—

University Partnership after World War II," *Bulletin of the History of Medicine*, XXXIX (May–June, 1965), 245–51.

Science and the Military—*Clarence G. Lasby*

There are no general studies which have as their central theme the relationship of science and the military, but there are a number of secondary works which contain useful, relevant material. Among these, A. Hunter Dupree, *Science in the Federal Government* (Cambridge, Mass., 1957), provides an excellent introduction for the period to 1940. It should be supplemented by Samuel P. Huntington, *The Soldier and the State* (New York, 1954), a brilliant analysis of the military profession. For the nineteenth century, William Goetzmann, *Army Exploration in the American West* (New Haven, 1959), and Frederick W. True, *A History of the First Half-Century of the National Academy of Sciences, 1863–1913* (Washington, D.C., 1913), offer stimulating accounts of particular episodes of the scientific-military collaboration. For World War I, I. B. Holley, *Ideas and Weapons* (New Haven, 1953), is indispensable; it is the best single volume for the effect of scientific developments on weapons and strategy. Important source material on the interwar period can be found in Vannevar Bush, *Modern Arms and Free Men* (New York, 1949); and in the volumes of the *United States Army in World War II* series, especially Constance McLaughlin Green, Harry C. Thomson, and Peter C. Roots, *The Ordnance Department: Planning Munitions for War* (Washington, D.C., 1955); Dulany Terrett, *The Signal Corps: The Emergency* (Washington, D.C., 1956); and Mark S. Watson, *Chief of Staff: Prewar Plans and Preparations* (Washington, D.C., 1950).

For World War II, James P. Baxter, *Scientists Against Time* (Boston, 1946), and Irvin Stewart, *Organizing Scientific Research for War* (Boston, 1948) are of primary importance and contain considerable otherwise unobtainable documentation. By far the most revealing study of this period, however, is Richard G. Hewlett and Oscar E. Anderson, *The New World, 1939–1946* (University Park, Pa., 1962), the definitive and perceptive official history of the Atomic Energy Commission. For the cold war, there is a dearth of detailed information of the impact of science on weapons development, although some pertinent information can be gleaned from congressional hearings. The scientists' influence on public affairs, in contrast, is thoroughly examined in Alice Kimball Smith, *A Peril and a Hope: The Scientists' Movement in America, 1945–1947* (Chicago, 1965). Various facets of the altered relationship of science and the military after 1945 are carefully analyzed in Bernard Brodie, *Strategy in the Missile Age* (Princeton, 1959); Robert Gilpin, *American Scientists and Nuclear Weapons Policy* (Princeton, 1962); Robert Gilpin and Christopher Wright (eds.), *Scientists and National Policy Making* (New York, 1964); Morris Janowitz, *The Professional Soldier* (Glencoe, Ill., 1960); and Don K. Price, *Government and Science* (New York, 1954).

The most useful primary sources for the pre-World War II era are the *Annual Reports* and *Proceedings* of the National Academy of Sciences, and the voluminous records of the various military agencies in the National Archives. For sources after 1940, the independent scholar faces special problems because most of the relevant documents are classified. One exception is the superb collection in the University of Chicago Library which records the postwar scientists' movement. The World War II Records Division of the National Archives, Alexandria, Va., is the principal archives for documentation concerning the scientific-military developments, but frequently individual services retain declassified material. The Navy Department's Bureau of Weapons and the Air University Library, Montgomery, Ala., have excellent collections. For access to and information concerning the material available through the military services, one should contact the Office, Chief of Military History, Department of the Army; the United States Air Force Book Program, Office of Information, Department of the Air Force; and the Director of Naval History, Office, Chief of Naval Operations, Department of the Navy.

Chronology*

Science and Institutions for the Promotion and Diffusion of Knowledge

1743   American Philosophical Society, Philadelphia.

1780   American Academy of Arts and Sciences, Boston.

1790   Death of Franklin. David Rittenhouse president of the American Philosophical Society, 1791–97. Thomas Jefferson president, 1797–1815. Philadelphia is national capital of the United States until 1800, and American Philosophical Society acts as semiofficial advisor to the government on scientific matters.

1796   American Academy of Arts and Sciences receives Rumford Fund for the advancement of knowledge in the science of light and heat.

1798   Doctor Samuel Latham Mitchell starts *Medical Repository*, first scientific journal in the United States, New York.

1810   *American Mineralogical Journal* edited by Dr. Archibald Bruce. One volume covers 1810–1814.

1818–current   *American Journal of Science and Arts* founded by Benjamin Silliman, known as "Silliman's Journal."

1820   William Wood establishes Apprentices Library in Boston, beginning the Mechanics and Mercantile Library movement. First U.S. Pharmaceutical Convention held. This led to the establishment of the American Pharmaceutical Association in 1852.

1824   Franklin Institute of the State of Pennsylvania for the Promotion of Mechanic Arts begins publishing its journal. The Institute also establishes a museum and planetarium and encourages research and applied science.

1825   Maryland Institute for Promotion of Mechanic Arts. Middlesex Mechanics Association at Lowell

---

* Compiled by Marilee Clore.

1826   Millbury, Massachusetts, Lyceum established by Josiah Holbrook, beginning the Lyceum movement.

1837   Mechanics Institute of Chicago founded.

1839   American Statistical Association, Boston.

1840   National Institution for the Promotion of Science, Washington, D.C., grows out of the Metropolitan Society of 1810. The latter becomes the Columbian Institute for the Promotion of Arts and Sciences in 1816. The N.I.P.S., chartered by Congress as a national organization, had eight sections and was erratically financed by Congress, 1841–42. The N.I.P.S. initiated the first national scientific congress in 1844.

American Society of Dental Surgeons established and begins promoting first dental school, Baltimore College of Dentistry.

1844   American Psychiatric Association founded by superintendents of 13 insane asylums.

1845–   *Scientific American* founded.
current

1846   Smithsonian Institution begins publishing *Annual Reports.*

1847   American Medical Association.

1848   American Association for the Advancement of Science, formerly the Association of American Geologists and Naturalists, is founded (modeled after the British Association for the Advancement of Science, founded in 1831 in England, by Charles Babbidge).
Smithsonian Contributions to Knowledge appears.
Projected Boston Public Library permitted support by public taxation. This was the first tax-supported library and served as the model for the public library movement.

1852   American Pharmaceutical Association.

1859   American Dental Association.

1861   Demise of the National Institution for the Promotion of Science.

1862   *Smithsonian Miscellaneous Collections.*

1863   National Academy of Sciences incorporated by Congress.

1868   James Redpath reorganizes old Lyceums as commercial venture under Redpath's Lyceum Bureau. Lecture circuits are outlined and highly paid lecturers supplied.

1872   *Popular Science Monthly.*

1874   American Association for the Advancement of Science divided into sections in its new constitution: (*a*) mathematics, physics, and chemistry; (*b*) natural history (increasing to 9 sections in 1892, to 12 in 1895, to 18 in 1961. Parent organization of the Geological Society of America, Botanical Society of America, American Physical Society, American Anthropological Association, and History of Science Society).

1874   Priestley Centennial Celebration, Northumberland, Pa., institutes movement for national chemical organization. This movement delayed because of the new section in the American Association for the Advancement of Science.

1876   American Chemical Society, New York City, initiates the formation of other local organizations. Reorganization on national lines in 1891.

1878   Bishop John H. Vincent founds Chatauqua Literary and Scientific Circle.

1883   *Science*, financed by Alexander Graham Bell, begins publication. In 1900 this periodical becomes the official organ of the American Association for the Advancement of Science.

1887   American Physiological Society, oldest of biological medical societies, spawns a number of specialized organizations. The Society was founded by S. Weir Mitchell of Jefferson Medical College, Philadelphia; Henry P. Bowditch, Harvard Medical School; Henry L. Martin, Johns Hopkins; at the Physiological Laboratory of the College of Physicians and Surgeons, New York City.

1887–
93   *Journal of Analytical and Applied Chemistry*, edited by Dr. Edward Hart.

1887–
1908   *Technology Quarterly* published at M.I.T.

1888   American Association of Anatomists, Washington, D.C., product of reforms in medical education begun in 1870, reflects emphasis on research in morphology, cytology, genetics, and hematology. First president is Joseph Leidy, Professor of Anatomy, University of Pennsylvania. In 1908 the name changes to Association of American Anatomists.

1888–
current   National Geographic Society publishes *National Geographic Magazine* to popularize geography in order to finance monographs, maps, and expeditions.

    American Mathematical Society, New York City. Geological Society of America, Inc., New York.

1888–   *American Anthropologist.*
current

1888–   *American Geologist* published in Minnesota.
1905

1888–   *Publications of the American Statistical Association.* In
current 1922 the name changes to the *Journal of the American Sta-*
         tistical Association.

1890   American Society of Zoologists, Boston.

1891   Dr. Edward Hart, editor of the *Journal of Analytical and*
         Applied Chemistry, merges his journal with the publications
         of the American Chemical Society, editing the new *Journal*
         of the American Chemical Society until 1901.

1891–   *Bulletin of the New York Mathematical Society.* In 1894 it
current becomes *Bulletin of the American Mathematical Society.*

1892   American Psychological Association founded.

1893–   *Journal of Geology* published by the University of Chicago.
current

1893–   *Popular Astronomy* published by Goodsell Observatory,
current Carleton College, Northfield, Minn.

1893–   *Physical Review* published at Cornell University. In 1903 it
current becomes the official organ of the American Physical Society
         and later of the Physical Institute.

1894   Botanical Society of America, Brooklyn, N.Y.

1894–   *American Journal of Physiology.*
current

1894–   *American Mathematical Monthly* published by Kidder In-
current stitute in Missouri. In 1916 it is made the official organ of
         the Mathematical Association of America.

1896–   *Terrestrial Magnetism* published at Johns Hopkins.
1930

1897   American Astronomical Society, Boston.

1897–   *Plant World* published. At various times it merged with *Asa*
1919   *Gray Bulletin* (1893–1900) and finally with the *American*
         Botanist, which published continuously from 1901 until the
         present.

1898–   *Biological Bulletin* published by the Marine Biology Labo-
current ratory, Woods Hole, Mass.
1899   American Society for Microbiology, New Haven, Conn.
         American Physical Society, New York City.

1900–   *American Museum Journal* published by the New York
current Museum of Natural History. In 1919 the name is changed to
         its present title, *Natural History*.

1900–   *Ohio Journal of Science* published by The Ohio State Uni-
current versity and Ohio Academy of Science.

1901–   *American Journal of Anatomy*. In 1906 the title becomes
1906   *Anatomical Record*.

1901   American Association of Pathologists and Bacteriologists.

1901–   *American Botanist* begins publication.
current

1902   Electrochemical Society, Inc., Philadelphia.

1904   Association of American Geographers, Philadelphia.

1904–   *Journal of Experimental Biology* published by Yale until
current 1908 when the Wister Institute undertook the task.

1905   Reorganization of Wister's Cabinet into Wister Institute of
         Anatomy and Biology with a $3 million endowment given
         by General Isaac Jones Wister, grandnephew of Caspar
         Wister.

1906   American Society of Biological Chemists, Inc., New York.
         Entomological Society of America.

1913   Federation of American Societies for Experimental Biology
         promoted by the American Physiological Association, Wash-
         ington, D.C.

1915   Mathematical Association of America, Columbus, Ohio.
         Ecological Society of America.

1918   Chemical Warfare Service of the Army initiated by American
         Chemical Society.
         American Council on Education founded.

1919   American Meteorological Society, St. Louis, Mo.
         American Geophysical Union, Washington, D.C.

1924   History of Science Society established.
         American Society of Parasitologists.

1930   Econometric Society
         Institute for Advanced Study, Princeton, N.J. Albert Einstein
         becomes director in 1933.

1931   Genetic Society of America, New Orleans, La.
         American Institute of Physics.

1935   Institute of Mathematical Statistics.

Association for Sybolic Logic.

1947   *Bulletin of the Atomic Scientists.*

1948   American Institute of Biological Sciences.

American Geological Institute.

1955   Geochemical Society, New Orleans.

1963   Scientists' Institute for Public Information, New York. Established as central coordinating agency by representatives of 19 independent information committees organized by scientific associations during preceding five years.

Science in Industry

1722   French scientist René de Réaumur's discoveries in the area of iron metallurgy.

1729   Appearance of Dutch scientist 'sGravesande's machines for measuring the strength of materials such as wood, glass, metal.

1785   First mechanized flour mill opens.

1793   Lead-chamber process for sulfuric acid production introduced in the United States.

1799   Alessandro Volta devises the first electric cell.

1808   Sir Humphrey Davy demonstrates a primitive arc lamp.

1820   Hans Christian Oerstad demonstrates basic principle of electromagnetism.

1828   Scotsman James Neilson perfects process for heating the blast in blast furnaces used in steel production.

1831   Michael Faraday gives his famous paper outlining the principles of the generator to the Royal Society.

American physicist Joseph Henry experiments with primitive telegraph system.

1834   Samuel Luther Dana begins his work to improve dyeing and bleaching processes.

1836   James C. Booth opens one of first formal chemical laboratories in the United States.

1840   First portrait utilizing the Daguerre process is taken in the United States.

1848   American Association for the Advancement of Science established.

1856   Discovery of a new dye made from coal tar opens the way for development of synthetic dyes.

1857   Lammot Du Pont produces an improved gunpowder.

1859   First oil well in the United States is drilled in Pennsylvania.

1860's Louis Pasteur's investigations into the nature of yeast.

1863   A chemical laboratory opens in conjunction with metallurgical works at Wyandotte, Mich.

1864   Columbia School of Mines established.

Englishman James Clerk Maxwell describes the properties of electromagnetic waves.

1865   August Kekulé develops the structural formula of the benzene ring.

1865   Spengel mercury vacuum pump developed.

1866   American scientist Moses Farmer discovers the principle of self-exciting electromagnets.

1869   Dmitri Mendeleev's periodic table of elements appears.

Nobel process of dynamite production begins in the United States.

1870   James B. Eads constructs a steel arch bridge across the Mississippi.

John Hyatt patents a process for manufacturing the synthetic solid "Celuloid."

1873   Henry Rowland formalizes basic principles of magnetic circuits.

1876   Edison laboratory opens at Menlo Park, N.J.

1880   Electrolytic process first used to produce aluminum from its oxide.

A German chemist produces the first practical synthetic indigo dye.

1882   William L. Rowland writes separate reports on the state of the U.S. petroleum and chemical industry, for U.S. Census, 1880.

1883   Chemicals and the chemical industry are first recognized in the schedules of the Tariff Act of 1883.

1884   Solvay process plant for sodium production begins operating in the United States.

1888   First commercially successful electric street railway appears.

Nicola Tesla develops a successful alternating current motor.

The existence of electromagnetic waves is first experimentally demonstrated.

1889   American chemists invent roll film.

1890's Herbert Dow establishes Dow Chemical Company.

1893   Martin Dennis introduces improved tanning solution.

1900   General Electric Corporation founds its research laboratory.

1902   Du Pont Corporation establishes its eastern laboratory for research purposes.

Monsanto Chemical Company begins operation.

1907   The first thermosetting plastic, "Bakelite," is developed.

1912   Eastman Kodak organizes a formal research establishment.

1913   Standard of Indiana chemist develops high-pressure, high-temperature cracking for gasoline production.

1927   Du Pont begins basic in addition to applied research.

1939   First successful fission of the uranium atom.

1948   The transistor is developed.

Science in Agriculture

1735   Important surveying instrument, the theodolite, is invented by an American.

1785   The Philadelphia Society for the Promotion of Agriculture founded.

1791   The Society for the Promotion of Agriculture, Arts, and Manufactures is organized in New York.

1793   Eli Whitney produces the cotton gin.

1794   Springfield Armory becomes a national institution.

U.S. government appropriates funds for training engineers.

1819   *The American Farmer* appears in Baltimore.

1839   Congress makes first specific appropriation for agricultural studies.

1842   U.S. Botanic Gardens established.

1846   Smithsonian Institute founded.

1862   Congress passes the Morrill Act for the establishment of land-grant colleges.

Department of Agriculture established.

1869   First land-grant college, Iowa State College of Agriculture and Mechanical Arts (now Iowa State University of Science and Technology), opens at Ames, Ia.

1878   A University professor proves that the plant disease fire blight is caused by bacteria.

1881   The U.S. Entomological Commission becomes part of the Department of Agriculture.

1884   Bureau of Animal Industry organized.

1887   Hatch Act, creating the Office of Experiment Stations, passed.

1889   Department of Agriculture elevated to Cabinet status.

1890   Test for measuring butterfat content of milk developed.

1890   Army Signal Corps' meterological duties transferred to Department of Agriculture and the Weather Bureau established.

1892   Department of Agriculture pathologist discovers cause of animal disease tick fever.

1897   First Bachelor of Science Degree in Dairy Industry established at Iowa A. & M.

1898   Department of Agriculture organizes agency to introduce new plants from other countries.

1900   Experimental Arlington Farm established by the Bureau of Animal Industry.

1901   Bureau of Chemistry, Bureau of Plant Industry, Bureau of Soils set up within the Department of Agriculture.

1903   Ford Motor Company founded.

1906   Adams Act, which provided funds to state experiment stations for basic research, passed by Congress.

1906   Pure Food and Drug Act becomes law.

1914   Congress passes Smith-Lever Act authorizing extension work by the Department of Agriculture.

1919   Experimentation in Russia in the problem of artificial insemination for breeding purposes.

1921   Airplane first introduced into agriculture with the development of crop dusting.

1922   Bureau of Agricultural Economics established within the Department of Agriculture.

1935   Bankhead-Jones Act for agricultural research passed.
        Soil Conservation Service established.

1935   Henry Ford founds National Farm Chemurgic Council to promote the industrial use of farm products.

1936   Major U.S. dairy associations using artificial insemination in cattle breeding.

1942   Agricultural Research Administration organized.

Science in Medicine

1752   Pennsylvania Hospital opens in Philadelphia.

1757   Benjamin Franklin articulates methods he devised for treating paralytic patients with electric-shock therapy.

1759   Physician John Bard's operation for extrauterine pregnancy sets precedents in the field.

1766   Medical School of the College of Philadelphia opens.

1768   Medical Branch established at King's College in New York.

1783   Harvard Medical School established.

1794   First cesarean section in the United States performed.

1798   Medical Department added at Dartmouth College.

1798   Federal government undertakes care of merchant seamen.

1799   Transylvania University in Kentucky adds medical department.

        Sir Humphrey Davy suggests use of nitrous oxide as painkiller in surgery.

1809   First ovariotomy in the United States performed.

1813   Federal vaccine agent established.

1818   South Carolina surgeon perfects extrauterine pregnancy operation.

        Army Medical Department organized.

1824   An English chemist discovers composition of gastric fluid.

1830's   Mesmerism or hypnotism introduced into obstetrics and surgery.

1831   Chloroform discovered.

1839   The American Statistical Society founded.

1842   Massachusetts passes a law improving the collection of vital statistics.

1844   First use of nitrous oxide as an anesthetic during dental surgery.

1846   First operation using sulfuric ether as an anesthetic assures future of chemical anesthesiology in the United States.

1847   American doctor devises method for surgical removal of vesico-vaginal fistula.

American Medical Association organized.

1867   Army Medical Museum established.

1868   Army Medical Library opens.

1870   Massachusetts establishes first adequate state system for registering vital statistics.

Reorganization of the Marine Hospital Service by the U.S. government.

1879   Medical bibliography *Index Medicus* established.

National Board of Health organized.

1880   Surgeon General's Office sets up Federal Registration Area for the collection of vital statistics.

1887   Hygenic Laboratory, Marine Hospital Service, established by the U.S. government.

1893   Army Medical School established as training and research center.

Johns Hopkins Medical School opens.

New York City sets up diagnostic laboratory for research in bacteriology.

1900   Yellow-Fever Board operating in Cuba.

1901   Government appropriates funds for a permanent Hygienic Laboratory in Washington, D.C.

Rockefeller Institute for Medical Research founded.

1902   Reorganization of Marine Hospital and Public Health Service.

John McCormick Institute for Infectious Diseases established.

Founding of the Carnegie Institute in Washington.

1905   American Medical Association creates Council on Medical Education.

1909   Flexner Report on Medical Education issued.

1912   Public Health Service founded.

1930   Hygenic Laboratory reorganized and named the National Institute of Health.

1937   Congress creates the National Cancer Institute.

Science and Higher Education

1802   West Point Military Academy founded.

1815   Albany Academy begins operation.

1824   The Rensselaer Polytechnic School is established in Troy, N.Y.

1824   Franklin Institute of the state of Pennsylvania for the promotion of the mechanic arts founded in Philadelphia.

1825   Civil engineering courses begin to be offered in universities.

1835   Rensselaer School gives first engineering degree.

1837   Massachusetts establishes the first effective state board of education.
          Oberlin College admits women for the B.A. degree.

1842   Francis Wayland, president of Brown University, publishes *Thoughts on the Present Collegiate System in the United States* in which he advocates broadening and modernizing the curriculum, especially in science.
          Massachusetts passes the first compulsory school attendance law.

1860   Sheffield Scientific School opens at Yale.

1861   Yale awards the first Ph.D. in America.

1863   National Academy of Sciences founded.

1865   Massachusetts Institute of Technology opens.
          Cornell University founded in Ithaca, N.Y.

1868   Charles W. Eliot, chemist, becomes president of Harvard.
          Cornell University, Ithaca, N.Y., opens; nonsectarian with emphasis on science in the curriculum.

1870   First comprehensive organization of graduate studies, Yale and Harvard.

1871   Increased emphasis on science in education indicated by Yale pamphlet *The Needs of the University.*

1876   Johns Hopkins University established.

1887   Clark University established.

1891   Opening of the University of Chicago.

1893   First American journal for research results in physics appears.

1899   American Physical Society organized.

1930   American Association of Physics Teachers founded.

Science and Private Agencies

1796   Benjamin Thompson sets up first research endowment in the United States.

1826   James Smithson's bequest for the benefit of U.S. science.

1828   Noah Webster publishes his *American Dictionary of the English Language*.

1838   First permanent observatory in the United States established.

1840   The word *scientist* coined by the English philosopher William Whewell.
       National Institute for the Promotion of Science founded.

1843   Harvard Observatory opens.
       Cincinnati Observatory founded.

1844   First national congress of scientific men ever held in the United States takes place.

1846   Smithsonian Institution founded.

1867   Alexander Dallas Bache Fund for scientific research established under the National Academy of Science.

1872   English scientist John Tyndall's U.S. lecture tour.

1873   First systematic research financing begun by American Association for the Advancement of Science.

1874   American Association for the Advancement of Science sets up permanent research endowment.

1878   Joseph Henry Fund established.

1884   Elizabeth Thompson Science Fund set up.

1888   The Lick Observatory founded in California.

1897   Dedication of the Yerkes Observatory of the University of Chicago.

1902   Carnegie Institution founded.

Science and Government Agencies

1802   Army Corps of Engineers established.

1803   Lewis and Clark Expedition.

1807   Coast Survey Act passed.

1825   New York establishes the first state weather service.

1832   Coast Survey reactivated.

1836   Patent Office organized.

1837   Pennsylvania establishes a state weather service.

1838   New York appropriates public funds for school libraries.

1842   Naval Observatory begins operations.

1853   Pacific Railroad Surveys.

1862   Morrill Act for the establishment of land-grant colleges passed.

1863   National Academy of Sciences Founded.

1867   Clarence King's Geological Survey of the Fortieth Parallel.

1869   Lt. George M. Wheeler's Geographical Survey of Nevada and Utah.

1870   John Wesley Powell's Geological and Topographical Survey of the Colorado River of the West.

1871   Fish Commission established.

1873   Ferdinand V. Hayden's Geological and Geographical Survey of the Territories.

1878   Old Coast Survey agency changed to the Coast and Geodetic Survey.

1879   All surveying work consolidated under the U.S. Geological Survey.

1880   Results of the King Geological Survey published by the government.

1881   Reorganization of the Department of Entomology, Department of Agriculture.

1884   Allison Commission organized.

1886   Division of Economic Ornithology and Mammalogy, Department of Agriculture, established. Leads to Biological Survey.

1887   Hatch Act for the creation of agricultural experiment stations passed.

1888   John W. Powell's Irrigation Survey.

1890   Meterological services transferred from the Army to the newly created Weather Bureau of the Department of Agriculture.

1891   Congress authorizes President to withdraw forest lands from sale.

1896   National Academy Committee on Forestry appointed.

1897   Legislation laying the groundwork for a forest-management policy passed.

1901   National Bureau of Standards established.

1902   Newlands Act and establishment of the Reclamation Service.

1906   Passage of the Adams Act for increased support to agricultural experiment stations.

1910   Bureau of Mines established.

1915   Organization of the National Advisory Committee for Aeronautics.
        Naval Consulting Board appointed.

1916   National Research Council established.

1918   Chemical Warfare Service of the Army instituted. National Research Council formally reorganized by Presidential order.

1923   Naval Research Laboratory.

1933   Appointment of the Science Advisory Board.

1935   National Resources Board organized.

1940   National Defense Research Committee.
        Weather Bureau moved to Department of Commerce.

1941   Office of Scientific Research and Development organized.

1946   Atomic Energy Commission. Office of Naval Research established.

1950   Organization of the National Science Foundation.

1957   James Killian named head of President's Science Advisory Committee.

Science and the Military

1802   West Point Military Academy founded.

1803   Lewis and Clark Expedition organized.

1819   Stephen H. Long's Expedition to the Rocky Mountains.

1830   Navy Depot of Charts and Instruments set up.

1838   Lt. Charles Wilkes's U.S. Exploring Expedition.

1842   Naval Observatory opened.

1847   Lt. W. K. Lynch's Dead Sea Expedition.

1849   Lt. James Gilliss' U.S. Naval Astronomical Expedition to Chile.

1852   Commodore Matthew Perry's Expedition to Japan.

1853   Captain John Rodger's U.S. North Pacific Exploring Expedition.

1863   National Academy of Sciences founded.

1870   Meteorological work began in Army Signal Corps.

1877   Simon Newcomb began project of summarizing planetary and stellar positions observed since 1750.

1879   U.S. Geological Survey organized.

1886   Heinrich Hertz's discovery that radio waves are reflected from solid objects.

1890   Meteorological services transferred from Army to newly created Weather Bureau of the Department of Agriculture.

1915   National Advisory Committee for Aeronautics.
        National Consulting Board organized.

1916   Appointment of the National Research Council.

1940   Radar development completed.
        National Defense Research Council organized.

1941   Office of Scientific Research and Development organized.

1944   Proximity fuse first used over land.

1945   May-Johnson Bill providing civilian control of atomic energy.

1945   Project RAND organized.

1946   Office of Naval Research established.
        Federation of American Scientists formed.

1949   Soviet Russia explodes its first atomic bomb.

Glossary*

Aneurysm.   A permanent abnormal, blood-filled artery.

Animalcular theory.   Hypothesis that animacules (minute animals invisible to the naked eye such as a Paramecium) caused diseases.

Astrophysics.   The science that deals primarily with the constitution of the celestial bodies.

Calomel.   Mercurous chloride much used in medicine as a mercurial purgative, and anthelmintic.

Chirurgeon.   Archaic form of *surgeon.*

Collodion.   A viscous solution of acetone or pyroxylin used as a coating; a major ingredient of celluloid.

Conic sections.   That branch of geometry which treats of the parabola, ellipse, hyperbola.

Dalton, John (1766–1844).   English chemist and physicist best known for his development of modern atomic theory.

Electric traction system.   Transportation system involving the drawing of vehicles by electricity.

Ecotype.   A subdivision of an ecospecies that maintains its identity through isolation and environmental selection.

Gay-Lussac towers.   Developed by French chemist Joseph Louis Gay-Lussac (1778–1850) in 1818 and used in the lead-chamber process of sulfuric acid production.

Gilbert, William (1540–1603).   Most distinguished English scientist during the reign of Elizabeth I and renowned for his important work on magnetism—*De magnete, magneticisque corporibus, et de magno magnete tellure* (1600).

Helmholtz, Hermann von (1821–1894).   German physicist and physiologist. He proposed a theory of color vision, worked with the measurement of nervous impulses, articulated law of the conservation of energy. In the area of sensation and perception, he attempted to account for the perception of quality of tone, finding that it depended on the order, number, and intensity of overtones.

---

* Compiled by Marilee Clore.

Henry.   An electrical unit of induction named after Joseph Henry. Inductance of a current in which an electromotive force of one volt is induced by a current varying at the rate of one ampere per second.

Hydrography.   Decription and study of seas, lakes, rivers; especially measurement of the flow of streams with reference to utilization of their waters.

Hysteresis losses.   A loss of energy due to molecular change manifest in heat.

Icthyology.   A division of zoology; the study of fish.

Lavoisier, Antoine Laurent (1743–1794).   French chemist who discovered and named the element oxygen (1775–1783). The latter date is the year of his formal attack against phlogiston theory.

Liebig, Justus von (1803–1873).   German chemistry professor whose American students made significant advances in chemical fertilization during the last half of the nineteenth century. His most famous work was *Chemistry in Its Application to Agriculture and Physiology.*

Linnaeus, Carl (1707–1778).   Swedish botanist who first ennunciated the principles for defining genera and species and adhered to a uniform use of specific names. His *Genera Plantarum* is considered the starting point of modern systematic botany.

Magnetron.   A vacuum tube containing an anode and a heated cathode, the flow of electrons from cathode to anode being controlled by an externally applied magnetic field.

Mendelians.   Those who adhered to the genetic theories of Austrian botanist Gregor Johann Mendel (1822–1884).

Mensuration.   That branch of applied geometry concerned with finding length of lines, areas of surfaces, and volumes of solids from simple data of lines and angles.

Newcomen, Thomas (1663–1729).   Invented the "atmospheric engine," the first practical steam engine.

Solvay process.   Process for making alkali (commonly called the ammonia-soda process) developed by Belgian chemist Ernest Solvay (1839–1922).

Stearine.   The solid portion of any fat; an ester of glycerol and stearic acid found in animal and vegetable fats.

Theodolite.   Invention used in surveying to measure horizontal and vertical angles.

Thermal and catalytic cracking.   Process by which complex hydrocarbons composing petroleum or similar oils are broken up by heat or pressure into lighter hydrocarbons of simpler molecular formula.

Torsion balance.   An instrument used to measure minute forces, such as electrostatic or magnetic attraction and repulsion, by the torsion of a wire or filament.

Tuyère.   The nozzle through which the air blast is delivered in a forge, blast furnace, etc.

Weismannism.   Social view developing out of the work of German biologist August Weismann (1834–1914) whose theory of the continuity of the germ plasm (distinct from body cells) from one generation to another uneffected by any alteration in the body cells, became an important principle of genetics. It gave substance to the argument of those stressing heredity over environment in human behavior.

Index*

A

Abbe, Cleveland, 256–57
Aberdeen, Scotland, 139n
Absolutes in science, 136, 152; see also Space, absolute; Time, absolute
Académie des sciences, 21
Academies, European, influence of, 29
Academies: science training at, 168, 173; research at, 193
Academies of fine arts: see Cincinnati Academy of Fine Arts; New York Academy of Fine Arts; Pennsylvania Academy of Fine Arts
Academy, military; see Military Academy, U.S.; Naval Academy, U.S.
Achromatic microscope, 10, 11, 17
Acids, and chemical industry, 55; see also Amino acid; Dichlorophenoxyacetic acid; Hydrochloric acid; Nucleic acid; Sulphuric acid
Adams, Henry, 33, 135, 138, 266
Adams, John, 21, 26, 34
Adams, John Quincy, 202, 204, 231, 254
Adams Act, 95, 160, 229
Aedes aegypti mosquito; see Mosquito
Aerodynamic design, 74
Aeronautics, 74-75, 261; see also Aviation, commercial
Aeronautics, National Advisory Committee for, 234, 240, 247, 261–62, 263
Aeronautics and Space Administration, National, 247
Aerospace engineers, sciences used by, 74–75
Aerospace industry, 74–75
Agassiz, Louis, 169, 176, 211
Age, old; see old age
Agencies, government, support of research by, 223, 236
Agencies, private: support of science by, 191–221; distinguished from philanthropy, 192; and education, 215; Smithsonian Institution as, 197; see also Foundations, private; Philanthropy
Agricultural Adjustment Act, 96

Agricultural Adjustment Administration, 96
Agricultural colleges, 31, 90, 93, 169–70; see also Education, agricultural
Agricultural education; see Agricultural colleges; Education, agricultural
Agricultural experiment stations, 95, 155–56, 198, 229
Agricultural research; see Laboratories, agriculture; Research, agricultural
Agricultural Research Center, 25, 96, 102
Agricultural schools, 31, 90, 93, 169–70; see also Colleges, land-grant; Education, agricultural
Agricultural societies; see Societies, agricultural
Agriculture: technology in, 35, 91–94; effect of science on, 44, 89, 94–97, 104, 160, 191; and biology, 44, 160; use of chemistry in, 73–74, 89, 90, 94–95; industrial uses for products of, 81, 96; use of airplane in, 81, 103; nature of, 82, 86–87, 194; achievements of, 82, 92, 104, 105; steam power in, 83, 91–92; government aid to, 87–91; government control of, 88; and economic research, 96; education for, 31, 90, 93, 96, 169–70; work of laymen in, 100–102; electrical power in, 104; genetics in, 104; in American social mythology, 160; and industrialization, 228; and Department of Agriculture, 237; weather forecasting as aid to, 256; see also Information, agricultural; Machinery, agricultural; Pathology, agricultural
Agriculture, Bureau of, 160
Agriculture, Commissioner of, 94
Agriculture, Department of: support of science by, 25, 131, 228; creation of, 94, 228; organization of, 94, 95, 228, 229; development of, 95, 96; financial difficulties of, 95; research by, 95, 96, 99–100, 102, 228, 230, 231; and Great Depression, 96; in-

*Compiled by Barbara J. Stockley.

323

This book has been set in 10 point Times Roman, leaded 3 points, and 9 point Times Roman, leaded 2 points. Article titles are in 18 point Bodoni Bold. Authors' names are in 10 point Century Bold. The size of the type page is 25 by 45¾ picas.